Brian Jackson is a Yorkshireman, born in Sheffield. During a successful career, he has travelled extensively in Europe and the USA, although he and his wife now live in Herefordshire.

He is an avid reader, mainly of history and biography. In addition, Brian shares a love of theatre with his wife, in which are both active, and he has won awards both as a performer and Director.

As a writer he has contributed a regular business column in the local newspaper as well as producing numerous technical works.

'The Tears of Autumn' is his first novel.

The Tears of Autumn

Brian Jackson

The Tears of Autumn

Vanguard Press

A CIP catalogue record for this title is
available from the British Library
ISBN 1 843860 25 2

*Vanguard Press is an imprint of
Pegasus Elliot MacKenzie Publishers Ltd.*
www.pegasuspublishers.com

First Published in 2003

**Vanguard Press
Sheraton House Castle Park
Cambridge England**

Printed & Bound in Great Britain

Dedication

To Jude – for all the kisses in the park

And Amy and Mary Rose

CONTENTS

PART 3. DOROTHY – 1946

PART 4. JUDITH – 1957

EPILOGUE

PROLOGUE
AUGUST 12th 1977

Disjecta membra...

From the wall above the canal where he is leaning, gazing across the allotments running down the hillside to the canal below, David is surveying the rows of terraced houses in the streets beyond, where he had lived and played so many years ago in happiness as a boy. The early evening sun bathes the scene in mellow light and beyond the lofty spire of St. Mary's the summer sky is bright. The streets across the canal are silent; only a flight of pigeons rises and wheels above the rooftops away towards the city where Worcester's great cathedral rears majestically, dominating the skyline. It is peaceful, and a bittersweet sadness for the past begins to well inside him as David surveys the scenes of his childhood, safe in the shadow of St. Mary's.

Along Northfield Street, beneath the church, stands St. Mary's school. A pretty Victorian red sandstone building, in size and appearance it is like a village school and seems almost out of place in urban streets. In a strange sort of way it conjures up an image of The Water Babies and Tom the sweep, though why it should be so David couldn't explain. His memory wandered to the party that had been held there after the war for all the local children. He saw himself with all the other toddlers at long tables festooned with red white and blue bunting and flags with Aunty Ame and Aunty Rose and the other mothers supervising and chattering in the yard with the church looming above them. But now the school has gone and the building serves as a home for the local drama club. Even St. Mary's has found a new role; it is converted into flats. Nothing remains and all is changed and changing. Beyond the city the sun is setting gold above the Malvern Hills and the few brilliant wisps of cloud appear as though limned in molten metal.

David shifts his gaze back along the road and surveys the rows of gardens running along the back of the terraces. They look so small; but small as they are they were never mean houses and although not affluent, they were never poor. Always in his memory they had been homely, welcoming and comfortable. The ghosts of childhood lie in David's view and unbidden tears begin to fill his eyes. It is over eight months now and although the wound is healing it still gives pain. Only time will be the healer and meanwhile David cherishes his memories of Aunty Ame.

His little knot of flowers lies where he had carefully placed it upon the bare mound of earth. A gentle breeze stirred the foliage of the yew beneath which they lay with the scent of summer blossom in the air, faint with the humming of bees and woodpigeons calling from distant trees. A peaceful place; such a peaceful place to rest. And with the bittersweet moment upon him David has paused to lean upon the wall high above the old canal and the streets below to savour the memories of his past.

"Don't forget us will you David. Don't forget us now that Ame's gone will you."

Dear Aunty Rose, how could he ever forget her, for she had been so much a part of his life too. David stands motionless for long moments drinking from the memories of his past. Then he turns to the car and drives down to the canal, across the white concrete bridge to Aunty Rose's house amongst the streets below.

Standing in the back porch which he had been overlooking just a few minutes before, David waits for the welcome he knows he will receive. The door opens; it is Uncle Bob whose aged face breaks into an immediate grin of welcome, his rheumy eyes twinkling in the deep lines of his face. Uncle Bob puts a finger to his lips and suppresses his greeting.

"Who is it Bob?" Aunty Rose's voice comes from the living room.

Uncle Bob beckons David inside and whispers, "Go on in. Be a nice surprise for her." Then as David steps quietly past him he calls back into the living room, "Nothing. Just the kids up the yard."

Aunty Rose is seventy but without any signs of encroaching age or infirmity and as David peers round the living room door she gives a cry of genuine delight. Rising from her armchair, Aunty Rose throws her arms about him and hugs him to her.

"David!" Aunty Rose cries, "What a nice surprise. What brings you here?"

"Oh I had to come down south on business." David has no need to elaborate. It is sufficient that he has come. "I'm just on my way back to Sheffield. Thought I'd just pop in and see how you are."

"How nice. Lovely to see you. Here come on, sit down here look. Put the kettle on Bob."

"Already done it." And Uncle Bob enters from the kitchen. "Had a good journey then? How've the roads been?" Always solicitous; never reproachful no matter how long it is between the unexpected visits.

14

"How long's you stopping?" asks Aunty Rose. "How about a bit of tea? Has you had anything to eat?"

David is reluctant to put them to any trouble. They weren't expecting him and so will not have made any preparations for his visit. And he knows they will give him the last thing they possess if he asks for it. So he replies, "No I'm fine thanks. Had something earlier."

"Have a sandwich," Uncle Bob prompts him and David is tempted. It would be churlish to refuse their hospitality.

"Well. Perhaps a cheese sandwich. If it's not too much trouble."

Trouble! Aunty Rose immediately goes into the kitchen and David hears her busy with plate and knife in the pantry.

"We'm going up to the Saracens later," Uncle Bob says. "You got time to come up with us?"

Oh of course, for David knows they like a drink; in fact it is their unfailing custom to go up to the local every night for a couple of pints of mild. In his youth Uncle Bob had been a great drinker just as Uncle Al had been, chasing down beer with rum chasers. His strawberry nose bears witness to it but now, although he still drinks regularly he drinks in moderation.

"Yes," David replies. "What time you going?"

"Nine o'clock. We always goes up then. Makes sure you can get a seat."

Of course David knew that. "Okay," he says. "I'll give you a lift up. Shan't stop all night though; I've got to get back to Sheffield. Still I'll come and have one with you."

David settles himself into the armchair vacated by Uncle Bob whilst they busy themselves in the kitchen with tea and cake on a tray on his behalf, the honoured guest, always a pleasure.

It hadn't always been so. Not on those final visits to Aunty Ame…

He had been away to London on business for a couple of days and decided to return back home via Worcester.

"You've come… a long way… out …of your way," Aunty Ame had said but David had shrugged it off. "Just a little detour. Just a little dog-leg instead of a straight run north."

Aunty Ame was still at home then, lying on the bed they had brought downstairs opposite to Uncle Al's in the living room so that he could be near her. She was propped high on cushions with a soft scarf loose about her throat. Her head was covered and her eyes were bright and alert in her flushed face, so pleased to see him. But her speech was impeded and slow and to his distress David could not understand everything Aunty Ame tried to say. He sat with her skinny hand in his, shocked at the changes being wrought in her, fighting his emotions and

15

trying not to show it. He remembered her as she used to be in her younger days, a vital, attractive woman. Now she kept her bony arms covered and for vanity wore a headscarf to hide her lost hair. But still she seemed indomitable.

Aunty Rose had been there with Uncle Bob, trying to make something of David's visit. "Here's David come to see you Ame."

"Aint that a nice surprise then Ame. Our David."

They fussed and hovered and with a sudden revelation David realised his visit was equally a relief for them, relief from the boredom and frustration and forbearance of having to nurse Amy. They pressed her to take her Complan, the only food Amy was capable of, and made careful and elaborate preparation of her cup of lukewarm water but Amy rejected it. She sat with David's hand in hers as though they were rocks in the turbulent sea of activity surrounding them.

She looked at him and talked uncomprehendingly, wiping the fluid that issued from her throat away from her mouth with tissues, willing him to understand the reality which was upon her.

Rose was saying, "Come on Ame, drink this up, you'll soon be on the mend again."

But Amy waved it away. Albert was talking about the birthday party he was planning for her with all the neighbours round but Amy knew better and with difficulty she told him so.

"Albert… you talks… daft."

Albert wasn't the least put out by her scorn of him and protested she'd be well enough soon. But David had seen the knowledge in Aunty Ame's eyes. He bent to kiss her and she turned her face from him with a cry so David raised her hand and pressed it to his lips as she watched him, and wished her well and took his leave of her…

Here is Aunty Rose with slices of fruit cake and a pot of tea on the tray, calling into the kitchen, "Bring the cups and saucers in will you Bob." And David emerged from his reverie.

He lingered to give them a lift up the road before setting off on the two hour journey home and everything is as normal and convivial as it used to be. Aunty Rose and Uncle Bob are greeted by the other regulars as they enter the 'Saracens Head' and David is proudly introduced.

"My nephew. Rose's sister's grandson. He's just come to visit us on his way back to Sheffield. Been down here on business."

The regulars, ordinary elderly working people are impressed. Rose and Bob are popular and the regulars murmur greetings and shuffle along the horsehair bench to make room for the unexpected visitor.

"I shan't stop for more than one. I've got to get back."

Aunty Rose is immediately solicitous. "No of course not. You'll be

16

tired; and all that journey in front of you."

"Have another if you wants," Uncle Bob offers, draining his first pint.

"No I'm fine, really. Here let me get you another one before I go."

They protest but David is already up and crossing to the bar with Uncle Bob's empty glass.

"Here," says Uncle Bob as he comes to the bar, "here's your Aunty Rose's glass. Are you sure you won't stay for another?" But David still has half of his drink left to finish before he leaves.

"How's Judy and the little 'uns? They keeping alright?"

"Yes they're fine thanks."

"Give her our love won't you."

Someone has slipped some coins into the jukebox. With a skirl of pipes 'Mull of Kintyre' rises over their conversation. Aunty Rose is looking at David.

"What's the matter love?"

"Oh nothing," he replies and then, with a sudden urge to confide his feelings, "It's just that she didn't deserve that. Not that..." A wave of emotion rushes over him.

"I know love," Aunty Rose replies. "It was awful for her, and for Albert too. For all of us really."

"She was good to me... She never deserved it... that way..." But David cannot form the words and tears begin to flow down his face. The last sound is smothered in a sob. "I'm sorry aunty..." He is crying inconsolably and now the others in the bar are beginning to turn and look at him. "I'm sorry... I'd better go..."

A touch on the arm, an earnest look of compassion passes between them and he is gone.

PART ONE
DAISY – 1940

CHAPTER 1

Afternoon in the park

The great city of Sheffield lies in the valleys of the Sheaf and the Don where the rivers meet beneath the high bracken moors of Derbyshire. In the west the moorland encroaches almost to the edge of the city and the comfortable suburbs of Ringinglow and Ecclesall end abruptly where the road winds upwards to the villages of north Derbyshire nestling beneath gritstone outcrops of moorland crags. This sweeping area of countryside, later to become Britain's first National Park, is still regarded as the lungs of the city. And the city of Sheffield needed lungs. For in the east along the river valleys lies the industry which made the city great and from which rises an eternal pall of smoke, clouding the horizon and turning the civic buildings in the city centre black.

Here are the steelmakers, the engineers and foundries whose names bear the legacy of Britain's industrial revolution. Thos. Firth and John Brown Ltd; Huntsman Works; Bessemer Foundry. William Lee, who pioneered stainless steel. And all the others, now focused upon one desperate purpose; to rearm Britain now that the country is at war. Armour plate for battleships and tanks and shells. Away down the rivers at shaper and lathe, men turn off vast coils of blue steel awash with oiled water to keep it cool. Don't dull the blade, don't waste it; only another hundred and fifty more then start another batch.

In the smoke laden foundries shadowy figures of men, diminutive in the erratic gloom hoist vast ladles of molten steel which cascade showers of lethal sparks and the smoke wreathes high into the darkness of the roof beyond the glaring arclamps. And the noise reverberates on the same vast scale. Pounding hammers driven by steam which vents and whistles in irritable ferocity from factory walls along the ruined banks of the Sheaf, the Loxley and the Don. The earth shakes with the violence of the hammerblows and men's minds are driven insensible by the brute noise. And the steam, as though impatient to be freed hisses and vents in frustrated clouds all along the river valleys. Night and day, night and day as the nation toils for life.

But it is a time for lovers. For who in those frantic, numbered days would not savour to the full the pleasures of life away from work and

21

war and desperation. For some, to eat and drink and sleep in weariness is enough. To be away, if only for a few hours respite, from the foundries and the forges which hiss and crash and shake the earth.

And who would not pause and listen to the soaring song of the skylark where the sun bursts out of the summer clouds? Or catch the delicate fragrance of carnations or the musky scent of a rose? Or the softness of a lover's hand in yours, the yielding delicacy of her skin and the light that dances in her eyes as she lies upon the meadow, shielded from the sun and gazing into the foliage of the tree above.

Away across the playing field beyond the belt of trees the park keeper's bell was ringing. Daisy's eyes refocused and she raised herself, reclining against the tree on her elbows. She turned to look at the young man sitting impassively beside her, staring morosely ahead.

"Bill," she pleaded, "come on Billy. Park's closing. We've got to go."

Bill ignored her and remained as he was with his arms clasped round his knees, his youthful good looks marred by a scowl of irritation.

"Billy come on. Park's shutting. Didn't you hear the bell?"

"Aw so what!" He turned on Daisy with a snarl. "And don't call me Billy. Me name's Bill." He felt thoroughly unreasonable and had no intention of hiding it.

Daisy tried again to mollify him. She laid her hand on Bill's arm and said, "Come on. Don't let it spoil our afternoon."

But he remained impervious to Daisy's appeal and stiffened against her gentle insistence. She reached to touch the waves of his dark hair. The frustration rose in him again and he shrugged her off, looking intently at the distant trees.

There had been few enough people in the park that afternoon. A group of children playing an impromptu game of cricket had sent the distracting sound of their play floating across the meadow, and the few strolling families had given Bill and Daisy a wide berth. Twenty yards or so behind the tree a dense yew hedge enclosed the formal garden and shielded them from view. Secure from unexpected intrusion they had spent the afternoon in the world of Sunday in the park. And Bill had become increasingly aware of Daisy lying prone on the grass beside him.

Her eyes were closed and her long blond hair was loose about her shoulders, framing her face. She was eighteen, two years younger than he was, with a freshness and vitality that accentuated her desirability. It wasn't that Daisy was exceptionally pretty – her nose was rather too straight – but she had an air of sensuality. The merest hint of lipstick accentuated the fullness of her soft mouth, inviting his kiss.

Bill turned his head to look at her. Her light cotton dress was lying loose across her legs. He reached out and twined his fingers through

22

hers.

"Daisy." His voice was a low murmur.

Daisy responded languidly, lost in the peace of the day. There was something vulnerable and unattainable about her as she lay.

"Daisy." Bill squeezed her hand gently and Daisy responded, squeezing his hand in return. But she remained as she was with a faint smile of contentment on her face.

"Whew it's hot!"

Bill removed his jacket and looked with casual intent all around them as he ran his fingers over the careful Brylcreem waves in his hair. At the bottom of the slope where the field levelled out near the trees the children were still engrossed in their game. There was no-one else about. The young couple with the toddler who had passed by earlier had vanished, probably round the yew hedge to the tea house in the formal garden behind them. Only the swallows were busy, swooping and flitting easily over the grass. Bill rolled his jacket into a pillow and lay down beside her. Once more he sought Daisy's hand and again she squeezed him softly in return. The simple response aroused passion in him and he felt the stirring of an erection.

He turned to look at her. There was a wisp of loose hair at her temple. He reached across and stroked it into place. Daisy twitched slightly at his touch but her look of contentment remained. Bill glanced about the field and again there was no-one, only the distant sound of the children at their play. He leaned across and kissed her desirable mouth, oh so gently. Daisy responded lightly, innocently and remained as she lay with her eyes closed and her smile of secret pleasure.

Bill savoured the scent of her and the pressure of her lips responding to his kiss. He looked about him again. Again there was no-one. His erection subsided and he lay down again and tried to sunbathe. But he was restless and conscious of her presence at his side. Through his closed eyes the sun was making him blink. Beside him Daisy was immobile. Bill thought of kissing her again but she was too still, too content.

He sat up and loosened the top two buttons of his shirt and tried to concentrate on sunbathing again. But in his mind he saw Daisy's dress falling between her slightly parted legs and the buttons at the front, the slim belt around her waist. It was as though she was waiting for his approach. He began to imagine how she would feel. The beating of his heart increased and he could feel another erection stirring.

Once more he gazed about the field, certain that he was observed. And once more they were alone except for the children intent upon their game. He bent to Daisy and kissed her, as she lay, with all the force and passion of his being. Daisy's hand stole around his neck and her soft

23

fingers held him to her in the kiss. He pulled her body to him in a surge of desire and kissed her again, burying his face in her neck and Daisy held him to her and kissed him and kissed him again; his eyes, his cheeks, his lips. With desire raging in him Bill sought Daisy's breast. He savoured its firm softness and bent to kiss it through the fabric of her dress, cupping it in his hands against his face. Oh God! And then passion subsided and they lay together breathless in each other's arms.

They kissed again. Long, slow and intense. Bill reached down and pulled Daisy's skirt above her thigh. She sprang back and pushed him from her.

"No!"

She began smoothing down her dress.

"Daisy."

"No."

"But there's nobody about," Bill pleaded. He drew her close again. "Come on. There's nobody here." He began kissing her again and again she wriggled and fought against his wayward hand as he held her in his embrace. She felt his hand above her stockings and on her thigh, his fingers seeking to push between her legs. She tore herself away and sat up breathless.

"Stop it Bill. You mustn't."

"Why not?" Bill lay back, breathing hard.

Daisy patted her hair back into place and looked defiantly ahead. "Somebody might have seen us!"

"But there's nobody about."

"No Bill. It's not right," Daisy insisted.

"Why not?" he pleaded. "You love me don't you?"

"Yes but…"

"Well then. Why not? Eh…? I'll go mad if… Daisy… Come on…" Bill reached out and pulled her to him. Once more Daisy shared his kiss until submission changed to abrupt flight and she sat up, darting apprehensive glances around the field.

"Why not? Eh? Daisy, why not?"

"It's… it's too open."

Bill's heart was pounding. "Let's go somewhere else. Where we can't be seen."

"No."

"Come on." He took Daisy's hand and tried to coax her to her feet. "Daisy. Come on Daisy." There was urgency and desire in his pleading. "Let's go into the woods. Nobody'll see us in the woods."

"No Bill," Daisy insisted. "I don't want to. Let's just stay here. I want to stay here."

And Bill sat morosely by her side with his arms clamped around his knees, busy with his thoughts and gazing into the middle distance. Finally the clanging of the handbell signalled it was time to leave.

Daisy stood and tried to smooth the wrinkles in her dress. She took her comb and mirror from her handbag and rearranged her hair and when she was ready she stood patiently at Bill's side until he rose in his own time and put his jacket on.

"Alright," he said morosely. "Come on. Let's go."

He strode off.

Daisy tried to take his hand but he wouldn't. She tried to match his pace but he contrived to keep half a pace out of step with her.

"Bill. Don't let it spoil things."

He came out of his isolation and turned on her in fury. "I could be getting me call up papers any day!" he cried. "I might never see you again! This bloody war! You don't know what it's like for a bloke!"

He pushed her hand away and strode off. Daisy scampered after him.

"Billy," she cried. "Bill... I'm sorry but... I can't. You know I can't. It's not right... is it."

She broke off lamely and Bill turned on her again.

"No! It's not right. None of it's right! You and going dancing and just holding hands." He began to stride away again but his pace faltered and he turned to her. "What d'you think I am?" He turned from her and Daisy heard him say, "I love you. I can't go on like this."

Suddenly the barrier between them had fallen. He allowed Daisy to take his hand. Then he kissed her, gently, and said, "I'm sorry."

Beyond the meadow and over the trees ahead the city spread out before them. The avenues and open spaces of the western suburbs were dotted with patches of green. In the city centre the unmistakable outline of the fine Victorian town hall stood proudly but beyond it the outlines became blurred under the haze of smoke hanging above the industry in the east like a perpetual fog. Above the city, in the still summer air the anti-aircraft barrage hung like grotesque marshmallow playthings. Bill paused in his step. The city looked so vulnerable.

"I'm not going in the army," he muttered, as though to himself.

"What?"

"I'm not going in the army." He spoke softly as though in self revelation. Then he turned to her and repeated, "I'm not going in."

"But you'll have to Bill." There was anxiety in Daisy's voice. "I mean, they'll send for you. You'll go to jail if you don't. You can't just not go!"

"I don't mean that Daisy." His eyes grew distant again. "I'll join the RAF."

"But... you don't get a choice! Do you?"

He didn't reply.

"You have to go where they send you," Daisy persisted. "Don't you?"

"I'll join up."

He was still gazing down at the city with its poor balloon defence hanging motionless in the air.

"I'll volunteer. Before they send for me." He turned to Daisy, suddenly animated. "We've got to do something. We can't just sit here and wait for something to happen. They're crying out for pilots. Look what's happening down south. They're sending everything they've got against us. Fleets and fleets of bombers. Just a few more squadrons and we could push 'em right back to Germany."

Daisy was out of her depth. But she knew that the aftermath of Dunkirk had left Britain defenceless. Only the airforce was holding back the invasion.

"Well I'm not going in the army anyway," Bill persisted. "I'm going in the RAF. I'm giving them a taste of what we're getting."

Daisy put her arm round Bill's waist and leaned close to him. It was inevitable. With the rebuilding of Britain's forces the demand for men would reach wider and wider until it crossed the boundaries of reserved occupations. Sooner or later Bill would have to go. She had tried not to think of it until now but Bill was right. Soon he would go and there would be no more afternoons beneath the oak soaking up the sunshine of a languid summer day…

The sun had gone down and Bill and Daisy were in the shadows at the end of the row of council houses. The privet hedges caught the moonlight but the houses were blacked out and dark.

"You'd better leave me here." Daisy turned to face him and Bill sought for an image of her face. Now it was Daisy's turn to feel awkward. "What you looking at?" Her voice was small and breathless.

"You. You're very pretty." He bent and kissed her. Then he squeezed her to him and kissed her again.

"I'd better go," Daisy said with a flutter. "Me mother'll be waiting for me."

"I'll see you tomorrow then."

"Yes." The dark figure ran into the shadows between the privets and Bill heard the soft rattle of the door closing. He walked back home across the city oblivious of the night, carried on by the memory of her softness and the flutter of her eyelashes on his cheek as he kissed her.

Nearing home he became conscious of the lingering scent of her powder. He took his handkerchief and surreptitiously rubbed at his mouth. Then, for fear that he had reddened his lips he licked them and wiped them more gently.

The backyard was dark and silent as he fumbled his key into the lock, trying not to make a sound. In the sitting room his mother was sitting by the embers of the fire.

"You're late aren't you?"

"Where's me dad?"

"Gone up. He's up early in the morning."

"Is our George in?"

"Yes. He's ever so disappointed you let him down tonight."

"Well he sometimes goes out with his mates."

There was no point in pursuing the argument and Lilly knew it. Her two sons couldn't live in each other's pockets forever.

"Well," she said, rising, "I'm off to bed."

Bill loosened his collar and tie and Lilly went to the kitchen to fetch a pan of water to damp down embers of the fire. She paused before him.

"You've got something on your coat."

"What!" Bill was startled, unnecessarily so. "Where?"

"Here. On your shoulder. Some white on your coat."

It was Daisy's face powder.

"Oh it's nothing. It'll soon come off." Bill took the clothes brush from the sideboard drawer and began brushing vigorously at his lapel.

"Don't forget to put the lights out when you come up."

Lilly watched her son, busy with his jacket. Suddenly so grown up and independent. And demanding too, with an inner, almost secret personality. So unlike his younger brother; easy going, tolerant George.

Bill finished brushing the jacket and draped it carefully across the armchair in the corner. Lilly turned away quickly and made for the stairs door in the kitchen as he looked up.

"Goodnight Billy."

"Goodnight mother."

CHAPTER 2

Air raid

The long hot summer faded into autumn and the golden sunlight gilded the dying leaves in tones of copper and yellow. But the evening breeze carried a chill which the sun, sinking in flames above the moors, was unable to dispel. And the wind gusting through the trees brought the leaves down. Just a few at first slipping silently from the boughs and then more and more until they fell like a defeated army, drifting through the branches to lay in whispering heaps which fretted and twitched on the ground as the wind passed amongst them.

Despite shortages and inconvenience life went on and the people clung to mundane things and the comfort of familiar routine amidst the chaos of the greater world around them. In the small four roomed house at the end of the terrace – two up, two down with the privy in a row with the others across the yard – tea was just coming to a close. Lilly was sitting in her blue wraparound apron at her corner of the table next to the kitchen door with Harold and their sons, George and Bill. She was a robust woman, sturdy and capable who cooked good wholesome food and enjoyed what she cooked. She looked up from her plate as her youngest son rose and carried his plate into the kitchen.

"Oh George you'll make yourself poorly golloping your tea like that," she called after him. But the admonition was mellowed by the satisfaction that he had enjoyed his meal.

George grunted a reply and started to fill the bowl with hot water from the kettle for his wash. Harold left a portion on the side of his plate and crossed his knife and fork on it before pushing the plate from him. It was his unfailing custom and he murmured his appreciation through the final mouthful before turning his chair from the table to stretch his legs.

"What about that bit?" Lilly asked.

"I'll have it for me supper," he replied.

"I thought a rabbit stew would make a nice change," Lilly said turning to Bill who was mopping up the last of his gravy with the crust of a home made loaf. "Was yours nice Billy?"

Bill ignored her and Harold rose from the table with his mug of tea. "Is kettle on? I'll have a wash and shave."

"I think our kid's just took the hot water," Bill said maliciously.

"I've put it back on!" George called from the kitchen.

Harold crossed to his fireside chair to unlace his boots and drink his tea while he waited for the kettle to boil.

"What you doing tonight our kid?" Bill called.

"Playing snooker with Billy Earnshaw. Why?"

"Just thought I'd come down and have a game that's all."

"Thought you'd be out with Daisy," George replied without interest. "You usually are." He frowned up into the mirror, re-ruffled his hair and set to again with the comb to get his parting straight.

"She's staying in tonight." Bill dipped the last piece of bread in the remains of the gravy on Harold's plate. "She's washing her hair or something."

Harold unfastened the buttons on his railway waistcoat and leaned back comfortably.

"I might have a walk over to the White Lion later," he said to Lilly. "Are you coming for one?"

"I've just got to wash these few pots," she replied. "You have your wash while I clear the table."

Harold sipped his tea and buried himself in his Daily Herald.

George took his jacket from the hook behind the stair's door in the kitchen. "Anyway I'm just going round to Earnshaws."

"Hang on a bit," Bill called, rising from the table. "I shan't be a minute."

"I'm only going to see if he's ready." George was impatient to get the evening under way. "Come down when you've had a wash." He paused to confirm that his chalk was in his pocket and then he was gone.

Bill made a rush to the sink and removed the pots that Lilly was putting in to soak. "I shan't be a minute mother."

"Well look sharp," Lilly responded tartly. "Your dad wants his wash and I want to get this washing up done."

Harold was not a heavy drinker but a couple of pints goes down well when you are in the mood for it. Lilly banked up the fire with a big lump of coal and piled slack around it to keep it in. The darkness of the backyard was sudden after the brightness of the kitchen and they made their way in silence together down the terrace and crossed the road to the narrow wooden footbridge over the river. The moon gleamed on its oily surface as it rippled over rusting debris and household rubbish.

Suddenly Harold said, "What d'you think of this lass our Billy's knocking about with?"

The question took Lilly by surprise. "Who?" she said. "Daisy?"

"Yes," Harold answered enigmatically.

"She seems a nice enough lass. I got on with her alright."

29

Harold and Lilly had met Daisy for the first time the previous Saturday afternoon. She had been to the house briefly with Bill. They were going into town and then to the pictures. Lilly had thought her pleasant enough and easy to get along with but Harold did not seem particularly impressed. There was something about his tone of voice as he asked the question.

"Why?" Lilly asked.

"Oh nothing really. It's just that I were talking to Len at work. He knows the family."

"There's nothing wrong with them is there?" Lilly cried in alarm. "They're not in any trouble with the police or anything are they?" The thought of policemen coming to her door was more than Lilly could bear.

"No," Harold said hastily. "It's nothing like that. It's... just something that Len said. That's all."

"Why? What did he say?" Lilly was wary now.

"Well, she's got sisters. It seems they've got a bit of a reputation."

Lilly pondered on the implications.

"Well she seemed nice enough," Lilly said finally. "In fact I thought how nice and quiet she was."

"Well it's just what Len said. I don't want our Bill and George getting mixed up with the wrong kind of lass that's all. They've got all their lives in front of them."

"He's been going round with her a long time now. You can't judge a girl on what one of your workmates says. What does he know? She seemed a nice girl to me anyway. Very quiet and polite."

They emerged from under the railway bridge and Harold took Lilly's arm to cross the road. The glass panelled doors of the White Lion, normally so bright and welcoming with the picture of Windsor Castle and 'Gilmours Ale and Stout' etched on them, were blacked out giving the pub a closed and deserted look. Harold made sure the outer doors were firmly closed behind them then they swished through the blackout into the saloon. The noise and conviviality was in sharp contrast to the darkness of the chilly street.

Most of the regulars were already there, nodding greetings around the room. Harold left his cap with Lilly then went to fetch the drinks. Then Reg and Ada came in and they fetched the dominos from behind the bar and spent the evening playing 'fives and threes'. Lilly and Ada won the evening's play, not much just a copper or two, but the main thing was the laughter punctuated by keen and spirited exchanges. The combined effect of the beer and the smoke hanging in layers under the ceiling gave a shine to their eyes and in between play they discussed the nonsenses that the war was introducing into their lives until it was 'time'. Then they filed out after one another and stood in discrete groups on the pavement saying their prolonged and noisy goodnights. But the night breeze was cold and they quickly dispersed. The moon no longer reflected on the oily ripples of the river as they hurried across the narrow bridge. Harold fumbled his key in the lock and they went inside to warmth again and the welcoming glow of the fire.

Lilly cut herself a slice of bread and dripping. "You want a bit of supper Harold?"

"No," Harold replied, once more busy with his boots. "I'm going up."

He wound the mantelpiece clock.

"It's time our Bill and George were in," he said. "Anyway I'm not waiting up for them."

Lilly cleared the bread away and damped down the fire for the night. After a last look round she checked the back door, switched off the lights and followed him up.

The alarm clock on the chest of drawers ticked away the seconds in the darkness. Harold lay with his head deep in the feather pillows snoring loudly but Lilly slept oblivious to his snores. Beneath the bed the half full chamber pot added its own contribution to the stale atmosphere. A subtle, sweet aroma heightened by the remains of the final cigarette floating on the surface of the amber liquid like a corpse. They slept undisturbed by the gentle ticking in the room.

In Lilly's dream the sounds were faint and indistinct like the insistent tapping of a dentist's tool in the dreamworld of gas. Far, far away but insistent. And langorous. A long tunnel of time like the approach of a distant express. Lilly opened her eyes in the darkness and sat up suddenly.

"Oh my God!!" Panic! She tried to make sense of the sound that she could hear.

"Harold! Harold!" She shook his back violently. "Harold wake up!"

"Wha..ss..?" He stirred, grumbling. "Bloody Hell! An air raid!!"

They leaped out of bed as the siren struck at them with its incessant wailing.

"Oh Christ how long's it been going on?" Harold cried as he struggled to get his legs into his trousers.

"Don't know." Lilly ran around the bed. "I'm going for Bill and George."

"Where's bloody gas masks?"

"Here!" Lilly snatched them from the headboard and tossed them onto the bed in the darkness. Then she crossed the tiny landing to the small back room that George and Billy shared, snapping the bedroom

31

light on as she entered.

"Put that bloody light out!!" Harold whispered harshly.

"They're not here!" Lilly cried. "Our George and Billy. They're not here."

"How d'you mean not here?" Defying his own edict Harold flicked the light again. The bed was undisturbed. "Oh my God!"

"Oh where are they?" Lilly wailed.

"Quick." Harold said. "We can't wait up here. Cellar. Quick."

The siren's wail continued and they stumbled in a panic down the stairs. Harold dashed into the living room for boots and shoes. Unaccountably Lilly grabbed the kettle and a loaf, repeatedly wailing, "Oh where can they be?"

"Coats." Harold ordered. "Quick."

They found the candles on the shelf at the head of the cellar and went down in the darkness. Fumbling with the matches they heard a footfall and saw a gleam through the hole in the wall which had been made in all the cellars to link the row of houses together.

"Is that you Billy?" Lilly called.

An uncertain voice replied, "Is that you Mrs. Wainright?"

"It's alright Lizzie," Lilly replied. "We're coming."

Lizzie appeared with the baby wrapped in a shawl in her arms.

"Is your Tom coming?" Harold asked.

"No," Lizzie wailed. "He's on nights." She was close to tears. "They bomb factories don't they?"

"What about Mr. and Mrs. Short? And Mester next door? Are they coming?"

"I think so. I called 'em as I came through. I think they're following behind."

Harold pulled some wooden orange boxes down onto the floor from the pile he had accumulated in the corner to use for firewood. "Here, sit on these."

Lizzie subsided gratefully onto the box. The baby slept on in her arms.

Harold took his candle to the hole on the cellar wall and bent to it. "Anybody there? Are you coming?" he called.

There were faint cries in response, then old Mr. Turner who lived alone next door appeared in the opening. He gave a grin of relief. He was followed by Mr. and Mrs. Short from two doors away with their gasmasks and an assortment of clothes in disordered bundles.

Harold began passing more boxes down for them to sit on.

"Listen!" Mr. Turner said. They turned to look at him. "Sirens have stopped."

They all looked at one another. Finally Lizzie said, "D'you think it's safe to go back?" Her voice was querulous, a far cry from the strident back yard gossip.

"No! No," Harold said. "Better wait until the 'all clear'."

They all nodded agreement.

"How long do you think it'll be?" Mrs. Short whispered nervously.

Her husband looked up at Harold in the gloom but Harold only shrugged. "Shouldn't be too long. False alarm I expect."

But Mr. Turner, perched on the pile of coal with his ear cocked to the cellar grate above raised his hand and 'shushed' for quiet.

Lizzie started to say, "I've forgot babby's…" but again Mr. Turner silenced her with a gesture.

Harold went to join him and they both stood alert, listening.

The silence remained until Mr. Short, who could stand it no longer said, "I think it's alright. I can't hear anything." He went back to his box and resumed his seat next to his wife.

"Shhh. Shhh…" There was a subtle change in the expression on the faces of the two listeners beneath the grate. Anxiety began to grow among the rest of them.

"Was that…?"

No! It's imagination playing tricks. But now they all sat alert and listened. Mrs. Short sought her husbands hand. Very faintly there came a sound which receded as soon as they heard it. Wait! There it was again. And it was getting stronger.

"I wish you'd come down from there Harold," Lilly pleaded.

Harold ignored her. He was transfixed, listening. Fighting her own rising panic Lilly went to Lizzie who had been seized by a fit of trembling. She offered to hold the baby but Lizzie turned away and clutched the baby to her.

Now they could clearly hear it. The roar of engines as aircraft began to pass overhead. The noise grew until it was intolerable, a ceaseless reverberation so great that they could almost feel it.

"Hadn't we better blow them candles out?" Mrs. Short said nervously. "They might see the light."

With unbearable tension they waited in the darkness as the noise continued until the main body was past them, on its way to the river valleys and the industry that lay there. And then above the noise of the bombers they heard another sound, as muffled as a heartbeat. Thump… thump… thump… It was joined by others, all making the same sound.

"My God what's that?" There was panic in Lizzie's voice.

"It's… I think it's alright. It's anti-aircraft. It's our boys. Giving them what for."

But the sound was drowned by a mightier noise. The crash of the first bomb in the distance followed by banshee screams falling through the air, and more bombs all blending into a murderous cacophony of sound. Fearfully they huddled together and waited for the one that would fall on them, the descending scream and...

Hardly daring to believe it, they heard the noise of explosions die away and the drone of aircraft faded as the anti-aircraft fire chased them into the distance, leaving them in a profound well of silence. Nobody spoke. They sat with relief in the darkness. Shaking with relief! But alive. Oh thank God!

The 'all clear' sounded, the mournful wail of the sirens rising and falling over the burning city. And in the cellars they stirred, the sound of their movements great in the profound solitude into which each of them had fallen. Harold re-lit a candle and they inspected one another, not knowing whether to try a smile, unsure and unable to trust their emotions.

They heard sounds outside. Small activity in the street above them. The distant sound of ringing firebells. A voice at the cellar grate, startling in its nearness.

"ARP," the voice shouted. "Is everybody alright down there?"

Harold looked around at the others in the gloom. "Yes."

"How many's down there?"

"There's six of us. All from this row. We're all alright."

"You can come out."

With a clatter of booted feet the voice was gone.

Mrs. Short looked around her. Her composure was returning. Suddenly it dawned on her. She took Lilly's arm and said, "Where's your Billy and George?"

CHAPTER 3

Lovers tiff

The problem for Bill and George was how they were going to get home. They had spent the night with others in a deep shelter, stricken with fear, listening to the bombardment above them and trying to imagine what was happening. When at last the 'all clear' sounded they emerged and stood in disbelief. Yesterday – last night – The Moor had been an avenue of department stores and multi-storey shops. Now the whole city centre was ablaze. Yesterday's showrooms were raging infernos with flames bursting through upper storey windows and lighting the night sky. The fires were burning out of control as far as the eye could see. Their ears were filled with the roar of flames, bells, shouting.

George burst into tears and began to sob. Bill looked round at the others who had been in the shelter with them. Thank God George wasn't the only one. Bill felt his own mouth trembling. But it wasn't tears. It was anger! And impotence at this, coupled with what else had happened last night. God, that was a year ago! He gazed at the scene before him with a deep sense of futility.

It was still dark. God knows what time it was. The city was illuminated in a ghastly flaring light and deep shadows with smoke and steam billowing into the darkness. They had no idea what to do. Heaps of steaming rubble and fallen masonry barred every way. Bill put his arm around his brother and they stood helpless outside the shelter for what seemed an eternity.

A warden ran across to them. "Come on, get out of it. Quick." They began to move as if in a dream. "Get a move on," he cried pointing upwards. "That lot's coming down!"

George was still weeping. Bill looked at his brother and felt ashamed. George had always been the weakest of the two, both physically and emotionally. It stemmed from the accident when he was a baby. It was a washday and Lilly had strapped George in his high chair on the hearthrug so that he should be warm in front of the fire. Although at twenty months he was getting big for the chair, George was into everything and, on this particularly cold washday morning with the backdoor open it was the safest place for him. It allowed Lilly to get on with the wash while he was out of harm's way. Billy, eighteen months older, was out in the yard playing. He couldn't get far and, with the kitchen door open Lilly could keep an eye on him. And then Lilly heard the most terrifying screams in the living room. She ran in and saw the high chair had fallen forward into the hearth. The firegrate in the Yorkshire range was deep with four narrow cast iron bars across the front to contain the fire within the grate. George's chair had fallen forward just short of these, but not far enough short to save George. It was angled up against the grate. George, strapped in the seat, was hanging forward with his face pressed against the burning bars and within an inch of the searing heat of the fire, screaming, unable to move. Lilly grabbed the chair and freed George from it and ran with him in hysterics to the neighbours.

George never recovered from the ordeal. He grew up with his face scarred and with nerves that were scarred as well. Riddled with guilt Lilly tried to make up for it but she knew that she never could.

Bill tugged at George's arm. George was gasping and sobbing. He turned and looked at Bill. His mouth was moving but no sound came. Bill led him by the arm. "Come on our kid."

They followed the others and picked their way across the sodden fire hoses, past the incandescent shell of a tramcar still ablaze, past rescuers already digging amongst the rubble. A nightmare journey, until they left it behind and went into a church for tea, a blanket and someone to tell them what to do.

Harold and Lilly were desperate for news of their sons. When daylight came Harold left Lilly distraught and went out to search for news of them. But all that he could find out was that the main impact of the raid had been borne by the city centre. It was almost completely destroyed. By some divine chance the industrial heart of Sheffield was largely untouched. So the forge at Shardlows survived and continued to produce the crankshafts for the Spitfire's Merlin engines. The works of Vickers and Browne Bailey, Osbornes and Firths were still intact. But Harold could find no word of Billy and George. The ARP couldn't help, the snooker hall was closed. His only consolation was the absence of their names from any casualty lists. He continued his search asking anyone he met if they knew where George and Bill had been last night.

Lilly was sitting at the table fatigued and sick with worry when they entered. They were unsure of their welcome and George closed the door carefully behind them.

Bill called, "We're back mother."

Lilly raised her head in disbelief. "Oh where've you been?" she cried and burst into tears. "We've been worried out of our minds about

36

you."

George evaded the question. "We got stuck in town." His reply was devoid of emotion.

"Oh let's have a look at you." Lilly took hold of George's shoulders and began to inspect him but he shrugged her off.

"Give over mother. Tired." He looked across at Bill and sat wearily on the settee beneath the window.

Bill leaned against the mantelpiece with his back to them both. He rested his head on his arms. He heard Lilly's irritating anxiety pour out of her. "...worried sick about you. Your dad's gone out looking for you. He's been out all morning. 'Time is it...? I don't know where he's got to."

"Oh shut up mother will you!" Bill turned away from the mantelpiece and sat at the table. He sprawled forward and lowered his head on his arms again but he couldn't block out the flow of his mother's voice.

"I don't know what your dad's going to say. He's been gone ages. Oh why didn't you come straight home. Oh I'm so glad you're safe. You've no idea what we've been through..." On and on. Do you have any idea mother? Do you have any idea at all? The road outside was unscathed. The smell of burning was drifting in from the city on the cold morning air but everyone was safe. The neighbours were out, sharing gossip and trying to create adventures out of trivia. On and on and on...

"Go and put kettle on mother." Bill could barely keep the exasperation from his voice.

"Well I don't know! Oh why didn't you come home?"

But Bill's head was resting back on his arms and George avoided the question again and turned his head away.

Lilly went and did as she was bid. Then she went up the yard to tell Lizzie and Mrs. Short and the others that George and Bill were safely back.

Harold turned wearily for home. It was cold and his search had been fruitless. A bit of breakfast and a pot of tea and then he would come out and try again. Only, what was he going to say to Lilly? She was desperate for news and what had he to tell her? Nothing! Oh God!

Lilly was still out when Harold walked in. The kettle was boiling, steaming up the kitchen window and turning the bit of lace curtain into a wet rag. He heard low voices in the living room. It sounded like...?

There were George and Bill sitting and talking like nothing had happened. Unreasonable anger flared in Harold. "Where the bloody hell were you two last night?"

Bill looked up in surprise to see his father in the doorway and he bridled at Harold's tone. What right had his father to speak to him like that! They were lucky to be alive after what they'd been through! The tiredness in Bill's sleep rimmed eyes vanished.

"Last night! Last night!" he cried. "Where were we last night? Have you been down there dad? Have you seen it? Have you seen what they've done?"

"Well we were worried sick about you," Harold retorted. "Stopping out all night like that. What d'you expect?"

"Dad. We couldn't get home," George said wearily. He bowed his head into his hands. "You've no idea have you."

The sharp response died on Harold's lips. Clearly his sons were exhausted. They had been closer to it than he had feared. "No." he replied at last. "They say it's pretty bad."

"Bad! I'll say it's bad!" Bill would not be placated and he continued angrily, "They've wrecked it! Whole bloody lot's gone. 'Moors gone from top to bottom. And Pinstone Street. As far as you can tell."

"Town Hall's still standing," George murmured but Bill railed on.

"…Gas mains blown up and rows of shops… they're all on fire, any what's left standing. Houses… They'll never get it straight again." Now, in the telling, Bill was close to tears, the tears that he couldn't shed last night. Harold tried to interject but Bill would not, could not be stopped. "…They're bringing in the injured in their hundreds… everything's on fire…" He began to sob. "There's bodies…" he broke off with tears streaming down his face. Harold searched helplessly for words but before he could say anything Bill was on his feet. "Where were us two last night? Where were us two?" He was crying uncontrollably. "We were in that bloody lot! Aren't you glad to see us?"

Bill stormed past his father into the kitchen and rinsed his face under the tap. How could his father speak to him like that! After everything they'd been through. Lilly returned and found him in the kitchen drying his face.

"Is your dad back yet Billy?"

"Aye," he shouted at her. "He's back! He's in there."

"There's no need to speak to your mother like that!" Harold retorted from the living room.

Lillly's relief turned to dismay. "Whatever's going on?" she demanded.

Harold was standing with his back to the fire, warming himself. The fire was sending dense plumes of blue smoke curling fiercely up the chimney but giving out little heat. In the cold morning light of the room George was still sitting in dejection on the settee.

"Whatever's up with our Billy?"

Harold raised his arms in a gesture. "I don't know," he said wearily. "I just asked him where he'd been and he flew off the handle. Can't get a word out of this one here."

George stirred and looked up at his mother and father. His face expressed shock and sickness beyond endurance. "It's awful," he said softly. "It's… it's…" and he bowed his head once more.

Bill appeared in the doorway behind them, as silent as a ghost.

"Well," he said finally, "you're alright anyway."

"Come on love." Lilly steered him to a chair. "Come and sit down. I'll go and mash that pot of tea."

"Sorry Bill," Harold offered, "but we were worried about you. We didn't know where you were, if you were alright or anything."

Bill sat rigidly at the table.

"We all went down our cellar," Harold continued doggedly. "There were me and your mother, Lizzie, Mr. and Mrs. Short. The old man from next door."

Lilly came in with the tray of milk, sugar and spoons and set it on the table. "You'll feel better for a nice cup of tea. Have you and George had anything to eat? How about some breakfast?"

"Don't want anything," George said.

"We had something at the ARP," Bill lied, glancing at George.

"I'll have a bit of something in a minute," Harold said.

Lilly fetched the big grey enamel teapot and poured out strong mugs of tea. Flecks of leafstalk swirled around as she carefully stirred in the sugar. They took the tea gratefully.

"But Billy – George, why didn't you come home last night? Me and your dad were home and gone to bed when 'sirens started."

"You don't stay playing snooker till 'early hours of the morning surely to God?" Harold grumbled from his armchair. He reached forward and placed his tea on the hob to keep warm. "Come on George, don't be so daft. Where did you get to?"

George looked across at Bill as though for approval but received nothing in response.

"We didn't stay in 'The Royal' more than an hour," he said.

Harold and Lilly waited.

"Well…" George paused. "Anyway we went for a game when this gang of blokes comes in with Andy." He looked across again. "Didn't they Bill?"

Bill remained silent.

"I didn't think you still saw Andy," Lilly said. "How is he? Thought he'd got his call up."

"He has, he's… Oh well anyway," George continued. "We were having a bit of a laugh and a joke and then Andy says, 'You've seen the light then!' Well of course our Bill didn't know what he were talking about." George took a sip of tea. "Well, one thing leads to another and he says he's seen Daisy out with another bloke so our Bill says…"

"Aw give up George," Bill mumbled from the table. "Shut up will you. It's nothing."

"But I thought you said she was stopping in last night." Lilly was nonplussed. "Wasn't she washing her hair or something?"

"That's what she said," Bill spoke softly, with an air of resignation. He didn't want to go through all this with his mother and dad. They'd never understand. But he knew it was inevitable. Only he didn't want George blabbering it all out. "That's what she told me," Bill continued. "Well I thought she was. Then this mate of our George's comes in and says he's seen her out with another bloke in the Albion."

Harold saw his previous suspicions justified. "How d'you mean?" he demanded, then turning to Lilly he said, "What did I tell you!"

"There wasn't just her," George protested but Bill looked sharply across to Harold and said,

"What d'you mean. 'What did I tell you?' What's going on?"

"It's nothing," Lilly put in quickly. "Just something your dad and me were talking about that's all."

George plunged in to save the situation. "She weren't alone. I mean there was a crowd of 'em. All out together."

Harold allowed himself the self-satisfied smile of confirmed prejudice and sipped quietly at his tea. They just won't bloody listen will they!

"Anyway," George was saying, "we went to see 'em. I didn't want to go…"

Bill interrupted quickly, "We went off to this pub where Andy'd seen 'em. That's all." It was like making a confession.

"The Albion?"

"Yes dad. The Albion! Our kid's just said that!"

"Only asking," Harold said.

Bill paused momentarily and took a breath to calm his angry retort. "Anyway, she was there with this crowd. We had it out and I asked her what she was doing."

"What did she say?" Lilly asked.

"She said she'd just come out for a drink with her sister and some of her mates."

"But you said she was staying in," Lilly persisted and Harold gave a small snort of derision.

"Oh mother I know I did," Bill replied with infinite patience. Weariness was beginning to overtake him just as it was creeping over all of them. They were sitting in a languid world of tiredness and reaction.

From the road outside came the sounds of traffic and people making their way to the city to see it for themselves. It all sounded so far away. Bill took up the story again.

Bill and Daisy had begun arguing and Daisy's sister's friends had rallied round her and there had been a bit of pushing and shoving.

"Come on, clear off! Can't you see you're not wanted." Then a couple of shoulder jabs and Bill had turned but there were too many. "Oh yeah? Want to make something of it do you?" It was humiliating and Bill had stood undecided whether to risk it. Then they had turned to George. "Got your bodyguard. Eh? Eh?" They began giving George taps on the cheek; not enough to hurt but enough to infuriate. George had coloured up in temper and they had mocked him. "Nah! He's not going to do owt. He's like his brother only yellow. Not even going in the army. Conchie! That what you are? Eh? Conscientious objector? Eh?" And more taps to the face.

"Leave him alone." Bill pushed them away from George.

"Oh yes!!" His adversary raised his face to Bill in challenge.

Bill tried to resort to reason. "Leave him! He'd go in same as the rest of you if they'd have him. Only he's badly. His accident! Look at him!" He resisted the impulse to square up to the fellow who was now facing him.

George turned away. "Shut up Bill. Come on let's go."

More shoving, more bravado. "Yes go on. Yellow. Pair of you."

Bill turned but now Daisy pushed forward.

"Leave him," she said and pulled away the one who was trying to provoke Bill. He allowed himself to be pushed to one side.

"Need a woman to fight your battles do yer?" he taunted.

Bill took half a step forward but Daisy intervened again.

"No Bill. Why don't you go. You'd no need to come here anyway."

The crowd parted with mock respect to allow George and Bill to pass and they received further jostles as they made their way between them.

They left, humiliated, and what was worse for Bill was that he'd been humiliated in front of Daisy as well as his brother.

But Bill told his mother and father none of this. Only that he had followed Daisy home to get it sorted out between them.

They had crossed town to the road where Daisy lived up Parson Cross, pausing on the way for a couple of fierce drinks. George had been reluctant but Bill silenced his protests. "We're going to have it out. You're always 'same you. Let anybody push you around. And anyway! She's not talking to me like that! Telling me to go away. Don't know what's going on!"

The road was dark and silent; street lamps unlit and not a glimmer of light from the blacked out houses. It was cold and the moon shone fitfully through broken cloud. Bill waited in the shelter of an overgrown privet. George paced the pavement, hunching his shoulders for warmth.

"Come on Bill," he whispered, thrusting his hands deeper in his pockets. "We don't want any trouble. Let it go. Come on. Let's go. It's getting late."

But Bill remained close by the hedge, fuelled by alcohol and his anger, oblivious to the cold. Determined to see her and wipe out the image of him slinking away beaten, protected by her intervention, her bloody charity. It was all her fault.

George was at it again. "Come on Bill it's cold! We can't wait here all night."

"Well go on then," Bill taunted. "You go home if you want. I'm staying here."

George stopped pacing and peered into the darkness from where Bill's voice had come but there was no further response. After a few moments he resumed his pacing again.

Bill stirred. "Keep your eyes open will you. I'm busting for a lag."

He went into a passage between the houses and George took up Bill's position against the privet. Until Bill returned and they stood together, waiting.

George began to whistle softly to himself to relieve the boredom

"Shut up will you! They'll know we're here!" George received a sharp dig from Bill's elbow. Then he felt Bill stiffen with alertness.

"What's up?" George whispered. "They here?"

Bill shushed him and began to move like a shadow along the street close to the hedge. "Aye," he whispered. "Sounds like there's a few of 'em."

They hid in a garden gateway and listened again. Bill felt angry and ridiculous creeping about like this in the shadows like he was a kid again. But he didn't want a confrontation with all of 'em and he didn't want his younger brother involved in any trouble. His mother'd never forgive him. Anyway, he wanted to see Daisy on her own!

Along the road the group had stopped. They heard the sounds of giggling and low chatter. Then silence. It lasted forever then faint giggling broke out again. Bill felt jealousy flare as the breathless sounds were carried to him on the night breeze. Then came the sound of farewells as the group dispersed, and footsteps tripping along the street, loud in the darkness as Daisy and her sister approached.

Bill held his breath. As they drew abreast he reached from the shadows and gripped her arm.

"Daisy." The fierce whisper in the darkness terrified her. Daisy screamed; Mary, her sister began to run. Then recognition dawned.

Daisy pulled her arm free and said, "What you doing…?" but Bill cut her short.

"Come here!" He grabbed her arm again. "What's going on then?"

Mary paused in her flight and turned. "Leave her alone!" she yelled.

"What you doing here?" Daisy repeated. She wriggled again but Bill held her firmly.

"What the bloody hell d'you think I'm doing here." He began to work himself up into a temper. "I've been here half the bloody night. And our kid!"

"Tell him to stop it," Mary wailed. "He'll have me mother and dad out!"

"I've been stood here waiting for you." Alcohol was evaporating the last shreds of Bill's self control. "I'm bloody frozen!!" he shouted.

"Billy. Bill, be quiet." Daisy looked anxiously about her in the darkness.

Now Mary intervened. "Why don't you mind your own business!" She turned on George. "Tell him to get off home. And you get off with him!"

"You're being ridiculous Bill." Daisy free'd herself again and set off along the road to Mary but Bill caught her and turned Daisy to face him.

"Who is he? Who's that bloke?"

"Let me go Bill." Daisy pushed against him with her free arm. "Let – go – of – me."

"Ey-up Bill you'll hurt her." George cried and tried to restrain him but Bill pushed George's hand away.

"What you doing going out with other fellers behind my back?"

"If you must know, it's Sally's birthday tomorrow!" Daisy cried with defiance. "We just went out for a drink with her and a few others. That's all."

"And who's Sally?"

"Friend of our Mary's!"

"Well why couldn't I come then?"

"You weren't invited. She didn't invite you! Did she!"

"You said you were staying in! You said you were washing your hair!"

"I changed me mind!"

Daisy set off again with Mary's arm about her. In his mind Bill heard the giggles and the silence in the darkness.

"And who's he?" he shouted.

"Shut up Bill. You'll have all the street out." Daisy broke into a trot. Her hand was to her face trying to hold back tears.

"Don't you tell me to shut up!" he shouted.

"Bill," George pleaded and Bill turned on him too.

"And you can shut up as well!"

He ran and caught Daisy again. She stopped and fiddled in her handbag for a handkerchief.

"Go and fetch me dad," Daisy sobbed and Mary ran on ahead.

"What you crying for? Eh? I saw you, up there at the end of the street. With him! You were necking! Weren't you? Weren't you?" Bill punctuated his accusations with prodding and pushing, making Daisy stagger where she stood. "Come on... who was...?"

"Oh shut up! Don't you ever get sick of the sound of your own voice?" Daisy set off again with tears streaming down her face. "Leave me alone!"

"Aw go on," he taunted. "Get off home. Back to your mother."

A door opened as Daisy ran down the path and her father stood silhouetted in the doorway.

"What's all this bloody row?" He was a big man, a foundryman and his voice filled the street.

"Dad..." Daisy cried.

Bill shouted more defiance and her father saw the two young men caught in the spill of light from the doorway.

"Get off home where you belong!" he shouted. Bill shouted in retaliation and Daisy's father turned on the doorstep. "Right! Ada!" he called. "Where's me shoes? Hey you! Just you wait there! I'll bloody well give you what for!" He turned his attention to Daisy. "And look at you! This is a fine time to come in! Look at the state of you! Get in!" He pushed her roughly inside and slammed the door.

Bill stood in indecision. His anger was unspent, still seeking an outlet. Confusions arose. Now he felt ashamed that he'd made her cry. It had all gone wrong! He was angry with the whole world. Self pity welled inside and he walked, not knowing where his path took him, not caring where he went. He needed a crowd, any crowd to cleave through and shoulder aside in anger, seeking confrontation to purge the bitterness he felt. But the streets were empty and he meandered, lost in misery with George like a phantom at his side.

"Leave her Bill. There's plenty of others."

Bill didn't respond. He wandered, anywhere but home. Can't go home. Can't face them yet... not yet... not just yet...

And the sound of sirens began to wail over the city and he allowed himself to be pulled unwillingly into the nearest air raid shelter.

"Well I don't know." Harold was saying. "Just because you've had a bit of a row with the lass, that's no reason not to come home is it? You might have got into all sorts of trouble like that. And what about me and your mother? And our George?"

"Oh you just don't understand do you!"

He looked at his pot of tea with distate. It was cold with a creamy layer of milk coagulating on its surface. Slowly, Bill roused himself, avoiding their looks.

"I'm going up for a lie down. I'm tired."

CHAPTER 4

Locarno

There was no consolation to be had. Bill's work in the heavy spring department was noisy and demanding and tiring and it failed to erase Daisy from his mind. He worked like an automaton, gripping each glowing bar of steel in the tongs as it rolled out of the furnace and dragging it forward to fit the end onto the coiling mandrel. Oh Christ! Daisy! The buttons of her dress undone, the softness of her breasts. Locate the tapered end into the gripper, straining to keep the red hot steel from twisting out of his grip whilst hot scale falls around his feet. Guide the glowing bar along the mandrel as it coils around it, then twist the tapered end into alignment, flat against the last coil. Release the gripper, reverse the rotation. Daisy lying on the grass by his side and her fingers stealing round his neck as she kissed him. Free the spring, designed to absorb the recoil from an eight inch naval gun, a hundredweight of hot coiled steel and swing it clanging onto the steel plate floor. His hand upon her stockinged leg, moving along her thigh beneath her dress whilst the spring was hoisted away for tempering in the bath of molten lead. Wipe away the sweat!

"Get your mind on your bloody work!" Bill looked round. Another glowing steel bar had slid from the furnace and was already rolling towards him on the conveyer. "You'll be having a bleeding accident!"

Get back in focus. Reach with the tongs, drag the bar forward, locate it beneath the gripper on the coiling mandrel, banish the memory of her eyes looking into his, heave the spring with anger onto the steel floor, slippery with scale. The pounding of the hammers beyond the furnace, beating tapered ends into the bars. The softness of her hair, the scent of perfume... the pounding of his heart...

Sometimes Bill almost succeeded in ridding himself of her spell. Nights out with the lads. Drinking. Snooker. But she was always there, haunting him like an unbidden spirit in his memory. And Bill's preoccupation became more intense and his mate's teasing became less tolerant.

"Pull your bloody self together. What's up with thi?"

"Are you supping up or what? It's thy round!"

If only they knew. His memories confused him. He'd determined to rid himself of her but he didn't want to. He had raged at her on that final night, sending her home in tears but he had been humiliated by her. It was only Daisy's intervention that had prevented the scene in the Albion from turning really nasty. He was guilty of treating her shamefully, repaying her concern like that. But she had been with somebody else! But it was a friend of her sister's. Or a friend's friend. Stupid, stupid jealousy!!

"Come on! For Christ's sake! It's your shot!"

"What? Sorry."

Bill leaned over the table and lined up on an easy red.

A snigger from the opposing pair. "Bloody Hell he's missed it! Again!"

A sneer from his playing partner. "That's seven and bloody six tha's cost me tonight!"

By the end of the second week Bill was casting about for a solution. Perhaps if he were to try to see Daisy again. If only to say how sorry he was that it had finished the way it had. No! That would make him look weak and foolish. Or would it?

His mates tried to cajole him out of it. "Forget about her. Come on." But the more they tried, the more Bill, despite his better judgement, resisted their blandishments. He suddenly realised that he had no-one he could really confide in about the way he felt. But, he told himself, you can't just switch somebody out of your life just like that! Not if you think anything about them! Trouble was, did she still care about him?

Well, he was going to do something about it! It was intolerable the way things were!

But what?

There came a night when Bill knew he had to see her. He had a shrewd idea of where she might be found. He didn't want to go calling, not after the slanging match with her father in the street. And anyway he couldn't be sure that Daisy wouldn't slam the door in his face. But the Locarno was a different matter. There he could arrange to bump into Daisy as if by chance and it would save face all round.

Wednesday night. That's when he would see her. Now, having resolved to do it Bill couldn't wait for the time to pass. He was impatient of some unforeseen delay.

"Is me best shirt clean mother?"

"Yes. Why?"

"I want to wear it. That's why."

"No need to snap me head off."

He washed and shaved early then fretted over the lethargic way his mother set about tea. He forced himself to take it at their pace and sat talking to George on the settee. He knew they wouldn't understand why he wanted to see Daisy again. Valiantly he tried to avoid their innocent questions.

"Where are you going?"

"Who with?"

"Well if not with our George who with then?"

"Well why not? We always play snooker on Wednesdays."

"Well what's the rush anyway?"

Was it always like this? Jesus Christ!

"I'm just going out. That's all. I always get dressed up when I'm going out! Look, how much longer's tea going to be?"

Inside the Locarno it was dark except for the stage where an energetic bandleader was taking the massed dancers on the floor through one of Dorsey's latest hits. Cigarette smoke hung in layers above their heads. The floor was jumping and alive with noise. Bill waited just inside the door and acknowledged a wave. He was standing in a crowd underneath the balcony. In the wall behind him and to his left was the cigarette kiosk, glowing in the darkness. At the extreme right of the balcony a crowded staircase led down onto the dancefloor. The bandleader brought the number to a stop and the dancers cheered and applauded.

Bill started to move beneath the balcony towards a group of tables beyond the staircase. My God! He was in luck. Straightaway! Daisy was sitting at one of the tables with a group of friends. The girls looked up at Bill's approach and Daisy turned to see him making straight for her. Only it wasn't Daisy at all. Bill hesitated disconcerted, gave a half smile and lost himself in the crowd again. Blond hair! That's what did it. Ah well…

He did a circuit of the dancefloor, scanning the girls cramming its perimeter but there was no sign of her. He checked his watch. It was early yet. There was still time for her to arrive and anyway he'd only… Someone punched him on the shoulder from behind. Bill turned, clenching his fists. Charlie Bradshaw was grinning at him, holding up his hands defensively. "Na then Bill. Alright then? I thought tha were going to hit me then."

Bill responded with a mock feint and grinned back. Charlie offered Bill a cigarette. "Seen owt tha fancies?"

Bill shook his head nonchalantly. "Not much. There's a couple at a table across the other side."

The floor began to jump as the band swung into another big number. Bill leaned into the match. "What you doing now then?"

Charlie leered at the girls around them. "Anybody! Has tha noticed there's more tarts than blokes nowadays. Thank God for deferment eh."

But Bill wasn't listening. He was scanning the floor for Daisy. "Listen," he said, "I'm just going up on 'balcony for a bit. Coming?"

"No," Charlie said. "There's plenty to go at down here." He preened, gave his hair a stroke and nodded toward two girls who were whispering together and casting glances in Bill and Charlie's direction. "Look at 'tits on that one eh. Coming?"

"You've no chance. I'll see you in a bit."

"Yeah." Charlie said without listening and headed for the girls.

Bill watched for a few seconds. Already the girl he'd targeted was smiling and they were both gesturing in Bill's direction. Charlie turned to him but Bill gave a wave and made his way toward the staircase. Charlie'd be alright.

The balcony was full as well and the counter at the back was busy serving the people who crowded round it. Bill leaned against the balcony rail, scanning the floor below. Suddenly she was there, moving along the edge of the dancefloor with two other girls, one reasonably pretty but the other a mousy, plain girl. They won't mind having her with them, Bill thought without charity. Her plainness makes the other two look good and she might get a boyfriend because of their attractiveness. They paused as a surge of people moving across the floor blocked their path. Bill looked hard again. No mistake this time. It was Daisy and now they had turned and were disappearing beneath the balcony.

Bill headed swiftly for the staircase. As he neared the bottom he leaned over the handrail, scanning the area where he had just seen her. Damn! Where had she got to? The exit doors were in the corner under the balcony. Surely she wasn't leaving already! Next to the doors the cigarette kiosk shone bright in the darkness and it was hard to recognise the people silhouetted against it. But she wasn't there! He peered again. He was sure she wasn't. He reached the foot of the stairs just as the dance number finished. Streams of people left the floor and headed for the stairs, impeding his progress. It was like trying to swim against the tide. Bill turned to shoulder his way through and suddenly he was face to face with Daisy. She paused, briefly recognised him then tried to push past with her friends. They followed with their noses in the air. Bill took Daisy's arm. She looked fleetingly up at him and took his hand off her arm.

"Do you mind!"

"Daisy."

But she continued aloofly on her way.

The band struck up again. Bill saw Charlie waving at him from the floor with the big breasted girl and a smirk of triumph. Bill responded with an absent grin of acknowledgement. He was nonplussed! He should have thought it through more carefully. He hadn't allowed for Daisy snubbing him. He lit up again and leaned against a pillar.

Now Daisy was on the dancefloor with an unlikely looking partner. She didn't seem to be all that interested and as the music stopped she left him with barely a 'thank you'. Bill stubbed out his cigarette and moved to her side.

"You look super tonight. New dress?"

"I've had it for months." She was scanning the people milling around.

"Well you look nice anyway."

"Thank you." She turned and ignored him as her two friends came over in response to Daisy's wave.

The plain one turned her back on Bill and said, "Come on I'm thirsty. Let's go and have a drink."

"No thanks," Bill riposted, "I've just had one." Daisy turned on him with a rebuke and he quickly added, "Unless you want one." He gave her a half smile of optimism.

"Come on Daisy." The plain one took Daisy's arm. "What's he doing here anyway?"

"Yes," the other added, "don't you think you've caused enough trouble!"

They gathered Daisy between them and bustled her away. Bill followed closely and leaned between them, chatting. "All right then, I'll buy the lot. I don't mind. Anything for a quiet life! But it's no good for you, you know. It makes you fat."

The plain one gave Bill a look. Bill smiled at her. She huffed and turned away. The other one said, "Why don't you just go away and leave Daisy alone!"

Bill leaned in close to Daisy and whispered, "Can I talk to you? I want to talk to you."

And he smelled the scent of her again, unique and special, just as he had tried to remember it. It came to him and was gone almost before he had time to register it. A wisp of Daisy's hair accidentally brushed his cheek.

"We've nothing to say Bill." She walked on with an air of aloofness to the admiration of her friends. Bill followed them to the balcony and pressed his way ahead to buy their drinks. Reluctantly they followed Bill across to a table.

"I'd rather have had coffee," the plain one said.

"Please yourself," Bill replied. Daisy was gazing over the balcony rail. Ignoring the resentful looks of the other two Bill joined her and looked out over the noise and swirl below.

"Will you come out with me tomorrow night?"

"No. I'm washing my hair."

The old excuse. How easy it sounded. Daisy continued gazing out over the rail.

"Monday then."

"I can't."

"Why not?"

"Don't want to."

"What about Wednesday? We used to go out Wednesdays."

"I don't know. I don't know what I'm doing next week yet." She turned away from him.

"Oh come on Daisy. We used to have fun together. We can come dancing again like we used to."

Silence!

Bill sensed indecision.

He repeated gently, "Come on Daisy. I'll call for you Wednesday night."

"No," she repeated.

"Why not?"

"No. Look, I'm here with my friends."

Bill glanced briefly at the others. They glared back. Their intervention now would finish his chances. Leaning close he whispered, "I've joined up."

Daisy turned to face him. "You've not!"

"I have."

"But I thought you were in a reserved occupation?"

"I am."

Daisy looked uncomprehending.

"I've not got my papers. I've joined up. Volunteered."

"But what for? Whatever for?"

There was concern in Daisy's voice and Bill's heart soared.

"I told you I would. Ever since that afternoon in the park. Remember? We stood on that field at the top and looked across the city. I said I'd fight 'em and I'm going to."

"But you don't have to!" Daisy cried. "You could have waited. Well... but anyway you can't... I mean... you're in a reserved occupation. Aren't you?"

"I've volunteered aircrew."

A light passed across Daisy's face. "Bill!" she breathed, with a kind of respect in her voice, "RAF?"

"Yes. I said I would. And I have."

At the table the plain girl was getting to her feet. "Come on Daisy. We're going down to dance."

51

"What?"

"There's them lads down there look."

Bill reached for Daisy's hand but she drew it away. "No Bill. I'm here with Sally and Brenda."

The plain friend persisted. "Are you coming then? I'm going to dance. Aren't we."

The other friend rose from the table. "I'm going down anyway." she said.

Daisy suddenly took Bill's hand in hers and released it just as abruptly. "Tomorrow night."

Bill was on the point of reminding her that she had said she was washing her hair but he checked himself and said, "I'll call for you."

"No," Daisy replied quickly. "I'll see you at the corner. Eight o'clock."

Bill watched them go. She could have danced with him! Oh well, what the hell. He left the dance hall and went to the Albion. George was there with Alma, his latest girlfriend. Oblivious to the fact that he was playing gooseberry, Bill spent the rest of the evening with them.

CHAPTER 5

Reconciliation and seduction

Bill and Daisy were drinking bitter at a round iron table with a pockmarked marble top in a little brown roomed pub. The bar was full, the regulars engaged in desultory chatter sitting on horsehair benches along the walls. From time to time the publican regarded Bill and Daisy with suspicion; they weren't regulars and they were young, out of place amongst all the older drinkers. But Bill and Daisy didn't care, they were too engrossed in each other, relieved and happy to be together again.

"Have you really joined up Bill?"

"Yes," he replied, "I've volunteered aircrew. I've got to go for final interview and medical next week."

The low chatter of the seedy room was punctuated by a burst of laughing at the bar and the clink of glasses.

"When will you be going?" Daisy's eyes were cast down, unable to meet Bill's as she asked the fatal question.

"If everything goes alright – just a few days I suppose. Couple of weeks perhaps. It all depends…"

"Why Bill? Why?" There were tears in Daisy's voice and she bustled with her handkerchief. Bill pushed his empty glass to one side and leaned across the table. He took Daisy's hand in his and the publican glared at them.

"I've got to go now Daisy. I've no choice. After that row there didn't seem to be nothing else for it. I just wanted to get out there and do something."

"But can't you get out of it?" she pleaded. "Can't you say you've changed your mind? After all you're in a reserved occupation. Can't you Bill?"

"No," he replied with gentleness and finality. "I'm going through with it. I can't stand by any more. Every time you hear the news we're being beaten here and beaten there." As he spoke, Daisy's hand in his Bill's eyes were elsewhere. "I've got to go don't you see? We've got to go and fight them…" He fell silent, his young face clouded beneath the dark wavy hair.

"Are you having a drink or what?"

Bill looked up dreamily at the publican standing over them at the table. "There's people want to use these seats." And he glared at them and cleared away their empty glasses.

They felt the shabbiness of the pub and its smoke stained, grimy walls oppressing them; the rudeness of the crowd trespassed on their privacy. They left and walked hand in hand in the darkness letting their desire for each other guide them where it would.

Crossing the road, oblivious to the cold they went into the park. Bill put his arm about Daisy's shoulder and drew her to him. She snuggled close and they savoured the intimacy of each other, the brush of thigh against thigh as they walked. She turned to face him. How pale and fragile she seemed in the moonlight and Bill's heart jumped as he looked at her. They paused and kissed, a little kiss, just the sweetness of her mouth and Daisy's nose cold against his cheek. Then they continued further into the shadows. They slowed as they came upon the bench. It was hung over by the dark mass of the trees, silent except for the murmuring of the little stream beyond flowing lightly over stones. Daisy would have sat but Bill turned her to him and kissed her again as they stood in the darkness.

Daisy trembled but not with cold. Despite all of Harold's misgivings and the reputation of her sister Daisy was still a virgin. But she knew it was going to be now. She was going to give herself to him. Her girl dreams, walking down the aisle in virgin white with the innocent veil were cast aside. Bill was here and he was going to go away and leave her. Oh and she wanted him. She wanted to go beyond the impotent fingering and caressing. She wanted them to belong to each other completely as man and wife, to please and keep him forever.

"Not here," she murmured tremulously. Bill paused and tried to see her face but now not even the gleam of moon showed as Daisy took Bill's hand and drew him down beneath the trees. His hands shook with dreadful anticipation and his heart pounded as he spread his raincoat on the cold grass. Awkwardly they sank to their knees and slowly reclined in each other's embrace until passion took over and she was pushing and moving hard beneath him. Bill struggled with furious patience to find her and uncover her and then he felt her hot, oh God so hot and wet… Daisy winced and drew herself back, "Wait." She struggled and arched herself, "Wait a second." He helped her to pull her knickers down and over her feet and then she was pulling him into her, "Be careful Bill." And kissing, kissing, kissing…

Afterwards he remembered how suddenly it became cold again. And how awkward it was then and ever afterwards to make the transition from passion to reality. He edged away from her, careful now not to soil his clothes. There was apology in Bill's movements. He began to tidy himself then bent to kiss her again, lightly. There was no response. Daisy lay without moving, without regret in her own world. The step is so easily taken and can never be retraced. So easily lost. For what? The excitement wasn't in his coming, only in the anticipation. Now Daisy felt empty and unfulfilled. For her it was over before it really began. The cold reached up into her but Daisy didn't care. Let it come and cleanse me and purge me of heat. She felt Bill's kiss. Was it duty? It was so different from his kiss of… was it an hour ago? Just a few brief moments ago. No more. She turned and tried to see him. She could hear him in the darkness brushing at his clothes, smoothing out the creases.

"Come on Daisy love. We'd better go."

Unwillingly Daisy stirred. Oh what a mess, wet and cold.

"Have you got a handkerchief or anything?"

"Yes." Bill replied hesitantly. "It's a bit… you know."

"Where's my handbag? Have you seen my handbag anywhere?"

In turn Daisy fumbled and tidied herself as best as she could. "Don't look."

Bill turned away awkwardly. "I'm sorry…" Wrong! His voice drifted off and he stepped down to the bank of the stream, leaving Daisy to it. He heard her clothes rustle as she smoothed them down. He heard the snap of her handbag and then her voice, soft in the darkness, "Where are you?" Bill returned and joined her where she stood. She handed his raincoat to him.

"There's some on it. Will it show?"

Bill rubbed at it with his handkerchief.

"It's mostly on the inside." But thinking better of wearing it he folded it carefully across his arm with the lining concealed.

Was there anyone to watch them as they emerged from the park? A quick glance along the road showed it as dark and empty as before. Why then did they feel so guilty? And step out so briskly to put the place as far behind them as they could?

CHAPTER 6

'Boy in blue'

Why did he have to go and do it? Lilly and Harold couldn't understand it. Not even George could understand it.

"Oh whatever did you want to go and do a thing like that for?" Lilly wailed. "You've got a nice safe job. There's no need for you to go. You were exempted."

"She's right." Harold's anger at Bill for giving up a reserved occupation was tempered with the voice of reason. "What you're doing down there is far more important than twenty soldiers going and getting killed. You're on essential war work Billy."

Oh God, why don't they ever understand! He didn't want a nice safe job doing essential war work, he wanted to fight back. More importantly for Bill, he wanted to be seen to be fighting back. Oh yes, he'd seen the way some people looked, people who didn't know. Conchie! That was the word they used. Well, he didn't want it used about him!

Harold and Lilly waited for Bill to fail the medical as George had done, for George had received his papers but much to his relief had been rejected on medical grounds. But not Bill. He passed A1 – even the stringent eyesight test for aircrew. He passed everything they put before him and was selected for training as a radio operator/air gunner on a bomber squadron.

Oh but his eyes shone as he told them on the day his papers came confirming his selection. He could hardly contain his excitement and how could they deny him when they saw him, bursting with pride. George solemnly shook Bill's hand and they had a get-together that night with the regulars at the White Lion. There was back patting and well wishing and despite their misgivings Harold and Lilly swelled with pride watching Bill at the centre of the admiring crowd. And they all had a drop too much and made their unsteady way home to sleep it off until the alarm dragged them out to another days work.

But when, the following night Bill told Daisy of his selection she became sullen and withdrawn. They couldn't talk without arguing and long silences built up between them. The evening was a disaster and Bill took Daisy home early. The goodnight kiss was a mere peck and his triumph turned to ashes.

Oh! but what the hell for the morning of his departure had arrived!

Bill's suitcase was open on the settee waiting for the addition of last minute items; his shoes were polished and gleaming on the hearth; there was a shave with a new blade and his best suit was laid out on the bed.

Lilly was bustling, afraid he'd miss the bus, the train or both. Finally Bill emerged and sat in his father's chair to lace up his shoes.

"Are you sure you've got everything Billy?"

"You've put me razor in haven't you mother?"

"Yes."

"That's it then. That's the lot."

He busied himself before the mirror with his collar and tie leaving Lilly to close and lock the case.

"Now don't lose these keys or you'll never get it undone."

"I don't need it locking." The fuss was beginning to get on Bill's nerves; all he wanted now was to get on his way. But Lilly still wasn't content and she went off upstairs for a leather strap and buckled it around the suitcase for extra security.

"There," she said with satisfaction, "that'll stop it bursting open only don't let it get lost will you. That's the one we use when we go on our holidays to your Aunty Ame's at Worcester."

"I won't." Bill tried to hide the exasperation in his voice, calling as he went back up the stairs, "I'll post it back when I get there."

He took his jacket from the bed, checking that his wallet was in the lining pocket and took a clean white handkerchief from the chest of drawers. He felt good in the suit and wearing it during the day in the middle of the working week when everyone else was at work gave the whole occasion a special feel. Feeling slightly self conscious Bill went back down into the living room.

"What time did you say your train was?"

Bill ignored the question; he had already answered it a dozen times. Standing before the mirror he busied himself with his breast pocket handkerchief, arranging it with three points neatly showing.

"You'll have to get a move on. You'll miss that bus."

Oh shut up mother I'm not a little boy! But he turned to check the clock against his wristwatch. Christ! A sudden surge of panic siezed him.

"Come on mother," he cried unreasonably, "we'll be late. Bus comes in a minute." And in a sudden flurry of coats and luggage they were ready and on their way.

"All the best Billy," Mrs. Whitehead called from the yard across the terrace as Lilly locked the back door. "What time's his train Lill?"

57

"Quarter past eleven."

"All the best then love." She stood and watched them set off down the terrace with her arms folded across her ample expanse of apron then she went off to tell the neighbours in her yard.

The station was crowded. It had an air of having been built with the crowds in it with only the faces constantly changing. Bill left Lilly with his suitcase at the platform barrier while he joined the queue at the ticket window. He felt more relaxed; now they were at the station he had plenty of time. Then they joined the stream of passengers and well wishers impatiently streaming through the barrier onto the platform. The ticket inspector punched Bill's ticket, examined Lilly's platform ticket and mumbled, "Blackpool train platform three."

Descending the footbridge steps to the crowded platform below they paused, searching for a gap at the platform edge when Bill abruptly took Lilly's arm.

"This way, come on." There was Daisy amongst the waiting travellers, searching for him. He stood for a moment before her, suddenly bashful in his mother's presence then he put his suitcase down and took Daisy's hands.

"What you doing here?"

"What d'you think? Come to see you off. Aren't you glad to see me?"

"Of course I am. Of course I am." He almost kissed her, thought better of it and hugged her to him instead.

"Bill." Daisy's eyes flickered momentarily in Lilly's direction and her voice carried a sudden edge of urgency. Bill released Daisy from his arms and searched her face. Again that earnest look. Oh why had he brought his mother along!

"It's good to see you Daisy. I didn't think you could make it. What about work?"

"I got an hour off." Daisy replied. Bill turned to look at Lilly; he wasn't sure whether his mother was disposed to be friendly towards Daisy or not. There was a frosty politeness about her and the earnestness in Daisy's manner evaporated. "How long before you get back?" Daisy's voice was low, no more than a murmur amongst all the bustle of the station and she clung to him.

"It's just a few weeks. I've got basic training and then some leave. It'll pass before you know it."

"It seems so long," she whispered, "So many things can happen."

Behind them there was a rush of passengers as a train arrived. The piercing shriek of a trainwhistle rose above the din of station announcements and amid blasts of smoke a Bristol express began to slide away from a platform at the far side of the station. Their moments together were too short; Bill's train clanked into the platform and he was caught up in the rush for doors. He vanished and they thought they had lost him forever until he reappeared, sharing a window with another parting serviceman. Along the train doors slammed and careful farewells, left too late, remained unsaid. Lilly begged him to take care and received an unexpected kiss then gave way to Daisy. But the fond farewell was oh! so brief. The whistle blew, a flag was waved and the coaches began to move. Daisy's reluctant fingers slid from his and he parted from her, one face among so many peering from the windows and waving as the train curved into the sooty tunnel and its enfolding clouds of smoke...

Basic training for the new intake was taking place 'somewhere in England'. Nowhere that you could find on a map but the wind blew thin off the damp grey Irish Sea and when it was a clear day you could just make out Blackpool's tower in the distance.

The weeks passed by quickly, though not quick enough for some who cursed, found difficulties in everything they had to do and made their own lives a misery. But Bill found it tolerable. He soon had pals and after day upon day of routemarching and squarebashing they exchanged remedies for blistered feet and getting Brasso stains off battledress blue. He discovered the cameraderie unknown outside the armed forces. They became tolerably smart; the warrant officers abused them less and they looked down upon the batches of new recruits who followed, amusing themselves by referring to the newcomers as sprogs. They learned the language of the R.A.F. and the air became thick with service slang, used freely amongst themselves but more cautiously when regular aircrew were about. One or two planned R.A.F. moustaches. Their final week of basic training was spiced with the anticipation of leave and the triumphal return home. And in the end, why it had seemed like no time at all.

Bill jumped from the bus at the request stop at the corner where the jennel from the footbridge across the oily river emerged into the road. It was a bright day, the sun was shining through a scattering of clouds, and the grimy privet hedge lining the river bank was thick with leaf buds. He pulled his tie straight and tweaked it to stand proud above the unfastened top button of his uniform. Just in case anybody should ask. Aircrew! And with his forage cap set at a jaunty angle Bill set off with his suitcase and knapsack on the final steps to home.

With growing pleasure he acknowledged the greeting of two neighbours who passed him, glowing with conscious pride at their surprise and feeling their admiring gaze upon his back. Then up the terrace into the backyard and the familiar door of home.

Lilly was in the kitchen seeing to Saturday dinner; a pan of cabbage was on the verge of boiling over and she turned as Bill entered and almost dropped her knife in surprise.

"Bill!"

All thoughts of cabbage forgotten she put the knife in the sink, wiped her hands on her apron and rushed and hugged him to her. Then remembering her stained apron and Bill's smart uniform she held him at arm's length in admiration.

"Oh Billy...!" she cried. Then suddenly remembering she returned to the cabbage, turned down the gas, gave her eyes and nose a wipe on the hem of her apron and turned to him again. "But I thought you weren't coming home 'till this afternoon. Your train don't get in until quarter to four."

"I didn't get the train." Bill walked through into the living room. Nothing had changed; why it might have been only yesterday that he had left and he was mildly surprised at the feeling of pleasure it gave him. "I got a lift back with one of the chaps. Quicker."

Lilly followed him through with pride in her eyes. Bill was preening before the mirror. How grand he looked in his new uniform. He turned and leaned back, posing against the mantelpiece and lit a cigarette. His buttons shone and the waves in his dark hair gleamed. Lilly said, "I'll put kettle on for a cup of tea. Your dad'll be home soon. And our George. Oh you do look..." And she turned and busied herself in the kitchen.

There was to be a party. It was all arranged and the upstairs room in the White Lion was booked. Charlie Bradshaw, Earnshaw and the others had organised it. Bill protested when they told him. "I've only just got home. Give us a chance. Only got in this afternoon."

"Its organised now," Charlie insisted. "So tha's got to come."

"But why a party? We could all have just gone out for a drink. I'm not 'only one in 'forces."

"Your 'only one we know that's going up there." Charlie pointed skywards, laughing. "Aircrew, boy in blue! Touch of class. So we're having a party. Hey – and don't go getting changed – we want to see thee in uniform. Right? Right!"

There it was, don't argue. Bill had no intention of arguing; he knew the uniform flattered him.

"What about Daisy? She's coming isn't she? I hope you've told Daisy about it."

George and Charlie looked at each other slyly.

"I don't know. Did you tell her George?"

"No, I thought you were going to…!

"No I don't think so."

"Oh come on!" Bill knew they must have invited her. Still… he doubted. "Surely you've… for Christ's sake. Somebody must have. Surely!"

Bill's self assurance, bordering on the pompous since his return was shattered. Charlie stepped forward and clapped him on the shoulder as George shook with laughter at the look of anxiety on Bill's face.

"Come here. Course she'll be there. Now then go and have thi' sen a wash and shave. We'll see thee down there about eight. And don't forget, keep that uniform on."

It was strange the effect his uniform had on his mother and father. They deferred to him as though he was an honoured visitor. After dinner when Lilly put Bill's mug of tea before him she stood back as though waiting for approval. He met Harold coming the opposite way through the kitchen door and Harold stepped aside. It was even the same with George. At first Bill enjoyed it but it soon began to irritate him. Perhaps, he hoped, it would change when he got into his civvies; he hoped it would but meanwhile he kept the uniform on. He felt good in it but he would have to find a way to get them off their best behaviour; it would spoil his leave otherwise.

Somehow they all managed to be ready in time and Harold stood and surveyed his sons. "Come on then. Its quarter to; they'll be starting without us."

"Do I need a headscarf?" Lilly was rummaging in the sideboard drawer. "Is it cold out?"

On an impulse Bill said, "Dad why don't you all go on ahead and I'll come up in a minute."

"Why, what's up?"

"Nothings up dad. It's been a busy day – its going to be a busy night. I'll just have two or three minutes to myself before I go. I shan't be long."

Lilly looked up from the sideboard. "We'll wait with you then. Then we can all go on together."

Bill wished he had never said it. Christ! Why was it always like this? "No mother. You and me dad go on with our George. I'll be along in a couple of minutes. Alright."

"But it's your party Billy. You've got to come along to your party."

"No mother." Why was it always so bloody difficult? He continued patiently, "I know it's my party and I'll come along in a minute."

Lilly started to protest again and Bill held up his hand and smiled at her.

"Just a couple of minutes. You go along and tell 'em I'm on my way. I just feel like a couple of minutes on my own. That's all. Shan't be long."

It wouldn't do though would it and their protests hung in the air. Not understanding and more than a little resentful they went along without him. But when they had gone Bill switched off the radio and savoured the silence; the intimacy of his home, the familiar surroundings and the first solitude he'd had for weeks.

Avoiding the usual Saturday night crowd in the bar Bill continued instead along the passage to the door marked 'private' and the stairs to the upstairs function room. Half way up he met a neighbour from along the street, an elderly widower, one of Harold's friends. He raised his empty glass.

"Billy!! You're here then. Just going down for a refill." He took Bill's hand and shook it warmly. "Well done young feller. Well done. We should have more like you. Well done."

In a congratulatory glow Bill continued upstairs. There was a shout, "Bill's here!" as he opened the door and a cheer rose as the crowd in the room surged forward with handshakes and pats on the back; kisses from the older women and coy glances from the younger ones. Bill made his way through them to his mother and father.

"See, not too long was I."

"Still don't see why you couldn't have come with us," Harold grumbled.

And what had I been wishing for earlier this evening Bill mused wryly to himself; business as usual? But he wouldn't be drawn into an argument, not tonight. He was filled with the elation of his reception.

"Never mind dad, I'm here now. Come on I'll get you and me mother a drink. Oh, where's Daisy?"

"Don't know," Harold replied without enthusiasm. "She was here a bit since. Perhaps she's gone down with our George." There was a moment's hesitation.

"Come on then." Bill turned for the door. "I'll get you and me mother a drink. Where's our George?" he called to the room in general, "Anybody seen our George?"

"Gone to the bar," came a voice in reply.

"Gone to the dogs." cried another, raising a laugh at Bill's departing figure.

His reception was the same in the bar, more handshakes and back patting. "Good old Bill." "Here Bill's not got a drink." "Pint of bitter for Bill…"

He made a smiling progress to where George was leaning against the counter with a beaming smile on his face. By his side in a powder blue coat with a smile combining relief and welcome was Daisy.

"Hello."

Bill's heart filled with joy. For a moment he stood transfixed without reply. Daisy lowered her eyes under Bill's gaze. "Aren't you going to say hello to me then." Bill could have taken her and kissed her there. Someone pressed a pint on him and he became aware once more of the noise and bustle surrounding them. Turning to George he fished some money from his pocket.

"Here George get you and me mother and dad a drink will you." He looked at Daisy again unable to say the things he was feeling. He was overjoyed and content, for the moment, just to drink in the image of her standing there. He bent to her. "You look terrific love. I don't know what to say."

Daisy flushed with embarrassment. "Billy... there's people looking."

"What do I care. Come on, bring your drink."

Daisy hesitated as Bill turned to George, "Oh get Daisy another one will you. Have you got enough?" He put his hand on Daisy's arm. "I thought you'd have been upstairs with the rest of 'em." Again Daisy hesitated. "Come on let's get back upstairs and join 'em."

"No Bill. I... I'm sorry. I shouldn't have come. They don't want me up there."

Bill was taken aback. This was a fine homecoming! "What's up? What are you talking about?" Didn't everybody know he wanted Daisy to be there! "Of course we want you... they want you... what do you mean?"

"I should have stayed at home. I'm sorry Bill, I'll just finish my drink, I'll see you tomorrow."

Bill was nonplussed. This wasn't Daisy. A drink was passed over from the bar for her. Bill turned to George, "Hey what's going on? Has something happened?"

"How d'you mean?"

"Has something happened between you and Daisy or what!"

Daisy took Bill's hand and pressed it. "Forget it Bill. It's alright, you go on and enjoy yourself and I'll see you tomorrow."

"I'm not forgetting it..."

George looked sharply between the two of them, recognising anger rising in Bill. He tried to mollify him. "Come on Daisy don't be like that. It's nothing. Nothing Bill. You know what me dads like. He were just a bit funny with her when she arrived that's all."

"How d'you mean, funny?"

"Oh just something he said. It weren't much. Come on Daisy, don't take it wrong way love. Come on."

But Daisy was reluctant to be cajoled. "I'm sorry George. It's just that… I don't think they like me. They don't want me here. I'd better go."

"Right!!"

"Now hang on Bill," George pleaded, "don't go and spoil things."

Bill turned on his brother icily. "Its not me that's spoiling things." He should be moving arm in arm with Daisy among the crowd, laughing, happy together. Home is the hero. But this! "All these weeks I've been looking forward to coming home… seeing Daisy again…"

"Oh and me too Bill." Daisy squeezed Bill's hand. "You've no idea how I've missed you. I've missed you terribly."

Charlie was in the doorway, calling, "Hey Bill. Bill, come on. We're waiting for you." He beckoned to them, pint in hand and came perilously close to spilling it over the people around him.

"I'm coming," Bill replied a little too sharply. He checked himself. "We're on our way; tell 'em we're coming up."

Charlie gave a knowing wink and vanished. Bill turned his attention back to his brother. "Go and tell 'em we're on our way will you." He felt Daisy stiffen in resistance. "We're coming up together. Alright! Go on George, go and tell 'em will you. And there'd better be no more nonsense from me dad either."

George departed and Bill turned to Daisy with a reassuring smile. "Come on. It's alright. I'm not letting 'em spoil things, it'll be alright. You're with me!"

Still Daisy resisted. "I still think…"

"Don't worry." He coaxed, leaning close, "You're with me and I don't give a damn about the rest. Come on, bring your drink and to hell with 'em. We'll just spend an hour and then we can slip off somewhere eh! Just you and me. Come on, just for a bit."

Daisy gave Bill a little uncertain smile and followed him weaving through the bar with a nod here, a wave and smile there until they reached the darkness at the foot of the stairs behind the door marked 'private'. Daisy paused and Bill turned to sieze the opportunity to kiss her. Daisy put her hand against his chest, resisting.

"Bill, wait."

"What is it love? Come on, you'll be alright. He didn't mean anything. You know what he's like. Stay close to me; you'll be alright." He put his arm about her and started for the stair but Daisy shrank back into the darkness in the corner.

"Bill listen." A pause then, "Do you love me?"

"Of course I do. You know I do." He gave Daisy a wicked smile. "Come on let's just show our faces and then we'll slip out. I'll show you how much I love you later."

But Daisy didn't smile back. She remained with her eyes cast down in the shadows.

"Bill."

"What is it love?"

"Bill." Her voice was low and fearful, no more than a whisper. "I… I'm pregnant." And she turned from him and hid her face against the wall.

Bill stood awkwardly, stupidly, wondering what it meant. He didn't know what to say. Bloody Hell! He took a sip of beer; suddenly his composure was slipping away.

"When? I mean… how did…?"

"Oy oy oy, here they are!" The shout came from above and two or three beery faces appeared in the open door. "Can't wait to get at it. Found a little corner have you Bill? Go on, don't just stand there, give her one!" More cheers, more faces. Christ go away and leave us alone can't you! Bill looked up at them with a grimace of a smile.

"Be with you in a minute. Just give us a minute will you. Go on, we'll be right up."

"Aye I'll bet you will!" More shouts and Bill turned back to Daisy as though to shield her from the intrusion. The door above them closed and they were alone again.

"Are you sure?"

Daisy nodded.

"When's the… when's it due?"

"I'm nearly two months gone…" Daisy started to cry, sobbing alone in the corner with her back to the world. "I'm sorry. I shouldn't have told you."

Bill reached out and touched Daisy's shoulder and she turned to him quickly and cried against his chest while he held her close and stroked her golden hair. "What am I going to do?" she wailed. Bill was thinking furiously; any time now they would be coming again to call them upstairs to join the party.

"Daisy listen. Come on love, we've got to go. Dry your eyes." He held his handkerchief to her. "Come on." There was urgency in Bill's voice now, "Come on before they all come out again with their stupid bloody jokes." He was desperate to get out of there and find somewhere that they could talk, to work it all out. God what a mess! He couldn't meet the crowd upstairs again. "What are we going to do?"

Daisy heard him say 'we' and felt a small flicker of relief. She dried her eyes, dabbing at her make-up and hair. "Will I do?"

"Come on. You're O.K."

Leaving their unfinished drinks on the stairs they left. And nobody who saw them go could tell there was anything wrong could they. Not much!

CHAPTER 7

The knot tied

They never forgave her; whatever she did was wrong. In a perverse way Harold took deep satisfaction in seeing his earlier predictions proved right and he emerged at periodic intervals from behind his Daily Herald to remind them all.

"I said right from the start she was no good." He recalled what his mate Len at work had told him. "The whole family's no good. I told you, he knows 'em. Told you back then didn't I but you wouldn't have it would you. No! Well, who's right now then! They're all the same. All of 'em. Her sister an' all." He launched into his recital. There had been that trouble the night of the first air-raid when Bill and George had gone missing all because of her. Now this! She had spoiled Bill's leave party. Leaving them all stuck up there like fools with not a word. Wondering what to say, trying to laugh it off. They had been made to look stupid in front of everybody. "And now this! Well, they're not getting married, I'll tell you that for nothing!" And Harold set his face against it.

But Lilly knew. Of course Billy had to marry the girl! He had no option. He'd got Daisy into trouble and now he had to do the right thing by her.

"But what I'm saying is, how does he know it's his?" Harold persisted. "There was all that time he didn't see her wasn't there." Lilly began to demur but Harold continued in his implacable damnation of her, "A couple of weeks they're back together and then he's away on basic training over in Blackpool or wherever it was they sent him to. How does he know it's his? That's all I'm asking."

It was all to no avail. Despite the twin assaults of doubt and innuendo from Harold on the one hand – "…all your young life in front of you…" – and Lilly's prim concern for 'doing the right and decent thing by the girl' on the other, Bill had no doubt at all. And on that first night home, back in the house after the party he had told them.

Daisy had protested at first, in some trepidation, fearful that Bill might take her protest at face value and leave her to go through the shame of her pregnancy alone. But no; Bill was steadfast. They would be married and Daisy's heart lifted with relief.

"What about your mother and father? Do they know yet?"

"My dad's ever so mad about it."

Bill could imagine it. He had still not met Daisy's parents for she had always been reluctant to take him home and introduce them. Bill's only sight of Daisy's father, a hammer driver in one of the forges, a big muscular hard drinking uncompromising steelworker had been of him standing in silhouette on the doorstep threatening to give Bill a good seeing–to and roughly pushing Daisy in through the front door.

"But mum's got over it now," Daisy continued. "And I've got our Mary. She's thrilled to bits about it. She's going to be an aunty."

It didn't help that the respective families had nothing in common. Each side blamed the other.

"Don't know who they think they are," Daisy's father said, "taking advantage of a young girl like that. He's only a railway labourer you know. His father. Oh didn't you know that? Works in 'Nunnery yard in 'LMS warehouse. Oh yes! They're nowt special."

"Forcing himself on her," Daisy's mother confided to the neighbours during a break in the concert room at The Cannon. "She had been going to have a really nice wedding. When she met the right young feller that is. Now what? We had it all planned; a nice white dress with a veil. In church…!" She took a dainty sip at her half of bitter. "But him! I mean, what is he? He had a nice steady job. And now he's thrown it all up. Well you can tell what he'll be like can't you. I mean, what sort of life's our Daisy going to have left alone with a babby and him off… Never knowing if she's ever going to see him again."

The respective families lined up in an air of mutual distrust and the wedding day was fixed. Bill returned to camp for further training before joining his operational squadron and Daisy looked with dismay at her clothing coupons and tried to reconcile her allowance with the need for a wedding outfit, maternity clothes and a layette. The families met to sort out the arrangements but nothing was satisfactory to either side. Daisy's parents certainly had no intention whatever of paying for all of Bill's lot to come and feed their faces. "And if you don't like it, you know what you can do…!"

The day of the wedding dawned grey with a hard rain driving in from the west and desolate clouds passing endlessly overhead. The grimy privet hedges lining the oil streaked river looked more lifeless than ever.

Bill stood uncomfortably in the small back bedroom he shared with George; the cold lino striking through his socks made his feet numb and his freshly shaved face felt stiff and taut. There was a curl at the side of his head that wouldn't lie with the others. He wasn't ready for it! He'd had no breakfast, just a mug of tea and he felt dull and nauseous.

George, with Myra his girlfriend, were waiting downstairs. Harold was in his best suit with brown boots and a new cap. Bill went down to face them. He felt as though his father would never forgive him. Lilly took the clothes brush and made him stand still whilst she brushed his shoulders and back. George, his own buttonhole fixed, handed one to Bill and Myra pinned it on for him but it was unsatisfactory and Bill re-pinned it himself before the mirror.

When everybody was ready and it was time to go they all trooped out of the house into the rain and caught the bus to town.

Daisy was wearing a pale green costume; it was the wrong colour for her but it didn't seem to matter and she showed! They scurried to the registry office out of the rain and spent the first few minutes in the waiting room repairing the damage to flowers, hair and makeup. Daisy's family stood apart. It was cold and the small gas fire, inadequate to heat the room, did nothing to thaw the chill that permeated the gathering.

The door opened and they were beckoned through to the office. With stiff politeness they deferred to one another and, like a visit to the dentist it was over before they knew it and they were on the doorstep again. Bill and Daisy posed together hand in hand. They didn't feel any different; they should have been the focus of attention but they weren't, everyone seemed more concerned with picking the right moment to make a dash through the rain to the reception at the Brown Bear. Mary and Myra threw confetti and it blew and swirled about the doorway. Another wedding party came dashing along the road beneath a gaberdine mack held aloft to keep the bride's hair dry and suddenly Bill and Daisy were in the way.

"Come on then," somebody said and they scuttled off in twos and threes around the corner to the pub. The landlord brought out a plate of sandwiches and they sat steaming round the fire, gradually becoming more relaxed. They raised their glasses and drank a self-conscious toast and George said a few words and hoped they would be very happy together. They stayed until it began to fill with the lunchtime crowd then they began to feel out of place all dressed up with damp confetti still clinging to them and the party broke up. The weather was just as bad; the driving rain had clearly set in for the day. So in honour of the occasion Bill and Daisy took a taxi to their new home at Daisy's Grandma Mason's.

CHAPTER 8

Advent

"Billy's coming home!" Daisy's joyful shout rang through the house, as bright and happy as the sunshine streaming through the windows. The news was greeted without enthusiasm by the old lady. Grandma Mason had not wanted her home invaded in the first place. The clash of her old ways with Daisy's young ways was creating strains that were beginning to show. It was not that she didn't care for her grandaughter. Of course she did. But it was bad enough with Daisy here alone; with Bill coming back to live with them the place wouldn't be her own any more!

"When's he coming?"

"What did you say gran?" Daisy shuffled into Grandma Mason's sitting room in carpet slippers with her cushion and Bill's letter in her hand. She was enormously pregnant and looked even more so with her long ill-fitting cardigan unbuttoned, gaping across her belly.

"I said when's he coming?" the old lady repeated testily.

"Middle of next week. Doesn't say exactly – Wednesday or Thursday I think. Looks as though he'll be home for good; something to do with going back to work or something. He doesn't say exactly."

Grandma Mason looked disapprovingly at her pregnant grandaughter. The prospect of her home being taken over entirely filled the old lady with malice. "That's him all over. Never know where you are."

"Oh gran, come on! He can't help it. He has to go where they tell him in the R.A.F."

"I suppose you want a cup of tea." She rose to go into the kitchen. "But I'm not bringing biscuits for you. Look at you, all that weight. You want to think how much they cost. Hope he's bringing some money with him this time…" She went off into the kitchen grumbling to herself and Daisy settled at the table to read her letter again with the cushion at her back for support. It was going to be any day now the nurse had said and Billy would be home in time. Everything was working out alright after all. Oh gran was awkward but she was getting on. Old people were always like that and if Bill was going to be home for a bit then things would be better. They would be able to give gran a bit of money more regularly. Oh and wait 'til she saw the baby! That would make all the difference in the world. She could dress her up in pretty clothes, dresses, bonnets and things. Gran was a good knitter; perhaps she'd be a bit more interested when the baby came and knit her some nice warm woollies for winter.

"You alright gran?" Daisy could hear the rattle of the tea things as the old lady pottered about in the kitchen. "Anything I can do?" But she made no effort to move and gran, in the kitchen made no response.

What a lovely morning, a perfect summer day with everything blooming. They would be able to take the baby out in her pram for walks together in the evening and maybe call in somewhere for a drink. Daisy hadn't been out for ages! Well, not out properly. Oh, she had done a bit of shopping but that wasn't going out. It was just right living here with gran. They had the front sitting room all to themselves with a table and a couple of old easy chairs and the back bedroom was theirs too. They shared the kitchen. It wasn't too bad. And when she'd had the baby, why she would be able to help gran about the house a bit more. Perhaps do a bit of cooking although there was nobody she knew who could cook like Grandma Mason. And if she and Billy wanted to go out alone together – say to the pictures or something – well gran would be there to look after the baby for them.

Daisy's back ached again. Ah well, soon be over. What an age it had been. The sun shone in through the glass warming Daisy's hand where it lay on the dark polished wood of the table. Birds were singing outside and roses were beginning to bloom in the garden. What a beautiful day it was.

Bill came home the following Wednesday. Daisy had made a special effort to welcome him, her hair was washed and set and she was at ease and perfectly relaxed when he arrived. Grandma Mason greeted Bill with reserve and retired to her room in the back parlour leaving Daisy, in a flattering brightly printed dress reclining in one of the easy chairs. She made to rise but it was a struggle and Bill dropped his suitcase and crossed swiftly to her side. He knelt and kissed her.

"How are you? How's the baby?" He placed his hand gently upon her tummy and Daisy stroked his hand where it lay upon her.

"We're fine aren't we Isobel. Any time now Billy, you're home just in time. She's due any time now." She clasped Bill's hand again and squeezed it. "Oh it's lovely to have you home again." And she drew Bill to her and kissed him passionately.

Bill crossed to the sitting room door and closed it. "How's the old lady?"

"I wish you wouldn't call her that. She's fine, she's alright. Really, she'll be alright once the baby's born. Just you wait and see."

"Not been giving you any more trouble has she?"

"No, no she's been alright Bill. Really she has. She's just old and she's been on her own too long. She's just a bit set in her ways that's all."

He wandered over to the fireplace and lit a cigarette, tossing the match into the grate. There was a shadow in his expression but Daisy was too happy to notice. Then he went over to the bay window and stood for a moment looking out at the tiny garden with the carefully tended roses. "That's all right then."

"What about you Bill, how long are you home for? When are you due back?"

He remained standing with his back to her, staring through the window. He was out of uniform, standing in silhouette against the brightness outside. He sighed and Daisy saw his shoulders drop.

"I'm not going back." The words, softly spoken sounded loud in the emptiness of the room. Daisy's voice was querulous.

"How d'you mean Billy. What's happened?"

"I've been dropped from aircrew training."

Daisy was shocked; he was so profoundly disappointed, she could see it now in the way he just stood there. It was as though all Bill's pride had been taken from him.

"Why?"

He turned from the window and she watched him pace about the room. Finally he sank into the armchair opposite to her. "I've failed the course." Daisy waited and he sighed again. "Got the gunnery, that's alright. Medical. Eyesight. All that's O.K." He paused again.

"It's the bloody wireless!" and he flung the butt of his cigarette into the hearth with venom. "Three times I've done it! Gone through the whole course. Three bloody times…! Missed it every bloody time by the daftest thing…"

Daisy waited. Bill wouldn't look at her, averting his eyes with his hand to his brow and holding his temples as though there was a physical pain.

"My standard's high enough in practical. I've got no problem there! It's the examinations… the theory… every time… something different…" Bill was speaking as though to himself.

"But if the other parts are alright…" but he cut her off.

"Three times I've done it. The whole damn lot," he cried. "They said last time if I fluffed it again it was my last chance." He bowed his head silently. Daisy couldn't think what to say to console him. Finally Bill raised his head and looked at her. "So that's it! I'm out; back to work. Monday I suppose. Or tomorrow."

Daisy eased herself forward and reached out her hand to him but

71

Bill ignored it.

"Well anyway," she offered, "we're glad to see you home. Aren't we Isobel."

"You seem pretty sure it's a girl." he mumbled. "How d'you know?"

Daisy brightened. "It's big. Big babies are always girls. That's what mum says anyway and we're glad aren't we." She patted her tummy again. "Isobel. Don't you think that's a nice name for her?"

Bill made no response. Finally Daisy said, "Can't you go without wireless?"

The question was lame and Bill raised his head and looked at her scornfully. "You just don't understand do you?"

He leaned back in the chair, closing his eyes as though in exhaustion. "There's a new gun they're working on. High elevation. I'm on a permanent secondment back to Tempered to work on recoil springs for it."

There was no pleasure in Bill's homecoming. Daisy recalled his earlier leave when Bill had come home talking of the things he was doing and what he was going to achieve. There had been excitement and fire in his voice. But not now. And other occasions when he had voiced his ambitions to her, the way he had stood and spoken that afternoon in the park. He wanted so much to play his part. And that fateful party. 'Aircrew, boy in blue'. Back to Tempered! How could he face it. Daisy was at a loss to know what she could do to make the occasion better.

"Would you like a cup of tea?"

He stood up and hovered about the door. "No." He hesitated then, "Better go and see me mother and dad. Shan't be long. See you later."

Two days later Daisy started. Her labour was long. She began in the early hours of the morning and Bill dashed off through the June dawn to fetch the midwife. They returned to find Grandma Mason in control. There was no rush and no need to worry, she said. Babies come in their own good time. The baby was a big one, everybody could see that and Daisy settled into a long and uncomfortable labour.

At 6-00 am Bill went off to work leaving the women to it. The midwife told him there was a long time to go and he was only going to be in the way. Later, trusting to her own judgement and Grandma Mason's competence she popped off to see another case and returned a couple of hours later. Daisy's labour continued. It was going to be another glorious summer day with faint wisps of cloud and very little breeze to bring some relief. They closed the bedroom curtains for some shade. And meanwhile in the Heavy Spring department Bill worked and sweated, his mind barely on the job wondering how Daisy was getting on, had she had it yet, was it a boy or a girl? Was she alright? Was the

72

baby…? Surely, she must have had it by now!

He couldn't remember exactly what he was doing that June day at ten past three but that was the time they came to him from the office to tell him he was a father! To a beautiful, ten pound four ounce baby boy. They christened him David.

CHAPTER 9

'Per ardua ad astra'

"I'm going out for a drink." The statement was made in the uncompromising flat tone that Daisy was coming to expect and her initial light of expectation flickered briefly then expired. A few weeks ago she would have said, "I shan't be a second Bill, I'll just get ready." But now there was no invitation to accompany him and she sat with resignation and watched as he got ready to go out, carefully avoiding Daisy's eyes.

"Where are you going?" she ventured.

"I've just told you, out for a drink."

"Where to?"

"What's it matter where to," he flared back at her. "I'm just going for a pint with the lads from work. Can't I just go out now without having to explain where I'm going? I'm going out with some of the lads from work. I might see our George. Anything else you want to know?"

"You're always going out. You used to take me. You never stay in with me and David."

"Oh what's the point," he sneered. "you're not even ready are you."

Daisy looked down at herself unhappily.

"I could soon get ready."

"Oh yes! And who's going to look after the baby eh? You know what she's like." Bill gestured at the door to Grandma Masons parlour beyond. "You can't ask her, we'll never hear the end of it." He began rummaging in the sideboard drawer. "Where's me tie?"

"Which one?"

"The blue one; you know which one!" he cried impatiently turning over Daisy's headscarves in the drawer.

"I've washed it. It wants ironing."

"Bloody Hell!" Bill went off upstairs muttering to himself to find another one. A few minutes later he was ready to go. He turned to look at her from the doorway. Daisy was nursing David in the chair with his bottle. There were nappies on the fender and ashes in the hearth; the dinner plates remained uncollected on the table and the room was overlaid with the rich, sickly smell of dried baby milk. He could no longer see her prettiness. She was completely given over to the child in

74

her old cardigan; her hair, once brushed out into sleek curls was dull and unkempt. It wasn't easy on clothing coupons, of course it wasn't... but still, look at her! There seemed to be nothing to say any more, nothing to share, just... "God! I can't do anything right. If I go out I'm never there; if I stay in I'm in her way. Bloody old woman!" Bill's misery had grown daily and the rift between them had widened, fuelled by bitterness over his rejection by the R.A.F. And if he didn't work overtime they were short of money. What was there to go home for anyway!

"Shan't be late." he mumbled. Daisy looked up at the door closing behind him. Not even a kiss!

There was only George waiting for him when Bill reached the 'Albion'. He wasn't expecting anyone else despite what he had said to Daisy. No mates from work; no gang of young men out on the town. Only George, his brother in whom Bill confided his frustrations and the drudgery of his marriage. "It's awful. I mean the old woman's always there, she never goes out. We never have the place to ourselves. You feel... I don't know... she keeps herself to herself but... It's as though she's listening!" he cried. "You can't do anything. You know... relax! Do anything!!"

It was a self defeating spiral. Living at Daisy's grandma's inhibited them. They didn't go out alone together because the old lady wouldn't be put upon to babysit. Daisy felt herself trapped with the child in a marriage that had no comfort and because of their inhibitions Bill wasn't interested in her any more. He was always 'too tired' but he wasn't too tired to go out nearly every night and that took money they couldn't afford for him to spend but whenever she mentioned it... Why bother! What was the point in dressing up just to sit alone with the baby night after night?

"And if she's not going to make an effort when I get home what's the point of just sitting round listening to the radio all night like a bloody old man?"

But this time George's eyes were shining with enthusiasm when Bill walked in. He ordered up Bill's pint even before Bill reached him; there was something he couldn't wait to say and he grabbed Bill's arm.

"I think I've got you and Daisy a house." He was almost jumping with excitement.

Bill didn't react. He was too busy scanning the bar looking for a seat.

"Did you hear what I said? Bill listen, we've got you a house."

"How d'you mean you've got us a house. What you on about?"

"Its Myra, she's got this friend who knows somebody what's leaving." George could barely contain his excitement having this good

75

news for Bill. "Only you'll have to move quick. They've not said anything yet. They're giving notice, I think its end of this week, I think that's what Myra said but you'll have to let her know so that she can let this friend know before anybody else gets in first."

"But where? I mean, what sort of house is it?"

George was impatient with Bill's lack of enthusiasm. "What's it matter?" he cried, "It's a place of your own. Just you two and the little'un. Come on, what's up with you? Here, sup this." He handed Bill's pint to him. "It's a new one; one of them they built up on 'Manor. It's only been up about four or five years!"

Now Bill's interest was aroused. The Manor Estate was one of the vast new corporation housing developments that had been built as part of Sheffield's slum clearance drive in the thirties. If it was true…!

"Are you sure?"

"Course I'm sure. She called round at teatime and told me to tell you. But you've got to let her know straight away before somebody else gets there first."

"Where abouts? I mean, where on 'Manor is it?"

"Christ I don't know. She's given me an address but I don't know whereabouts exactly." George fished in his wallet. "Here, it's on here."

"Let's have a look."

George gave Bill the paper with the address on it. There it was. God, if only… "When does she need to know by did you say?"

"Right away. If you're interested that is."

"Course we're bloody interested."

"What about Daisy?"

"She'll be interested an' all."

The house lay just behind one of the shopping centres near the top of 'Prince', the main road named after the Prince of Wales that ran the length of the estate like an artery carrying the main tram route down to the factories in the Don valley below. Situated on a corner position it boasted a long triangular garden at the front that extended round the house to a little patch of ground in the rear. The front door was at the side, opening into a small lobby at the foot of the stairs with a door into the living room. Bill and Daisy had acted quickly to get the key and their furniture in, now they stood at the garden gate with David in their arms looking across the garden at their new home. They savoured the words; their home. At last a home free of the restrictions that living with Daisy's grandma had imposed on them. They walked self consciously along the path in the warmth of spring sunshine to the front door feeling the eyes of the neighbourhood on them. Bill unlocked the door – why does it always fumble at times like this? – and then they were inside and

76

a great surge of relief overwhelmed them.

The living room had a desolate air; Bill and Daisy had acquired very little furniture, only the old easy chairs in faded moquette, a draw leaf table and four dining chairs. There had been a scramble around second-hand shops for a gas cooker due to be fitted this afternoon and they had been given a square of redundant carpet by one of Daisy's aunties. There was a mirror that had a crinoline lady in a garden painted on it over the mantelpiece and Bill had hung a calender on the opposite wall. But it was home. Almost too good to be true! Their future was bright with hope; Daisy would make the house sparkle and Bill would work with a renewed sense of purpose. They walked through the house savouring the sense of ownership and belonging.

"Cup of tea?"

Bill turned to look at Daisy, standing with her child in her arms. She was wearing her best dress and coat, her eyes were bright with happiness and he saw again the prettiness that had captivated him. It seemed so long ago. She crossed to him and lifted her face for a kiss. Bill embraced her gently, enfolding the child between them, all three, together as one family. And holding her in his arms Bill felt warmth and love surge within him as she responded with gentle eagerness to his kiss.

"No," he said, "I don't want tea." He took Daisy's hand and she followed him to the stairs. Long neglected words of love passed between them and Bill waited impatiently, listening to the beating of his heart while Daisy laid David in his cot in the other bedroom. The child began to cry and he heard Daisy talking to the child, shushing him. Then she returned, leaving David crying in the cot. "He'll be alright, I've covered him up and closed the door." Bill was sitting on the edge of the bed. The morning sun beamed through the window catching motes of dust in its light and there was a moment of awkwardness as they listened to the muted sounds of the child across the landing. Daisy pulled Bill up to stand before her and unbuttoned his shirt, then the buttons of his trousers as he fumbled with her dress. Relief and freedom overwhelmed them; Daisy raised her arms and her dress came over her head then she was in Bill's arms again, pulling his shirt off, throwing it to the floor and stumbling onto the bed, down, down, down, away from the world and all its cares and giving themselves in a frenzy of passion.

They made friends with their neighbours. Rita and Jack next door both worked in the cutlery industry; their son Andrew, barely a year younger than Daisy and waiting for his call up papers, delivered bread for a local bakery. Across the side garden the Wilsons, an elderly retired couple were pleased to have them as neighbours. Their own children

77

had long since left the city and the Wilsons rarely saw their grandchildren. Mrs. Wilson called round occasionally to see Daisy and especially David.

Bill was still working long hours and overtime and in the middle of July he began working alternate weeks on night shift. The extra money was useful despite the exhaustion and inconvenience it brought and they began to accumulate some extra pieces for the house, culminating in one of Daisy's proudest new possessions, a kitchen cabinet with a pull down front that became a working surface. Daisy invited Rita and Mrs. Wilson round for a cup of tea the morning after it arrived to admire it.

"Very nice," Mrs. Wilson offered. "'Course we're too old for anything like that now. Oh but what a difference it makes to your kitchen Daisy."

Rita was equally complimentary. "Matches your paintwork too," she said, looking about the kitchen. It was the first time Daisy had really taken notice; the cabinet was painted brown and cream whilst the kitchen walls were green. It wasn't a match at all, more a complementary colour but she was pleased to receive the compliment. "Oh by the way," Rita continued, "our Andrew's got his papers yesterday." She spoke in a matter of fact way without emotion; it was to be expected and there was no good getting all upset about it. "Infantry! We were hoping he'd get in the engineers. Still…"

"When does he have to go?"

"A few more days. 'Course he's thrilled to bits about it. Well you know what lads are like."

"Yes," Daisy mused, "I know only too well."

The others looked at her and Rita said, "Oh yes I was forgetting your Billy's in the airforce or something isn't he?"

"When does he have to go back?" Mrs. Wilson asked.

Daisy didn't want to get drawn into the reasons for Bill's return to civilian life. "Oh he doesn't have to go back. He's on a special job. He can't say too much about it."

"Oh."

Daisy suddenly found herself enjoying the unexpected sense of mystery that her words provoked. Mrs. Wilson was impressed but Rita felt that she had been snubbed. Her news about Andrew had been upstaged by Daisy.

"Well anyway we're having a bit of a 'do' for him before he goes," Rita said. "Only up at the Manor but we want to give him a bit of a send off." Daisy's mind went back to Bill's party again. There must have been lots of these parties going on all over Britain she thought and then, a sudden revelation, 'I suppose they're doing it in German families too'.

"So why don't you and Billy come up," Rita continued. "We're having it tonight."

"We can't come up." Mrs. Wilson put in. "Mr. Wilson doesn't like to be out at night. Not now. Not since air raids started."

"Oh I'm sorry Rita. We can't either. Bill's on nights this week. He'll be going to bed as soon as he gets back from town."

Rita's face fell. To be turned down by both! Daisy sensed the change in Rita's mood. Her mind ran quickly. "Well… it's just a thought…" Daisy turned to Mrs. Wilson. "I don't suppose… I mean with Bill being on nights… I don't suppose you'd mind coming round for an hour to keep an eye on David would you?"

Mrs. Wilson immediately became cautious. She didn't want to find herself with an unexpected new job. Anyway Mr. Wilson wouldn't like it, being left on his own. "And what about Bill? Won't he have something to say about it, you going out on your own without him while he's at work?"

"Oh he won't mind Mrs. Wilson. Not just for once and it's not as though I'm going on my own; I'll be with Rita and Jack. Be nice to give Andrew a proper send off."

"Just this once then. As long as it's alright with your Bill."

"Oh thank you Mrs. Wilson. What time you all going up Rita?"

"About half past seven. We'll call round for you shall we?"

"And you're sure you don't mind Mrs. Wilson?"

"As long as you're not going to be late. Mester won't like it if it's late."

They departed and left Daisy with eyes shining in anticipation of the evening ahead.

Daisy had expected Bill to be back from town by half past ten but it was much later than that when he arrived home in a mood of irritation.

"Their Andrew next door's got his papers." Daisy said when he walked in but Bill made no comment. The trip had taken longer than expected, his shift began at eight o'clock and he needed to get some sleep.

"Did you get everything done you wanted to?"

"Yes," he replied absently then, "No, not really."

"What was it you went for?"

"Nothing. I could do with a cup of tea then I'm going to bed."

"I can get you some dinner if you want something now," Daisy called from the kitchen

"No." Bill was shaking the baby rattle at David lying in his pram beneath the window. "I'm going on up. Bring me tea when its ready. Tired."

Oh God! Daisy had to tell him now – it was no good leaving it until teatime when Bill got up to go to work.

"They're having a bit of a party for him," Daisy called, busying herself with the teapot.

"Who?" Exasperation; he wasn't really interested.

"I've just told you. Andrew. Next door; they're having a bit of a do up at the Manor. You know, a few drinks. A party."

"Oh aye!"

"They've asked if I'd like to go with them. If it's alright with you."

Bill feigned disinterest. "Go if you want to."

Daisy came through from the kitchen. "You don't mind do you Billy. Just for an hour."

"What about David? What time you supposed to be going?"

"It's half past seven. Mrs. Wilson said she'd come round for an hour."

"Sounds like you've got it all planned!" Bill felt quite unreasonable about it. They hardly ever went out together by themselves and now she had it all cut and dried with babysitting organised and everything without even asking him first. And meanwhile he was going to be at work all bloody night! In a perverse sort of way Bill knew that if he hadn't been on nights he probably wouldn't have bothered going anyway, beyond putting in a token appearance. But because he couldn't go even though he didn't really want to he made an issue of it. "You'd better go then hadn't you!"

"Oh Billy don't be like that. It's just a family do that's all. It's for their Andrew."

"Oh shut up," he cried. "I'm tired. I'm going to bed. Do as you like. Give me a call at half past five."

"Your tea."

He stamped off through the door to the stairs. "I don't want it!"

"Oh please yourself then!"

Daisy took care getting herself ready. David was fed and changed, sitting in his pram while Bill had his tea alone at the table.

"Aren't you having any then?" he demanded morosely.

Daisy was too excited to eat, besides she wanted to make sure David was settled down for when Mrs. Wilson came round.

"I've had what I want," she replied. "Keep an eye on him while I go upstairs will you."

"I've got to go in a minute!" he called after her.

Mrs. Wilson arrived and added to Bill's aggravation.

"It is a shame you having to go out to work instead of enjoying yourself. Of course in my day young married women didn't go out drinking alone without their husbands."

That made it look even worse, as though he was condoning it. But what could he say? That she was going out despite his disapproval? That he wasn't even master in his own house?

"Can you keep an eye on him a minute. I've just got to get my things." He went upstairs to escape her further comments.

He could smell fresh facepowder and Daisy was in the bedroom dressed in her best frock putting on her lipstick. Her hair fell in waves to her shoulders. Bill stood at the door in his blue overalls and stained sports jacket and watched her.

"Now you'll be careful now won't you?"

"Mmm?" She finished a last stroke, then she put the lipstick down and turned to him. "Course I will. I'm only going up the road. I'm going to be with Rita and Jack."

"Well just be careful."

There was a knock at the front door and Mrs. Wilson called from the foot of the stairs, "Shall I get it?"

"That'll be Rita now. Yes please, tell her I'm nearly ready." Daisy called.

"I'm going then." Bill felt he was in the way. Somebody, he thought, should be saying sorry to the other; he'd been on the verge of it but... "I'll see you in the morning then."

He went to kiss her but Daisy averted her face. "Mind my lipstick."

He gave a gasp of exasperation and left.

Daisy had a wonderful evening with drinks and jokes, gaiety and laughter. Andrew had a couple of mates still in civvies and there were uniformed young men, all intent on having a good time paying flattering compliments to the young women in the lounge. Daisy was amongst the most attractive of the girls there and what added to her attraction was the knowledge, when it circulated amongst the young studs that she was a married woman out alone. She had never known such attention. She didn't have to buy a drink all night after the initial one for Rita and Jack. As the evening wore on she spent less time at their table but circulated amongst different groups who were there, people of her own age, from just turned eighteen and old enough to buy drinks on their own account to young men in their twenties swaggering with boisterousness and alcohol. They vied with one another for the opportunity to see her home. An opportunity that almost certainly, in their beery imaginations, offered other opportunities too in the dark shadows of the paths between the houses.

One man in particular, whose name Daisy never caught, attracted her attention. Less ardent than the rest he had dark good looks and a pencil thin moustache and he gazed intently at her from the periphery of the crowd, smiled and raised his glass. It was as though he knew he

81

didn't have to compete on the same terms as the herd. Daisy had a fleeting temptation to leave the rest and go across to accept his invitation for a drink. She smiled back but then her attention was distracted by someone telling a joke and she remembered that Jack and Rita were only just across the room. But their eyes met from time to time and they exchanged smiles throughout the evening.

It was such a long time, well before she had the baby since Daisy had had such a good night out. What a shame that Bill couldn't have been here to share it too. Her thoughts of Bill made Daisy suddenly realise that time was moving on and she ought to be thinking of going home. Pity, for the evening was still in full swing. In the corner by the piano a sing-song had started and now the whole room was singing.

"Whats the time Rita?"

"Ooh look its quarter past ten. What time did you say you'd be back?"

A flicker of dismay siezed Daisy. She had told Mrs. Wilson she'd only be an hour or so.

"I'll have to go. Thanks for a lovely time. Where's your Andrew? Oh he's over there look. No! I'll see him before he goes anyway. Goodnight Jack. Thanks Rita." And she hurried from the pub back down the street to home.

Daisy slipped the key in the lock quietly so as not to wake David.

Mrs. Wilson was sitting in silence in the living room.

"Sorry I'm a bit late. Have you had a cup of tea?"

"No," Mrs. Wilson replied, "I expected you back long before this."

"I'm sorry. We were having such a good time we don't know where the time's got to. They're still at it up there. How's David? Has he been alright?"

"He's cried. Every time I put him down. And then when I finally got him off he woke up again when I put the radio on." Clearly Mrs. Wilson had not had a successful night with the child and Daisy coming home late was the last straw. Mrs. Wilson braced herself to speak her mind.

"It's not right Daisy, young married women being out on their own. I said so this morning. And your Bill wasn't too happy about it either was he?"

"But it was only up to the Manor. I'm sorry if he's been any trouble. Can I get you a cup of tea?"

"No! Its late! Mester'll wonder where I've got to. I told him I'd be home long before this." Mrs. Wilson drew on her coat like a shroud of disapproval. "But I'll tell you this Daisy. I don't know what your Bill's thinking about letting you go out like this 'till all hours. And him working nights and all. And that baby. They didn't do it in my day. No they didn't! War or no war."

Daisy had heard enough. She had enjoyed a lovely evening with a few drinks, jokes and laughter. She had left while the sing-song was still under way. There had been no impropriety, just a lot of teasing and fun. Nothing wrong. And then to come home to this… this criticism!

"There was nothing wrong tonight Mrs. Wilson. It was just like a party, that's all. I'm sorry I'm a bit late…"

"Bit late! You said you'd only be gone an hour."

"I'm sorry. Are you sure you won't have that cup of tea?"

"No. I must be off. It's late enough as it is."

"Alright Mrs. Wilson. Goodnight. Thank you." But the departing figure was gone.

There was no question of any more babysitting after that. Daisy knew that for Mrs. Wilson once was enough. What made it worse was that Bill knew that the opportunity for he and Daisy to have the occasional night out together had been squandered. Just because Daisy had got carried away and lost track of the time. Like bloody Cinderella!

"We could still go out Bill." she pleaded, trying to mitigate herself. "We could settle David in his cot and just slip out for half an hour."

"Oh yes," he replied scornfully. "I know what your half hours are like." He was still bitter over the fact that she had gone out without him.

"If we just went up to the Manor I could slip back to see that he's alright. We don't need a babysitter." But Bill would not hear of it.

The war dragged on. Rationing became more severe as the U-boats continued to take their toll in the North Atlantic. At home George and Myra were still courting and there had been some talk of a wedding but no dates had been mentioned. Lilly was working in armaments making wooden handles for machetes and Harold had been made up to Ganger. With his team of labourers he toiled at the goods depot loading endless freight onto long trains of wagons that came and departed with daily urgency. For Bill the development work on the gunspring was complete. He transferred to other jobs in the testhouse and sometimes his frustration at being stuck in civvy street showed in bouts of ill temper, but these generally didn't last long. David grew chubby and they had a small party in the house for his first birthday. Life continued on its unnatural course and summer passed into another autumn.

October came in wet, putting paid to the remnants of the Indian Summer. On a stormy night with hard rain driven by a wind increasing to gale force Bill dashed the quarter of a mile home from the bus-stop with his hair plastered to his head and water running down the inside of his turned up raincoat collar and down his neck. He was tired, thoroughly disgruntled and looking forward to a good wash and an evening before the fire after tea. Daisy was waiting for him with a look of suppressed anxiety. He shook the water off his mac in the kitchen with barely a look at her then hung it across the back of a chair in the living room to dry.

"Rotten night. Bus was late. Soaked."

Daisy called from the kitchen. "There's a letter for you."

"Who from?" He returned to the kitchen to towel his head.

"It's here." She took it from the window sill. "Ministry of War."

"What do they want?" Bill called from beneath the towel. "What's it say?"

"I don't know. I haven't opened it. It's for you." Daisy held it up for him to see. Bill took it from her and held it up, examining the envelope.

"Looks like call-up."

In dismay Daisy saw the weariness lift from him. "Can't be," she said, "you were sent back by the R.A.F."

He studied it, towel in hand in an agony of anticipation.

"Well aren't you going to open it then?" Daisy cried. "Come on Bill; see what it says."

He turned from her and opened it, read it and read it again. Without moving he said softly, "R.A.F."

"What!" Daisy held herself, desperate to know but afraid of what she might hear. "What does it say?"

In an agony of tension she waited whilst Bill examined the letter once more. And then with dismay she heard him say,

"R.A.F. I've got to go back. Groundcrew. Bomber Command. I'm to report on the 19th." He could barely conceal the joy in his voice.

CHAPTER 10

Fleeting consolations

Sitting in the worn armchair by the littered fireplace with Bill's latest letter in her hand Daisy observed without interest her child at play beneath the table with his coloured wooden bricks. David was eighteen months old and into everything. His sodden nappy, a discoloured smelly rag was hanging between his legs but Daisy didn't move, neither to reach for the child nor for the cup of tea growing cold on the mantelpiece above her chair. She didn't want to distract David from his current preoccupation. That would only set him demanding her attention and crying for her, to be picked up, given something to drink, or changed. Or something! Daisy wasn't in the mood for it!

A row of nappies hung steaming on the guard rail before the small fire where Daisy had hung them to dry. It would soon be dinner time but she hadn't any interest in it. Just let the day drift by and don't bother me. Leave me to daydream in bitterness. Daisy almost wished Bill hadn't written to her. It didn't make her feel any better; it was so full of his life, how he was getting on, the people he was meeting, new mates. It wasn't fair. He was having fun! But what did he know about it really? Or care about it for that matter; he was only getting service pay now and it was impossible to get by on what he sent her. And all the fun had gone from Daisy's life.

Only two and a half years ago – less than that even – Daisy had been carefree, soaking up attention from young men in dance-halls and pubs. Now where was she? Not yet twenty one and trapped in a cold impoverished house with a crying child. Her life was over. Some mornings Daisy didn't even bother to get up. Well, what was the point! With no fire lit and not enough coal and it was a dirty, messy business anyway with yesterday's ashes to be taken outside to the bin and the kid wanted changing, crying for his breakfast… So some mornings Daisy stayed in bed. David had a drink and a rusk in his cot and God help him if he spilled it and made her more washing! Well – he couldn't come into bed with her either, not 'till he'd finished his breakfast and not even then, he was always wet and smelly and cold, fidgeting about and letting the cold air enter the bed. This wasn't what Daisy had dreamed of, what they'd planned together, endless days alone in the house. This was rotten.

Daisy read Bill's letter again. Sends his love. Hoping to get a bit of leave soon. But he doesn't say when. Won't even be home for Christmas!

Rita seldom came round these days, nor Mrs. Wilson. There was no welcome in the house and anyway what Daisy really wanted was young company, people her own age to talk to with the same interests, not just war and rationing all the time. So she sat in isolation and brooded.

When Daisy visited home – for that's how she thought of her parent's house, as her home, not this desolate house up on the Manor – she had an unformed idea that perhaps she could move back to live with them. But that plan was stifled as it was born; Daisy's sister Mary was still at home and there was no room for her and David as well.

Mary sensed the change in Daisy's manner. There wasn't the same sparkle; some of her gaiety had gone although Daisy tried not to show it. It wasn't that her innocence had gone, it was her air of self assurance. Although the younger of the two sisters Mary had always been the more outgoing whereas Daisy was the serious one, the more romantic. Now Mary sensed barely concealed desperation beneath Daisy's weak smile.

"Just pass me his coat will you Mary. We'd better be on our way if we're going to get that bus."

Daisy's mother had David on her knee for the umpteenth time, trying to hold him there against his struggles but if she let him go he'd be after her ornaments again. She had already moved some of the pieces out of David's reach but he was so quick! He was into everything and her exasperation was beginning to show. Mary looked quickly across at her mother. "Oh you can stay for tea can't you? Can't she mum?"

"Well if she's got to catch… what time is it?"

"No," Daisy exclaimed but it was a half-hearted protest. It had been such a relief these past couple of hours to have someone to share in keeping David amused, "No I think we should really be…"

"You haven't got anything to get back for have you?" Mary persisted.

"Well…" Daisy looked across at her mother and sensed the lack of invitation.

"There you are then," Mary concluded triumphantly. "That's alright i'n't it mum." With a growing sense of mischief Mary saw her mother's face remain expressionless and added, "And we might get up the road for a quick drink before you have to get back. You don't mind do you mum."

Daisy heard her mother sigh but Mary was saying that she couldn't stay long up at the club anyway; she was meeting some of the others later. It would only be for an hour at the most. Daisy's heart lifted for the first time in..? It was so long ago she couldn't remember.

Her mother rose with resignation. "Here, you'd better keep an eye on him then while I put 'kettle on."

"I'm not really dressed to go out," Daisy protested as she took David from her but there was a gleam of anticipation in her eye all the same.

"No you look fine," Mary reassured her. "You can use some of my makeup if you want…"

"Mum didn't like it much," Daisy confided to Mary as they walked to the bus stop. "Shan't be able to do that very often."

"I'm sorry we couldn't have stayed longer," Mary replied, "only I've got to meet the others. You remember Sheila? Well she's got a boyfriend now only he's a miner so it depends what shift he's on. Well, it's just that it's arranged. Only we'll probably be late back or else you could…"

"No!" Daisy protested, acutely aware that even with fresh makeup on she wasn't dressed for going out; she would have felt terribly out of place. "I've got to get back. It's late enough for David as it is. But I'll come on over again. In a couple of weeks. That is if me mother'll…"

"Tell you what!" Mary interrupted with a sudden inspiration of sisterly generosity, "Why don't I come over to see you. Then you can get David to bed and you won't have to worry so much about the time then will you." Mary gave David's cheeks a little squeeze. "And you'll be alright too won't you. Oh look, here's your bus. Got your fare ready?"

"Yes. Thanks Mary I've really enjoyed this afternoon. Yes come on over, that'd be great if you could. Really." The bus drew alongside. "And make it soon. How about next week?" she called, half turning on the platform with David in her arms. She heard Mary call, "Wednesday," as the conductor pressed the bell and the bus drew away. And then Daisy's world became flat and colourless again as she returned to the routine emptiness, waiting for Wednesday to arrive.

How does a child know? On Wednesday afternoon Daisy washed her hair and set it up in curlers. She gave David a bath and spent an hour with him on her knee in the chair before the fire cuddled in his towel. Then she dressed him in his nightshirt and left him to play, ready for his tea whilst she combed the curlers out of her hair. David stood at the arm of the easy chair watching her.

"What do you think of mummy then?" Daisy looked at her reflection in the mirror. Her hair shone, longer than it had been when she was single, before the child. Now it curled in waves about her

87

shoulders and swung over the front of her collar when she tossed her head. "Don't you think you've got a pretty mummy then?" On the visit home to the family Daisy hadn't anticipated going out; tonight she was going to make the most of it and she wasn't going as Cinderella either.

"Come on then. Time for tea."

Maybe the problem was that Daisy tried too hard, sitting with David at his chair, coaxing and talking to him, trying to get him to finish his tea quickly so that she could concentrate on getting herself ready. Whatever it was, David would not be coaxed and Daisy started to become impatient which only made things worse.

"Here, here's a nice drink of tea. There's a good boy. Come on, drink it nicely." She proffered the cup but it was hot and David jerked his head aside and pushed it away, spilling the tea from the cup onto Daisy's lap. "Now look what you've done you naughty boy. It's a good job I haven't got my best dress on. Here, now come on, drink it." She poured some into the saucer. "Look I'll blow on it and make it nice and cool for you." But again David, expecting it to be as hot as the first time pushed it away. The tea slopped about the saucer precariously, David started to climb down from the table, Daisy fought to keep him in place whilst balancing the saucer of tea at the same time but David was determined to get down and he wriggled from Daisy's restraining arm lashing out wildly. The saucer fell from Daisy's hand, spilling tea over them both.

"Now look what you've done!" Daisy screamed in exasperation. "You naughty boy, look at me! Wringing, sopping wet! And you too! Well you can just stay like that, I'm not changing you again. Come here!" She seized him and, holding him by the arm gave him three or four good sharp slaps on the back of his legs. David shrieked and sobbed. "Shut up!" Daisy commanded. "You're a very naughty boy, you can just go to bed for that." She dragged him across the room and out to the stairs. "I'm sick of you. If you don't stop it I'll give you another. D'you hear. Shut up! Stop it or I'll give you something to cry for." Kicking and yelling the child was dragged up the staircase and Daisy dropped him crying into the cot and pushed the covers over him. David scrambled to his feet and began screaming against the cot rails for her. "Get down!" she yelled back at him. "Get down! Go on, lay down. Oh look at you. You're soaked. Well you'll just have to stay soaked. Look at the time and I'm not even started to get ready." Daisy marched back to the cot and David raised his arms to her. "No! Lay down." She pushed him down and pulled the covers over him and again and again David threw them off and scrambled to his feet reaching out for her. "No!" Daisy glared at him. She strode from the room and slammed the door against David's cries. "Shut up!!"

He was still crying when Mary arrived. She glanced quickly up the darkened staircase and closed the door carefully as she followed Daisy into the living room.

"Sorry, did I wake him?"

"No, he's been a real little bugger all day. Never stops. I wish he'd grow out of it. Here let me take your coat a minute. Shan't be long. I'm nearly ready."

Mary looked with approval at her sister. Daisy was wearing one of her best dresses, a bright floral print with squared shoulders and a full skirt. "Looks nice."

"Thank you."

"You meeting anybody special?" Mary teased.

"Ronald Coleman." Daisy paused in front of the mirror with her makeup. For an instant she looked dreamily beyond the image reflected there, then focused on Mary sitting behind her at the table. "And Clark Gable for you eh."

They laughed and Daisy finished at the mirror. "Shan't be long." she repeated brightly and went upstairs. Sitting there Mary couldn't help contrasting Daisy's air of gay anticipation with the poverty of the room. It wasn't the poor furniture, the sparseness of the room nor even the clutter of babyclothes and things pushed hurriedly away under cushions. There was a poverty of spirit which Daisy's air of expectancy could not dispel. A lack of caring and warmth. From upstairs Mary heard Daisy's voice raised in anger, a brief silence and then David cried out and Daisy shouting at him again as a bedroom door slammed against the faint cries. Then Daisy's footsteps on the stairs.

"D'you want me to go up to him?"

"No leave him alone. He's been asking for that all day." Daisy looked flushed as she entered the room, as though she had been making some exertion, "He'll be alright in a minute."

Mary decided not to pursue it; Daisy knew what was best for him and she changed the subject. "When's Bill coming back? You heard from him lately?"

"Got a letter day before yesterday. Doesn't say anything about any leave though."

"He must be due some leave soon mustn't he? I thought they got passes or something." Mary reached across for her coat.

"I know. But he's down near Hereford or Wales or somewhere. It'd take him a couple of days just to get back from there. I don't know what we'll do when he does get some. Anyway you ready to go?"

The cries of the child could still be heard upstairs and Mary looked quizzically at her sister.

"What about David? Aren't you going to settle him down first? Who's looking after him?"

Daisy busied herself with a scarf at the drawer. "Is it cold out? D'you think I'll need this?"

"No, it's not too bad." Mary let her question hang in the air.

Daisy saw Mary's look of misgiving. "He'll be alright," she said. "I'll pop back down just to make sure later on. It's only just up the road."

Mary shrugged off her concern. After all Daisy was David's mother and she must know. "Right then. Ready?"

Daisy took a fleeting look about the room. "Right, come on then. You go first and I'll put the lights out."

They left the house and gaily tripped off along the darkened road leaving the thin winter breeze to carry the sounds of the crying child away into the night.

And what a night they had. In truth the evening seemed better than it actually was for they only had three or four drinks each. But there was someone at the piano in the concert room and every so often when somebody did a request they'd all join in the singing. It was warm, convivial and smoky; noisy and bright. And fun!

Daisy had almost forgotten what this other world was like. It wasn't the same when she had come out with Rita and Jack; that was like being under the eyes of a chaperone. But tonight she could respond to the interested glance of a man, the offer of a drink and the innuendo.

"Where is he then? Gone abroad and left you all alone has he?"

The excitement and the teasing banter, playing the coquette.

"He's in the R.A.F. on a bomber squadron. Doing something to win this war. Not like some."

"Don't you worry about that." The man leaned in close to Daisy, confident with beer and gave her a pat on the arm. "Here, let me get you a drink."

"Already got one thank you." She smiled at him and pushed his hand aside. Why, he was nearly as old as her father.

"I'll get you another," he insisted.

"That your daughter waving?"

He half turned, paused, then grinned back at her. "Here love, have a drink anyway."

Daisy leaned and kissed his cheek. "Next time eh." And she left him to join Mary.

"You alright?"

"Course I am," Daisy replied. "Having a great time. See him over there, by the bar, look he's chatting to the woman with her hair up. He's just tried to pick me up. Doesn't waste his time does he!"

"I wouldn't want him in my knickers."

"Oh I don't know. Just now I'd welcome…" Mary looked across quizzically as Daisy spoke and Daisy laughed. "Well perhaps you're right. Shut your eyes and think of England."

"There's a bloke over there keeps looking at you."

"Where?"

"There look, by the end of the bar. With the moustache."

"Don't let him see us looking." Daisy nonchalantly moved and gazed about the room. "Oh I've seen him before. I came up once, weeks ago with Rita. He was here then. Never said anything though."

Mary was staring openly at him. "Nice looking." He smiled and started to make his way towards them. "He's going to say something now anyway."

"Hiya." His smile was attractive beneath the carefully clipped moustache and it was directed at Daisy although the greeting addressed them both. "Seen you before haven't I?"

"Might have done," Daisy replied.

"A week or two ago. Oh, might have been longer."

"Don't think so," Mary put in. "Never been in here before."

He glanced briefly at Mary. "Never said it was here did I."

"You alone?" Mary asked.

"No why?"

"Two's company."

His smile broadened. "Wait here. What you drinking?"

"Half of bitter for Daisy. And mine's a red label."

"Alright then Daisy. A half of bitter; in a stem glass."

He turned and moved easily to the bar to where a small group of friends waited and they saw a small discussion take place while the drinks were ordered, then one of his mates detached himself from the group and returned with him as he brought Daisy and Mary's drinks.

"So," he began, "my name's Len, this is Roger; you're Daisy and who's this then?"

Daisy took up the introductions. "This is my sister. Mary."

"Hello Mary." Roger moved alongside her. "What do you do then…?"

Len turned his attention to Daisy. "You don't come up here very much then." Not a question, a statement. Daisy felt as though he already knew all about her.

"No," she answered shortly.

"So where d'you usually go?"

And suddenly Daisy found herself talking freely to Len as he primed her with questions about herself. It was so exhilerating to be out as though she were free and single again. She didn't want to tell him about Bill but against her own instincts she told Len about him being in the forces and Len commiserated.

"So is this just a special night or are you going to be able to get out a bit more often?"

He was such a sympathetic listener and it was so flattering to have a mans attention again even in innocent conversation.

"Perhaps next week."

"That'll be nice. I'll look forward to that." He saw a brief look of doubt. "If you don't mind meeting again. Just for a drink."

"Yes." Why not! What harm was there, stuck in the house all week? "Anyway it's our turn now," Daisy said. "What about you and Roger? What're you drinking?"

"No, put your money away. It's his turn anyway."

"Just one more then. And then we'll have to go." Daisy hadn't mentioned David in her conversation and she was suddenly aware of the time. She'd been away almost too long for peace of mind.

"Oh well. If you've got to leave I suppose that's it." Again Daisy was aware of the confidence that Len exuded. He wasn't trying to rush his fences, he had all the time in the world to play it at Daisy's pace.

"You'll be here next week won't you?"

"Oh yes."

He looked at her and gave her a searching smile until Daisy began to feel uncomfortable, almost fidgeting for some way to break that concentrated gaze. "Right then. A half of bitter. In a stem glass."

To Daisy's relief – and she was surprised at how much of a relief it was – David was sound asleep. His covers were kicked all over the cot so she lovingly re-covered him and went off to her own bed. Len. She savoured the name. He hadn't even tried to make a pass or kiss her or anything like that. But he was so good looking. She lay in the darkness and drifted off into a contented sleep.

Wednesday couldn't come too soon. She made careful preparations to get ready and again by some divine intuition David seemed to know and was more than usually fractious, crying for her and demanding constant attention. But Daisy was not to be distracted no matter how difficult David made it for her.

"He was alright then when you got back?" Mary said when she arrived again the following Wednesday.

"Oh yes. Good as gold." Daisy spoke the words against the background of David crying in the bedroom above. Mary looked apprehensively at the ceiling. "Oh don't worry, he'll be alright."

"If you're sure."

"Oh yes. You ready? Come on then." And Daisy, looking as radiantly pretty as Mary had ever seen her put out the light and locked the door behind them.

What if Len wasn't there? Well, she could still have a good time like last week; a few drinks, singing with the others and flirting mildly with the few single men who were there. Perhaps she had tried too hard. Perhaps she shouldn't have gone to so much trouble with the make-up and getting ready. He hadn't seemed to have tried very hard last week. Oh! what was she thinking of! All they had done was just talk together like friends. But despite all the rationalising to herself Daisy's heart was racing as they walked into the pub.

He was there and waved, pleased to see her! Everything else was forgotten. They stayed with the others no more than an hour and a half. Then Len said, "Come on, let's go somewhere."

"What? I can't. I mean, what about our Mary?"

"She'll be alright," he said. "I want you somewhere alone. God you look wonderful tonight." He leaned and brushed his cheek lightly against Daisy's. "I want you." he whispered, "I want you."

"Mary, hey Mary," Daisy called across the table to her sister, deep in conversation with Roger, "I'm just going to the ladies. Coming?"

Mary collected her handbag. "Shan't be a minute." They went off chattering with excitement.

"How you getting on?"

"Great! I wasn't sure last week," Mary said, "but he's really nice when you get to know him. He wants to see me home. What about you and Len?"

"We're going to leave. You'll be alright won't you?"

"Well yes but… I mean… What about you and Bill?"

"It's alright. Anyway don't worry. He's not here anyway is he. He could be up to anything as far as I know. It's him what's got me in this mess anyway. You don't mind really do you Mary. Just this once?"

"You sure you know what you're doing here?"

"I've told you, don't worry. Oh you don't know how he makes me feel."

Daisy and Len left the pub to knowing winks from Roger with Mary giving him playful pushes and admonitions not to be so awful. Outside, in the darkness of the pub yard Len pushed Daisy into a corner of the wall and kissed her, releasing such a longing in her that she thought she would lose her breath forever. "Oh Len," she moaned, hugging him to her.

"Where do you want to go?"

"Anywhere," Daisy replied, her mind suddenly in a whirl, "take me anywhere."

"Where do you live? It's not far is it?"

"What?" Daisy had a momentary misgiving.

"There's nobody there is there? Babysitter?"

"No but…"

"Come on then. We can't stand out here all night. Come on Daisy let's get inside."

Oh yes, inside and warm beneath blankets. Who was to know? And if they did? There was only Mary and she wouldn't say a word. Oh yes… oh yes…

It was even better than making love with Bill, this sudden flood of passion with a man she hardly knew, whom she might never see again. This was a frenzied orgy of unbridled desire. She gave herself to Len without inhibition, with greater freedom than she and Bill had ever done and derived so much more satisfaction. Afterwards Daisy lay in the darkness and watched him in the flare of the match as Len lit a cigarette.

"I never knew it could be like this."

"I'm going to have to go." He drew deeply on the cigarette and the glow illuminated his face as he leaned in equal satisfaction against the headboard. "Got the time?"

"Wait a minute." Daisy reached across him for the alarm clock, savouring the smell of his body. "Quarter to twelve."

"Oh Christ. I've got to go."

"You sure? You could stay 'till morning."

Len drew Daisy to him and kissed her. "I've got to leave." He got out of bed and began dressing in the dark. Then he turned to her. "You're wonderful, do you know that?

"Oh Len so are you. Do you really have to go?"

"Sorry." He pulled his shoes on. "Next week eh?" Daisy made to get up. "Don't get out of bed. I'll let myself out."

"No, no it's alright. I'll come and lock the door up after you. Are you sure you can't stay?"

"Next week."

And next week and the week after and then three nights a week after that Daisy met Len for a drink and then they returned to the house, always careful not to make a noise, not to wake the child who was eventually asleep in the lonely room beyond.

And then Len was no longer there. Without any hint or apology he just failed to show up.

"Didn't he say anything?" Daisy demanded and Roger shook his head, an expression of bland innocence in his face. Daisy stood with her drink in her hand feeling so foolish with Roger and Mary looking on. "Well he must have said something! He must have said whether he was going to meet you tonight."

Again Roger shook his head. "We just, well, meet up when we're going out for a drink. That's all. Just, well, mates really. He doesn't tell me when he's coming and going." Again the bland expression. Daisy looked at Mary for support but Mary just raised an eyebrow with a small inclination of her head as if to say, "Don't ask me, nothing to do with me."

Feeling stupid and humiliated Daisy finished her drink and left them. She wasn't going to see Len again. She knew it! She'd been had! Cruel bastard. She should have known, with that devil-may-care attitude of his. He was off with some other fool of a girl now. She stormed off angrily back to the house and slammed the door. The sound echoed through the house and from upstairs she heard the bloody kid begin to cry again.

CHAPTER 11

Tonsils and tribulations

For two days the tops of the low hills surrounding the airfield had been white with the snows of March but last night it had settled over all the farmland of Herefordshire. Through the window behind the M.O's desk Bill could see a section of the big runway between the hangars. Now that was covered too and everything was temporarily grounded. Bill shuddered involuntarily; the office was barely warm and the single bar radiator on the floor adjacent to the desk, placed there to supplement the central heating was directed not at Bill but towards the M.O's feet. The M.O. resumed his seat at the desk and tossed the spatula into the wastebin.

"Sorry airman, they'll have to come out." He said it quite matter-of-factly. "How long's it been like this?"

"Well, a few days now." Bill watched with interest and a little trepidation as the M.O. began to fill out a short report.

"No I mean have you suffered much with tonsilitis before this?" he asked without looking up.

"I used to get it a bit as a kid but our George, me brother, he was worse than me. He had his out when he was ten."

"Well," the doctor replied, "it's your turn now. There's excercises coming up soon and then overseas I shouldn't wonder. You don't want this flaring up again." He finished writing and reached for a docket. "Report to the surgery, Tuesday morning 9-15 with your pyjamas. There's the address." He pointed to the docket and handed it to Bill. "No breakfast. I'll notify your C.O. and arrange seven days sick leave. Anything else?"

"No sir. Thank you sir." Bill saluted and left.

Skirting the parade ground Bill made his way towards the feeder runway and the hangars which faced it, passing the ground crews working on three Halifaxs who were grumbling at the cold, sweeping snow from the windscreens and the concrete aprons upon which the bombers stood. Seeing them working out here in the open he was bouyed up by the thought of his coming leave and the comforts of home. He called out to them. "Go on lads get to it. Soon get nice and warm."

A snowball missed him easily and more of the airmen with jeers and catcalls joyfully bent to scoop up handfuls of snow to bombard him but a warrant officer appeared from the hangar and the men sullenly returned to their brooms and shovels. Entering the hangar Bill collected his overalls from his locker and joined Mako at the bench.

"How'd you get on."

Bill put on a swagger. "Tonsilitis. Got to go and have 'em out." Mako pulled a face. "Ah but wait for it," Bill continued. "Seven days leave haven't I!"

"You have not!"

"Next week. Go in on Tuesday then back home. Back to the missus. Few pints, feet up by the fire."

"Jammy bugger. Oh you'll miss fight day with the home guard too."

Fight day was a regular weekly exercise designed to keep the base at peak alert and also to afford the Local Defence Volunteers an opportunity to participate in military supervised training. It was compromised by the fact that personal weapons were in short supply for the civilian soldiers and those that did exist were largely useless through lack of firing pins or breech bolts. The station 'other ranks' tended to regard it in the same spirit as school sports day.

"Never mind." Mako was one of Bill's particular mates and Bill didn't want to be too cocky. "Still going over to Leominster tomorrow?"

"I'm alright," Mako replied, "but you won't get one. I mean with having a seven day coming up."

"Course I will. Got my Saturday night pass all organised."

"But we're supposed to be getting a new training group in to go with the new tugs."

"Nowt to do with it," Bill responded "Anyway there's that Mavis. I want to see if I can get her interested."

"No chance!" Mako scoffed. "Not if there's officers about."

"Ah… ah…" Bill jabbed at Mako playfully, "we'll see then shall we."

The Flight Sergeant appeared in the hanger entrance and called the Corporal over to him, nodding in Bill and Mako's direction.

"Aye up. Better get on." Mako turned his attention back to the radio chassis on the bench. "Wallsie's in."

The Corporal approached across the hanger and halted stiffly three feet behind Bill who was diligently searching amongst the tools in his bench drawer. Both were conscious of Flight Sergeant Walls silhouetted against the open hanger door.

"Where've you been then?" the corporal demanded.

"Sick parade sir." But Bill didn't display the deference that the rank of corporal demanded. He remained preoccupied with the contents of the tool drawer.

"Whats wrong with you? Anything?"

Turning to face the corporal he gave a slight cough. "Tonsilitis, Sir. Got to have an operation, Sir."

"When's that then?"

"Next week, Sir. Tuesday, Sir." Bill looked him boldly in the face; it was a challenging look and the corporal didn't like the attitude that was being displayed. And the Flight Sergeant was still hovering in the hangar door.

"Right then. Close that drawer up and report to stores for a brush and shovel. I want that runway swept clear."

Bill was incredulous. "But I'm sick corp. I've got tonsilitis; I've got an operation coming up."

The corporal raised his voice in imitation of the manner he'd seen Flight Sergeant Walls adopt so many times. "Not today you haven't. You aren't sick until next week. Get out there. At the double. We've got three aircraft to return to operational service this morning! Jump to it! Come on, left right, left right..."

The next seventy-two hours were a torment. With the runway clear and no further snow forecast night training operations were resumed both for glider pilots and their tugs and Bill's pass for Saturday night was cancelled. But that was overshadowed by the discomfort of his tonsilitis and lurid memories of George arriving home after his operation with a bleeding throat, unable to swallow from the pain but being forced to eat dry cereals. Other childhood friends had also undergone the operation and come home bleeding and in tears. He was troubled by fears of how, as a grown man he was going to cope with it. He swallowed; it was exquisitely painful and he swallowed again. Perversely he tried to imagine how much more painful it was going to be after the op. He could think of nothing else and his mind obstinately focused and refocused on his coming ordeal. He remembered with misgiving the stories he had heard about service treatment. Rough and ready! No frills! Come on, come on, you're in the forces now, no bedside manner necessary. You, you and you report for amputation at the double. Yes sir! Right, Next!!! Wheel 'em in. Come on, look lively there we haven't got all day! What d'you mean there's nothing wrong with you? Course there is. Says so here! All right, let's have it off. Come on, stop wriggling about man... hold him down somebody. Right? Right then, here we go...

Bill woke up abruptly, the dream rapidly fading in the darkness of the billet as he groped for his watch. It was Tuesday morning.

It was not so bad after all. Not an experience he would want to repeat and his throat was so tender and sore. But in the matter of fact way of the services he had been treated well by competent and caring medical staff. Of course! The R.A.F. looks after its own. They need fit men, not invalids.

Bill was looking forward to the unexpected bonus of a few days at home. It had been a long journey with two changes at Hereford and Birmingham. Now his train was passing through the familiar outskirts of Sheffield; the park, with the stream and the woods behind, evoked a memory of that dark, cold night when Daisy first gave herself to him. Seduced! That wasn't the word; he wasn't a seducer. She had given herself freely to him. Under a bridge and the park vanished. Now there were familiar factories and a slow surge of activity developed, fellow passengers rising from their seats put on their coats and hats and began thronging the corridors with luggage and jostling towards the doors as the train drew down beneath the bridges into Midland Station.

The familiar surroundings immediately embraced him giving rise to a warm inward glow of welcome. Trams glided along, crackling across the junctions of overhead wires; there was a railway dray behind a stolid chestnut shire returning from the market. The smell of malting drifted in the steam from the brewery. And the dialect – Yorkshire but unmistakably Sheffield in its coarse warmth – in the chatter of the throng in the station forecourt. He caught a tram in Pond Street and went upstairs for a smoke and a look around the town. Best trams in the country, Sheffield trams; not boneshakers like the ones in Leeds or Glasgow but smooth and comfortable. The ruin of the city was appalling but it was surprising how quickly these ruins seemed to have become accepted as normal, a commonplace unremarkable landscape.

Bill approached the house in joyful mood. The privet hedge was rampant and behind it the garden was wild. He paused briefly at the gate and a fleeting pang of conscience siezed him. "I'll get that tidied up this week," he mused and went inside, tossing his knapsack in the lobby at the foot of the stairs.

In the living room Daisy waited to greet him with apprehension. She had gone to some trouble to look her best; her golden hair was rolled in a snood into the nape of her neck and she was wearing a woollen dress with a brightly printed floral pattern. But she looked out of place in her surroundings. There was a knowing look about her which distanced her from Bill.

He stood and glanced quickly round the threadbare room, at the dirty carpet lying dead before the hearth, nondescript in its faded stickiness. The furniture the same, not as he remembered it. The air was heavy with a sour smell, the odour of dirty water, ashes in the hearth.

Uncared for, littered, abandoned and lifeless beyond redemption the house closed in upon itself, the winter gloom encroaching from the dismal corners and filtering through the shapeless rags of curtain at the windows. Daisy tried a bright smile. Bill searched dumbly for words and the smell of the house assailed him.

"What the hell...?" He was lost, the happy greeting was gone, a will o' the wisp, his dream of home a mere fantasy.

"Billy," she began. Bill looked at her, searching for the girl he had come to see, frowning in disbelief.

"For Christ's sake Daisy. What's the matter? Place's gone to pot!"

"Bill... Billy... welcome home love." She spoke with hesitation; despite herself the greeting lacked sincerity.

"But look at the place," Bill gestured helplessly. "You never said anything... don't you ever clean up... I mean... Christ."

"You don't know what it's like," Daisy cried. "You've no idea! Living here with no money. And rationing... and... Bill... come on." Daisy went to him and put her arms around him. Bill just stood without response. "Oh come on, come on take your coat off." She drew him in from the doorway. "Come and sit down and I'll get us some tea in a minute."

He slipped his greatcoat off and handed it to her then sat gingerly on the arm of one of the chairs. He examined the seat as he did so, giving it a cursory wipe then brushed his hands together and fished out a cigarette. "Where's David?"

Daisy re-entered from the lobby where she had hung Bill's coat. "Oh, he's upstairs in his cot. Having a nap."

Bill rose. "I'll just pop up and fetch him."

"In a minute Bill. He'll be getting up soon. Come here, you haven't kissed me yet." Daisy put her arms around his neck and kissed him. Bill responded without feeling. Leaving her there he went to the kitchen; it was the same. He lit the greasy stove and put the kettle on and stood with his hands on his hips, bemused and disappointed. Daisy came and stood in the doorway. Bill swept an arm around, "Daisy... I just don't know what to say. Just look at it!"

Daisy bit her lip and made no response. A cry came from upstairs. She hesitated, then, "That's David. He's woken up. I'll go and get him."

Bill wandered back into the living room. 'He'll soon be two, and he's walking now.' His heart was filled with love and at the thought of holding his son and feeling his little arms around his neck and snuggling into his shoulder all the chaos around him faded into nothing. He could hear Daisy talking to the child, the clatter of footsteps on the stairs and Daisy brought him in. "He just wants his face washing a bit."

Bill stood horror stricken. A stink rose from the reeking nappy hanging between his legs where the bright red inflammation of the rash on the inside of David's thighs was peppered with clusters of hard pimples. His unwashed hair was lank and matted; there was something in it, on his scalp – scurf – scabs?

David grinned at him and Bill turned on Daisy beside himself with rage. "Bring him here!" he roared. "Look at him, look at him! What the bloody hell's been going on?" He brushed Daisy aside and carried David into the kitchen. "What have you done... what have you done..." The kettle was just coming to the boil and he poured the water into the bowl then he carefully undressed the child for a thorough wash...

He took David to the doctor. Daisy had been unwilling to take him herself. Perhaps she didn't see the need. Maybe this is the way all kids were. Living on the estate she saw all manner of urchins and little scruffs. Perhaps she just didn't care! Perhaps she was ashamed!

The doctor gave Bill some stuff to paint on David's head. "That'll soon clear that up. But you must keep his hair regularly washed and it'll deal with the lice. And get some cream for those legs. He must be kept dry. I know kids wet their nappies but he must be changed regularly. Vaseline's good." The doctor sighed; he saw so much of it these days.

"Couldn't you have done something mother!"

"We didn't know!" Lilly declared hotly. She resented the accusation and Bill's assumption that it was their responsibility. "We never gets to see him. She never brings him down to see us."

"I'm not surprised," Harold added. "She wouldn't have wanted anybody to see him in that state!"

"But you could have gone up there sometimes. Couldn't you!"

"Well we did at first. You know we did." It wasn't fair and Lilly wasn't having it. "But your dad's on firewatch when he comes home. He's dog tired as it is when he gets home from work. And its not easy crossing town these days, you has to change trams you know."

"You'd think she'd be able to look after him properly." Harold added.

"Oh don't keep going on about it," Bill cried, exasperated with their self righteousness. "She could have done with a bit of help."

"She was never very welcoming anyway. Never even offered a cup of tea last time we was up there."

"I knew she was no good," Harold put in for good measure. "I said so right from the start."

"Oh bloody hell! I've got to go back in a day or two!"

"Well there you are," said Lilly. "You've made your bed and you must lie on it."

"What are you talking about mother?"

"You! If you hadn't gone and joined up you wouldn't be in this situation now."

"Your mother's right. You had a nice steady job. Well paid and safe and you've gone and thrown it up. I don't know what you were thinking of."

"You wouldn't listen would you!" Lilly continued. "Well, there you are. We knew right from the start. You should have known better."

"Oh for Christ's sake mother...!"

Bill left, seething with resentment. Why was it suddenly all his fault? He'd gone to seek sympathy and support. All he'd got was the standard attrition. He ignored the trams and buses that passed him and began to walk it off. 'I mean what can I do?' he thought to himself. 'I've only got a few days then I've got to go back!' He walked into town past the screens hiding the derelict bombsites. Alright! He'd chosen to marry Daisy! It was easy for them to be wise after the event but damn it all he'd done the right thing by her and honoured his son.

Rusting girders, skeletons of once thriving shops rose either side of the road around him. He paused to look through a hoarding. There was nothing remaining, only a great hole where the shop floor used to be and the basement crater filled with water and rubble. So this is what you get for giving up a safe civvy job; betrayal! His wife living in squalor and unable to cope. And all they could say was, 'I told you so.' Oh to hell with all of you!! Ahead was The Marples Hotel. By some quirk of fortune the shell of the building was still standing and at first glance it looked as though it could be still open for business. Until you took in the glassless windows and through them the roof open to the sky and each floor below that missing where the bomb had punched a hole straight through the building to explode amongst the hundreds sheltering in the cellars below.

This wasn't what Bill had intended when he'd joined up. Now he had no option but to try and get things under control again before he went back. What could he do? He only had three more days. He caught the tram in Fitzalan Square and went home.

That same afternoon Bill took Daisy down to the co-op and they chose some paint, a pale green gloss and some wallpaper with a cream and green pattern to match. As soon as they got home they started; Bill gave the living room paintwork a good wash down and Daisy took the curtains down and pinned paper to the windows. They worked together with joy, to a purpose. Daisy followed Bill round the woodwork, wiping it clean and dry with an old towel then they paused for a cup of tea and some sandwiches. Daisy took care of David and after his supper she brought him in to say 'goodnight' to his daddy. Meanwhile Bill started painting. By eleven o'clock the skirting boards and doors were finished.

Set against the rest of the drab furnishings it looked garish and overbright. Bill had worked fast and the paint had smudged off the skirting boards onto the floorboards; some of it was on the wall but that wouldn't matter when it was papered over.

Daisy brought in a pot of tea and stood with Bill, admiring the results of the days work.

"Oh Bill, it'll be lovely. Do you think we'll get it finished by tomorrow?"

He took his cup and wandered over to the door inspecting his handiwork closely. Turning to look at her Bill saw Daisy standing radiant. In a wrap-over pinafore, her hair beneath the headscarf tied in a turban Daisy's face was flushed with the day's achievement and her eyes were shining.

"Yes," he replied, "We'll finish it tomorrow then the rest of the time's our own."

"Perhaps me mother's got an old pair of curtains we can have. They'd be better than the others."

"Come here."

"I don't think these would stand a wash and anyway they wouldn't be dry in time. What could we put up to the window?" Waiting for Daisy to stop Bill started to picture her beneath the working clothes; the feel of her body, her warmth and animal softness. "I'll go and see tomorrow. Or perhaps at weekend…"

"Come here."

She came and stood before him, looking at his face, studying it closely. Did he mean it? He took Daisy's face in his hands and kissed her gently.

"I'll just put these pots in the sink…" she began but Bill forestalled her and switching off the light he led her to the stairs. They kissed again, passionately, behind the newly painted door and then Bill turned her and with his hands on her waist he guided her up the stairs ahead of him. "Sod the pots…"

There wasn't time to strip the walls and re-paper so they papered straight over the existing walls after pulling off the loose bits first. The effect was immediate and much more satisfying to see the change it made to the room. Even with the battered furniture the room began to take on a look of freshness; more important than that was the smell of fresh paint, overwhelming the smell of neglect.

"Oh Billy. It's going to look super."

Bill took the praise with modesty. "We should've stripped it first but it'll have to do. It's better than it was anyway."

"Would you like a cup of tea?"

103

"No, no we'd better get on. Anyway I want to finish this bucket of paste before it goes off. Is there any more left? Should be another packet."

"We'll have a cup of tea then when you've mixed the next lot up." They continued with renewed vigour.

It was while they were taking a break with tea and a sandwich that Bill set to thinking. "It's not long enough is it."

"What's not?" Daisy glanced about the room. Had they cut and pasted a piece too short?

"This. Our time together. There's not enough time is there. This leave, it's too short. Spending it like this I mean. We should be making more of it, going out, enjoying ourselves instead of this bloody working all the bloody time."

"Oh but it looks lovely Bill."

"That's not what I mean!"

"I know that things had slipped a bit." she said with some hesitancy. Truth to tell Daisy was relieved that their preoccupation with the decorating was absorbing so much of their time and so much of Bill's leave. There was less chance of accidentally bumping into somebody that she would rather Bill didn't meet. While Bill was home that other way of life was shut away. It didn't exist, and why should it? It was only a diversion to get her through the interminable emptiness. There was no need even to mention going out for a drink. After the day's work on the house it was enough to put David in his cot and sit upon Bill's knee in the armchair, caressing until it was time for bed. "I'm sorry it was such a mess when you came home Bill," Daisy continued. "It was just that, well, things were getting on top of me and I didn't know when I was going to see you again."

"That's what I mean," Bill cried in exasperation. "I only got this leave because of the tonsilitis. God knows when I'll get another. Best I can hope for is a twenty-four hour. Generally it's just an evening pass. Quick drink in Pembridge or Leominster." He looked around him at the half finished room and raised his arms in exasperation. "And then there's the garden."

"Oh Billy no." There was only tomorrow left.

"I've got to," Bill insisted. "I've got to do something about it. I can't go away and leave it like that. I mean… look at it. We'll just give it a bit of a tidy up. It won't take long if we set-to in the morning. Just for an hour."

"Billy! Tomorrow's your last day!"

"I know. But it'll be done then." Bill saw the look of disappointment in Daisy's face. "Listen, I've had an idea. Well, it's just a thought. There might be nothing in it."

"What?" Daisy felt a twinge of apprehension.

"Oh don't worry. Listen. You know I've got some relatives in Worcester? You know, you've heard me mother talk about 'em. Her sister; they go to visit 'em every year for their holidays. Well, they used to before the war. We used to go and stay with Aunty Ame and Uncle Albert. There's two of 'em; Aunty Ame and Aunty Rose. Anyway, just a thought, maybe you could go down there for a couple of days."

"What do I want to go to your Aunty Ame's for? I don't know her!"

"No listen. It's not that. But you see, Worcester's not far from Leominster; I could easily get a train or something and get to Worcester or you could get from Worcester to Hereford and we could meet. Even if it was only for a few hours."

"But…" Daisy was taken utterly by surprise. "I mean…! How long would you get off?"

"Well, perhaps… I don't know. I've told you, I can only get a few hours. Occasionally… Well… it was just an idea that's all! I just thought it'd give us a chance to be together. Even if it's only for a bit… Oh forget I ever mentioned it!!"

"No Bill, don't be like that. It's just that I don't know 'em. And how much is it going to cost? I mean it's alright for you. You get your travel warrant. And anyway, they might not like it."

"Oh forget it. Sorry I mentioned it. Come on, let's get this finished."

"Oh come on Bill. Don't let it spoil it; you've only got tomorrow."

"I know! That's what I'm on about! There's never any time!"

Daisy let the subject drop. It wouldn't work and anyway there was no good getting into an argument over it.

"That paste should have thickened up by now," she said, changing the subject. "Are you ready? Come on, we'll get it finished by teatime."

Bill raised himself with an air of overwhelming weariness. "Aye. I suppose so."

With the redecoration of the living room complete Bill started on the garden. It was the last day of his leave.

"Don't you think you've done enough?" But Daisy's plea went unheeded. Bill was determined, like a man given one last chance. He wasn't a natural gardener but it didn't call for skill. He hacked with a pair of shears at the rank grass and weeds. David was out with him, wielding a pair of scissors and sawing unsuccessfully at a wayward branch of privet.

"Look, come on out of there," Bill cried, "Go and do that bit over there. Out of the way. You'll get hurt if these clippers get you." He took David's hand, leading him to the corner by the path where the grass had already been cut into ragged tufts. "Here you are look, this is your bit. See if you can pull these weeds up here. Like this."

Bill took a handful of rosebay willow herb and pulled; it lifted easily from the stale black earth. David took hold of a stem in imitation of his daddy and pulled. The leaves stripped off leaving him with a wet handful of leaves and the stem of the plant still firmly rooted in the earth. Bill laughed and pulled out another one. "See, like this."

It was beginning to look better already and Bill felt good. The sun came out and shone on them, the man and his son working together and Bill stooped once more to his task. 'This is what it's all about really, tilling the earth and living together in harmony. And each life becoming in some small way better than the previous one. So man fulfils his destiny on earth.' Bill was slightly surprised at himself, at the direction his thoughts had taken but it was so right for that moment and brought a sense of fulfilment. The sun was warming and David was playing happily amongst the debris of the grass. A beetle ran across his hand; David watched it in fascination for a second then he shuddered and flung it away and ran screaming across the garden. Bill picked him up and cuddled him and stroked his head and kissed it. It was getting better already.

"It's just a little beetle that's all. Here, theres lots of little animals. Look, let's see what we can find."

Bill scoured the uncut grasses beneath the privet. "Here's a web look. This is where the spider lives. He spins the web to catch his dinner. And there's a ladybird. See! A pretty red ladybird."

He extended his forefinger and the ladybird ran onto it. Bill turned and twisted his finger around to keep it in view as David gazed in fascination. "Here, do you want it? Come on it won't hurt you. Look."

Bill took David's hand, placing it alongside his own and the ladybird ran across onto it. David gave a shiver of delight until the little creature began to run along his arm. Then he took fright and waved his arm about until the ladybird flew off. Bill laughed at David's antics again. "Come on," he said, "let's find some more." He dug the point of his shears into the earth and turned it over. The tail of a worm protruded from the lump of earth. "Here we are, look at this then." He broke the lump open and lifted out the worm inside. It was a great red thing, long and glistening, writhing over and over on Bill's palm. David stepped back with a shudder. "Noooh," he wailed.

Bill held it out to him. "Here, come and look at it."

David leaned forward gingerly but wouldn't come closer. "Ooo-ugh," he said again. "Horrid."

"It's only a worm." Bill offered it to him and the child retreated. He picked it up and dangled it writhing from his fingers. "Come on, hold your hand out."

"No!"

Bill grasped David's arm and drew the child towards him. "Here," he said, "just touch it. It's only a worm. It won't hurt you." But the worm was a horrid slimy thing and David struggled and screamed in Bill's grasp. "Come on," Bill coaxed, "it won't hurt. Don't be silly."

But David would not be convinced; it was fat and red, its pulsing redness threatened him. "No. No!" he shrieked desperately struggling.

"Oh come on. It won't hurt you!" Bill was getting exasperated with David's silliness. What was wrong with the child? Other men's children played with frogs and worms and things. Why wouldn't he?

"No! No! No!" David tugged himself free at last and ran off into the house crying and leaving Bill glaring angrily after him. Bill tossed the worm back onto the ground. He picked up the shears and surveyed the garden. It didn't really look much better at all. The cut weeds lay scattered in the grass where he'd been working and he'd not done half of it yet despite all his morning's work. Just a waste of bloody time! 'Oh what's the point? It'll only grow again as soon as I've gone.' He took a brush and began to sweep with irritation at a scattering of earth on the path.

Daisy was calling from the back door. "What's the matter with David? What's he crying for?"

"He's being bloody silly over nothing!" Bill retorted. Gardening was over! Bill went back indoors taking a sour mood of irritation with him. What a way to spend your last day of leave!

CHAPTER 12

Moon river

Life resumed its pattern of drab weariness with shortages and penny-pinching poverty. But with the evening the drudgery of the day was cast aside and the seedy grubbiness mellowed in the glow of electric light as she washed and powdered, brushing her hair into long rolling waves falling to her shoulders. And then out beneath the muttering gaze of the neighbours leaving the house in darkness and the child stamping and raging alone.

Thank God for the pub at night and the gaiety of admiring company; the teasing and the ardent, beery men who were willing to show Daisy a kind of life, a life that might have been instead of wasting her youth cloistered with a child who clambered about everywhere, dragging his stickiness around the house, crying, demanding, spilling things. It was all too much. And so Daisy endured another year of poverty. The year nineteen forty three promised to be little better.

During the day the child was to be seen, like the little vagabond he was, sitting on the pavement, grubbing about in the dirt at the base of the privet, a solitary child. His second birthday passed unremarked. Playmates didn't stay long for with the acute sense of moral propriety so marked in the working classes other kids' mothers didn't want their children associating with 'her' child. David's few brief attempts at friendship faltered in indifference and name calling. The outbursts of bullying resulted in David running inside in tears. "I'll tell my mummy of you."

But there was little comfort to be had. "Oh dry your eyes and shut up." And Daisy continued with her reading or brooding or whatever other preoccupation had taken her.

Oh, but sometimes there was that joyful moment when her knee was open to him. Then he would climb aboard and cling to her, sobbing out his story in the comfort of her arms. But alas, too few and far between, those golden moments stood like oases in the otherwise barren experience of the child's existence. For the preoccupation of Daisy's life was the good time evenings in the pub and the raucous cheer of friends, treacherous beneath the glittering veneer of drinks and the sparkle of light on glasses in smoky bars and lounges. To Daisy's delight Len

108

reappeared on the scene after an absence of some weeks with neither explanation nor apology. Now the child was something to be denied; like some item she had borrowed and forgotten to return she bustled him away.

"Upstairs to bed. And don't you dare make a noise."

And later when they returned he lay awakened in the darkness listening to the sounds. The low murmer of his mummy's voice, a whisper echoing in the night, "Sh, shhh. You'll wake him." The rasp of a hoarse reply, a stumble, suppressed giggles and the awful silence of intense unseen activity. He lay there between dreaming and sleep in the dark world of his night whilst Daisy, so near yet far away indulged her awful passion. 'Was that an Uncle Harry? Was that an Uncle Len, recently discovered?' Sometimes they would meet the child. Uncle Len offered discrete patronage. A toffee. "…only mind me coat with them sticky hands." A penny, "…for an ice cream." whilst she looked on with benevolence until the brief acknowledgement was over and she shoo'd David hastily away once more.

"I shan't be a minute Len. I'll just take him up then we can go."

And David is scooped into Daisy's arms and carried off upstairs to his cot where his struggles and protests begin.

"Now I shan't be long. Come on, lie down and go to sleep, there's a good boy. Lie down!"

Her coat hangs in folds about her as she leans over the cot and the scent of her powder lingers in the air, carried on the eddies of her departure.

"Mummy, mummy, mummy, mummy…" He calls incessantly after her, dancing and fighting against the cot rails and crying, crying, oblivious to the silence of the deserted house…

Until blessed daylight comes at last and David sits amongst the covers with the doll Isabel and the sucked and balding woollen dog. Daisy is not yet awake. The sun glows at the window accentuating the drab gloominess within and a shaft of light breaks through a crack in the curtain, a bright dagger point upon the wall. David is wet, the reeking nappy hanging from him, chafing against the tenderness of his legs aflame once more with the burning of his urine.

Across the landing Daisy stirs groggily from her bed, pulls her workaday cardigan about her and goes downstairs for a cup of tea and a cigarette. She needs time to herself to think before the day comes rushing at her. Last night had been unsatisfactory. Fine friend he'd turned out to be! Buggered off as soon as the heat was on. Now what?

So Daisy sat with the cup of tea before the ashes of the fire. The sounds from above became urgent, incessant. She couldn't think straight and the cries broke in on her concentration. Mary was coming on

109

Thursday; she'd talk it over with her and see if she could help. And she hadn't seen Brenda for ages; she was married now with a family. She might know what to do.

The cries from above continued and Daisy finished her tea and went to fetch him. God! But he stank and she held him from her as she lifted him over the cot rail. She poured another cup of tea and a milky one for the child and sat again and pondered. Perhaps she'd got it wrong and it was Bill's. But it was only three weeks since his leave. The bubble of hope vanished. Idly she watched David wandering about the room slopping tea over himself as he went and adding more stains to the carpet.

"Oh! Look at you," she flared. "Come here, let's get you changed." She took the soggy square of towelling from him and added it to the heap in the kitchen. "What are you going to have for your breakfast?" The rusk packet was empty save for half a biscuit and some crumbs. There was nothing else for it; she would have to cook! She measured out porridge oats, milk and water; while she was at it she put the kettle on for another cup of tea. In her preoccupation Daisy forgot the porridge and the strong smell of burnt milk filled the kitchen. So she stirred a healthy flood of cold milk from the bottle into the dish and stirred it in. "Come on, sit up here and eat it like a good boy."

David dribbled and spat it from his mouth. "Ugh, it's horrid."

"Come on," she said, "it's nice."

"Don't like it." David pushed the dish away.

"Oh come here!" Daisy pushed another spoonful into his mouth and again David spat it out.

Exasperated Daisy forced the spoon into David's mouth and again he spat it out. "Well you're not getting any more so you can just sit there until you've eaten it. I've made it specially for you." She flung the spoon into the dish and David started to climb down. "Oh no you don't." She pushed him back into his seat. "You naughty wicked boy. Eat it all up do you hear!"

"Don't want it!" he screamed, scrambling down from the chair.

"Oh shut up will you. Give me a bit of peace." She went into the kitchen and slammed the door on him.

David wanted to go out to play. Reaching on tiptoe he could just reach the doorknob but the door was still locked so he went to her to have the door opened.

"Oh go on," she said, "and give me a bit of peace and quiet."

The road was deserted and quiet in the early morning sunshine, the only sound coming from the foundries on the faint breeze from the Don valley below. Breakfast was forgotten as he skipped along the pavement. Before him lay the whole world. David decided he would go where the big boys went but they wouldn't be there now and he could have the whole playground to himself with no-one to push him down. It was across the road and round the corner with a railing round it and a clanging metal gate. He pushed the gate open and ran across joyfully and gave the see-saw a push down then back up again. Now for the swings!

"Hey! What you doing!" The voice was loud and grown up. David turned and saw a man at the gate all dressed in black with silver buttons and a shiny cap. The man's voice was angry. "I said what you doing?" it demanded.

David's jaw dropped in dismay. "I've come to play."

"Well come on. Get out of it."

"Can't I play?" David asked, bewildered. There was no-one else about. "I want to play."

"No. Bugger off home." David began to cry. The man stood guard near the gate and David would have to pass him. "I said come on, let's have you. Out!"

The man produced a padlock and raised his arm in a gesture as David approached. "Go on clear off. If I catch you here again there'll be trouble. Get off home where you belong."

David scampered off up the road in tears and after a few yards he paused and turned to look back. The man had locked the gate and stood testing the padlock. "Yes," he said, "I'm watching you."

David returned home and played for a while with the twigs and stones on the pavement beneath the privet until it lost its appeal. A neighbour silently passed him on her way up to the shops. David knew where there was a scooter! He would play with that! Tommy wouldn't ever let him play on it or have a ride. But if he took Tommy's scooter it would make up for the times Tommy had said you can't play with us. David dropped his twigs and stones and set off up the road to Tommy's house.

It was silent going down the garden path between the houses. David crept down the side and peered round the corner into the back garden. There was the outhouse door. David reached for the latch and lifted it; there was a click and the door swung open. David looked inside. It was stacked with coal and lengths of wood but just inside the door, why, there was Tommy's scooter. David stood and wondered whether to take it; it was so quiet he wondered if anyone was watching him. He looked back around the corner to see but there was no-one so he reached into the outhouse to take it. But some of the coal began to fall as he moved it making a terrible noise and, engrossed as he was David suddenly felt vulnerable with the open door behind him. He turned to see! There was no-one so he grabbed the scooter and began to make off with it but some of the wood fell down and inside the house a dog began to bark. As he was halfway along the garden path the door opened; David dropped the scooter and ran, his heart pounding, followed by the shouts of outrage, "Why you bloody little thief…"

He went back home to play in the garden. He sat in a corner far away from the side door where he could see if anybody came in from the road. But no-one came. There was no hue and cry. No-one bothered. No-one was interested.

Now he was hungry and getting cold and so he went back inside. The postman must have been. Mummy was sitting in the armchair with a letter. She was pursing her lips as though she was trying to make up her mind. David ran across to her and began to scramble on her knee.

"Oh come on then," she said and David climbed up and sat happily on her lap. He turned to look at her and she put her arm around him. "What have you been up to then?" David buried his face against her. "Oh you are a little soppy aren't you. Fancy making all that fuss over your breakfast. We'll get you some dinner in a minute." Daisy picked up the letter to show him. "This is from your daddy look. He wants us to go to see him. All the way to Worcester. But I don't know. Whatever are we going to do eh?" For that was the paradox of Daisy's life. She had begun going up to the pub initially to fill the gap that Bill's absence had brought into her life. Now the chance to go and see Bill, if only for a fleeting visit, was an interruption. And she still had this other bloody business to sort out! Daisy shrugged and gave the child another hug. "Come on then," she sighed, "Let's go and get you some dinner shall we."

Moonlight was dancing on the Severn as it slid seductively below the high banks of the meadow at the edge of Worcester racecourse. Bill and Daisy's cigarettes glowed briefly, illuminating their faces framed in the turned up collars of their coats, each turned toward the others. With their arms about each other's waist they walked and talked softly as the river gurgled and eddied against the bank. Above them loomed the latticed iron framework of the railway bridge silhouetted against the moon.

"I wish you'd brought him."

"I couldn't Bill. I mean, I wasn't sure how your Aunty Ame was going to manage to put us up." It was a weak excuse and Daisy knew it. She didn't want to bring him and that was it! Besides his rash was back and he was getting all scurvy and oh…! How do people manage with kids? Anyway she'd had no intention of bringing him to Worcester in that state for everybody to comment on. Mary would be alright with him and anyway it was only a day or so.

"They said he'd be no trouble, they said they were looking forward to seeing him. I told you so in the letter." Bill harboured rosy memories of David as he had seen him last in the garden, pottering about together.

"Oh well," Daisy said, "I did it for the best." She snuggled close to him. "I just wanted us to have time just to ourselves."

Bill flicked the butt of his cigarette into the river and turned Daisy to him. She dropped hers on the floor grinding it with her foot. "I love you," he whispered. "Oh God, you don't know how I'm missing you."

"I miss you too." She responded to his kiss. "When will you get another leave?"

"I don't know. It's not easy." They were approaching the high brick pier supporting the railway bridge high above them. "Oh come here." They kissed again. "I want you. I want you so much. Oh it's no good is it."

"What?"

"This! Just a couple of hours. I mean... there's no time..." He kissed Daisy again and pushed his body against hers, moving and pulling her hard against him.

"Oh Bill," Daisy gasped, aroused. "I want you too."

"Come on, come up here." Bill led her up the bank until they were safely out of sight behind the brickwork of the pier in complete darkness.

"Not here," Daisy protested. They were too close to the towpath. "Somebody might come."

But Bill wouldn't be denied and he kissed her again fiercely. She was so sweet and soft and perfumed and he laid her on the bank and pulled her skirt up and felt between her thighs. Daisy wriggled and tugged at her knickers then reached for the buttons of his flies. A train rumbled slowly across the bridge above them, masking the sounds of passion. Soft, urgent, yielding, demanding, fierce and sweet beneath him; Bill was consumed with desire until, breathless he opened his eyes to the unseeing world and heard once again the distant city sounds. "Oh God Daisy. I love you."

"I love you too."

CHAPTER 13

Wire!

Another starshell burst in the cloudless blue sky above him leaving a brief trace of grey smoke and Bill threw himself to the ground almost landing on top of his companion and cracking his arm painfully against his rifle. Then he sat up and looked around, rubbing his arm ruefully. There was no sign of the main body; somehow they had become separated from the rest of the unit.

"Where's the others? Come on Mako where are they? Can't see any of 'em anywhere."

Mako rolled lazily over onto his back and discarded his helmet. This would do, up here on the Brecon Beacons with nobody to worry them. Time to lay back and relax for a bit with a cigarette. He lit up without offering one to Bill. "Take it easy will you. You're always bloody wittling. They'll be miles behind, we'll have a rest up here for a bit."

Bill peered anxiously about as another shell whined overhead, bursting somewhere to the rear of them. He leaned forward then suddenly gripped Mako's arm and pointed. Down the shoulder of the hillside and well ahead of them a group of airmen were making their way along the valley, following the path of the stream.

"There's one of 'em... and another! Looks like our flight. That's Flight Sar'nt Dean in't it. Look, just down there!"

Mako continued to lie on his back, smoking and occasionally casting a disdainful glance in Bill's direction.

"Come on Mako! We've got to try and join up with 'em!"

"Why don't you sit down before they see you and let me finish me fag."

"Oh come on," Bill urged, crouching and giving Mako's arm a shake. "If we don't link up with 'em we'll never get across the ridge never mind about making the objective."

Another shell burst above them but much closer this time. Fragments showered about them and Bill threw himself flat on the ground again. Mako rolled onto his face, scrabbling for his helmet. Then he raised himself on his elbows and examined the broken remains of his cigarette.

"Bloody excercises," he moaned, "It'll be bad enough over there without having to get half shot to hell before we get there. Where are they?"

"Just down there." Bill replied raising himself to a crouch. "Come on, before another one comes over."

Picking up their rifles Bill and Mako set off running half crouching and stumbling across the hillside to intercept the rest making their way along the valley below them. Up on the ridge, away to their left they could just make out the referee's observation post. Another salvo of shells passed overhead.

"Looks like they've pinpointed base," Bill panted.

"Save your breath."

The ground was rough and treacherous, strewn with boulders and covered with heather and bracken amongst which potholes were concealed. After two hundred yards they paused for breath and checked their bearings.

"Can you see anything of 'em?" Bill gasped, leaning forward with his hands on his knees and drawing in great lungsful of air.

"They're moving off again." Mako was equally out of breath, winded by the sudden sharp exertion. "Come on." He was blowing like an old horse. "We'll just about make it."

A crackle of rifle fire came from above them on the ridge.

"Jesus!" Mako said, "that's where they are. If we cut across here we'll join 'em on the flank before Dixie spots us."

They set off again, cutting at an angle across the moor towards the shoulder of the hill and down to the stream below.

"Oh Christ!" Reaching the edge of a gully Mako suddenly exclaimed with dismay. "Wire."

A double row of barbed wire coils barred their way, extending away to the left and below them to the right as far as they could see.

"What!" Bill joined him and stared. "Oh bloody hell! Now what?"

Undaunted Mako said, "Come on, we'll go through it."

"How?" Bill replied. "We've got no cutters!"

"Here, like this." Mako thrust his rifle into a coil and lifted. The wire looped and sagged. The bottom coil raised a mere three or four inches off the ground.

"Come here," Bill cried hastily, "I'll prise 'em apart." He had just caught a glimpse of the main body again beginning their advance towards the ridge. They were going to miss them and fail to rejoin them if they weren't careful and then there'd be hell to pay.

Mako withdrew his rifle from the coil, gingerly holding the wire between finger and thumb as he did. The coil sprang at him and one of the murderous barbs scratched the back of his hand, drawing blood.

"Ouch! Christ! Bloody excercises. What the bloody hell's the airforce doing out here like this for anyway? We're not the bleeding commandos!" He sucked the blood off the back of his hand.

Bill put his foot on the base of one of the barbed coils, pushing the adjacent coil open with the butt of his rifle.

Here," he said, "quick. Get through here while I hold it open. I'll sling your kit across then you hold it for me."

Mako dropped his rifle and pack. Gingerly he crawled into the coil. "For Christ's sake don't let it slip will you?" he muttered anxiously, then with relief he stepped out of the other side.

Bill heaved their kit across the wire. "Here," he said, "catch!" Mako caught the rifles and imitated Bill's technique with the wire.

"Right, come on then."

Mako held the loop open for him; Bill dropped to a crouch and entered the roll of wire. Another starshell burst above them, instinctively Bill started to drop but checked himself before he became prostrate in the wire. Shell fragments puttered about them, the coil slipped off Mako's rifle butt and the wire sprang shut pinning Bill in a hundred barbed claws. He shrieked and panic took him and like a slow motion marionette he started to struggle.

"Hold still! Hold still!" Mako shouted at him desperately.

"Mako! Mako! Oh God! Get us out quick!" Bill was close to dancing with agony on the ends of the barbs.

"Hold still a minute! For God's sake keep still!" Mako put his foot on the base of the coil again and prised it apart gingerly with his rifle butt. The barbs tore threads from Bill's battledress and Bill cried out again.

"Hold it a minute." Mako released the wire carefully and put his knapsack on.

"Where're you going?" Bill cried. "For God's sake Mako you can't leave me here."

Desperately Mako tried again, this time pushing his back with the pack for protection against the coil opposite the rifle butt, forcing it wider and wincing with pain as the barbs found him.

"Right," he grunted, "quick! Try it now."

Bill crawled stealthily forward, straining against the barbs that still gripped him, trying desperately not to trigger the lethal coils to spring in on him again. He felt his uniform tear; something was holding him. His arms were free but one of the coils passed down the inside of his thigh between his legs. He raised his left leg warily and the coil moved with him.

"Bill! Come on, for Christ's sake!" Mako urged, straining in agony against the barbs.

116

"Hold it Mako. I'm stuck. Just a second more."

Panting and bathed in sweat Mako screwed his eyes against the pain as tears began to roll down his face. Bill tried once more against the coil between his legs. He pulled it barely free with his left hand and the coils above him began to close. Reaching up he pushed them back. The coil within his thigh leaped up and stabbed him viciously in the groin. Bill shrieked and eased his leg over it and with his face twisted in agony Mako saw Bill roll free. With a cry Mako released the wire and jumped free as the wire zinged and sprang back into coils again. Oblivious to the mock battle beginning to take place around them Mako and Bill lay and carefully examined themselves for damage.

CHAPTER 14

Indecisions

"Come here. I want you to go and fetch me fags, there's a good boy."
Daisy was sitting at the table writing on a page torn from an old
notebook. She was out of cigarettes, out of money and out of humour.
Dying for a smoke to settle her nerves and still bloody pregnant.
Nothing seemed to have worked! Perhaps that trip to Worcester could be
the answer after all. Going with Bill like that. Depends if…? How many
weeks gone was she when they did it under the bridge by the river?
Would he take it as his? Daisy's mind went back to it. She'd almost
forgotten what it was like with Bill. She wished she could have been
more relaxed and at ease about doing it, she could have enjoyed it a lot
more. There had been something very erotic about doing it so close to
the path, only just out of sight of other passers by and laying there with
her knickers down in the darkness. But with all the creeping about and
fumbling she couldn't remember if he'd used a johnny. She came back
to the present with a jolt; so it didn't solve the bloody problem did it? If
Ada wouldn't let her have some fags she didn't know what she'd do.

David was at her elbow, peering up at the edge of the table, trying
to see what Daisy was doing.

"Tell Ada I'll pay her at the weekend only I've run out." She
finished writing then folded the paper and gave it to David. "Give him
this and when you get back if you're a good boy you can have a piece of
bread and jam."

David gave her a grin but the effect was spoiled by the angry red
rash spreading around his mouth.

"Look at you. You little scruff." David threw his arms across
Daisy's knees and tried to scramble up onto her. "Go on. When you've
done your errand. Then perhaps. Oh," she exclaimed in sudden
exasperation, "Where's your other sock? Where is it? Oh, come here!
I'll never get me fags at this rate. What've you done with it?" She
dragged him up onto her knee and put his sock on and then his shoe.
"Now then. Have you got that note? Let me see! Alright go on then.
And come straight back. Do you hear!"

David scampered off leaving the front door swinging open, up the
road and round the corner to the next street where Ada and Sydney

118

lived. The heady scent of wallflowers hung about their garden path as David approached the door. Ada was throwing a shovelful of ashes into the dustbin when she saw David approaching. She smiled to see him coming down the path and David ran to her.

"Come on then." She beamed at him in greeting. "Come and see what I've got for you." Taking David's hand she led him indoors. "Look who's here Sydney."

Sydney, a florid man in his fifties was sitting at ease in his shirtsleeves and waistcoat when David entered. He looked up from his newspaper. "What are you doing here then? Come an errand for your mammy have you? Here Aunty Ada, haven't we got something for him then?"

David looked expectantly round the room. The sideboard had its normal adornment of ornaments, two glazed vases with pictures of highland cattle against a background of mountains, and a picture of a soldier, a young man in R.E.M.E. uniform smiling from the frame. The clock was on the mantelpiece and, at either end the candlesticks carved in dark oak spirals like sticks of barley sugar were just the same. Nothing that David could see was different.

"Shall we give it to him?"

"Oh I don't know Uncle Sydney. Depends if he's been a good boy or not. Have you been a good boy today? Have you?"

"Yes." David replied, his eyes wide in anticipation.

"Are you sure now?" Ada asked with mock severity.

"Yes." the child replied. "Mummy says I'm always a good boy. Sometimes."

Sydney and Ada laughed. "Ah! Bless him," she said.

"Now you just wait here then." Sydney went to the sideboard and rummaged in one of the drawers. David heard a rustling of paper; could it be a bag of sweets?

"Here you are then. Here's a toffee." And Sydney held it out to David, holding it by one of the paper twists at the end. It was one of the perks of Ada and Sydney's sideline in black market sweets and tobacco which they sold on to their private regular customers at inflated prices in return for 'tick', that favoured children sometimes received an unexpected gift.

"What do I get then?"

David threw his arms about Sydney's neck and gave him a moist kiss which Sydney discreetly wiped away.

"And what about Aunty Ada? Does she get one too?"

Ada picked David up and hugged him, giving him a kiss on the cheek.

"Now you sit there and eat your sweetie." Sydney pointed to the armchair he had just vacated, "While I go and get your mammy's ciggies." He went off and returned with two packets of Gold Flake and wrapped them in a sheet of old newspaper on the table. Then he wrote on the back of the note which David had brought and handed it back to him together with the cigarettes.

"Tell your mammy she's not to send you round for any more until she's paid what she owes. Give these to your mammy won't you. Now don't forget. Here's your parcel. And here's the note. Keep it safe and give it straight to your mammy there's a good boy."

"Going now," David said unintelligibly through the mouthful of toffee.

"Well go straight home then won't you." Ada admonished him. "And don't forget to tell her what Uncle Sydney told you."

She watched from the kitchen door as David strode importantly along the road with his parcel. An expression of pity mingled with warmth passed briefly across her face. "Poor little bugger." she murmured to herself, then she went back in and closed the door.

Daisy received the parcel from David with disappointment. It didn't look as big as expected.

"What did Ada say then?" she asked as she opened it.

"I've had a toffee," David replied.

Daisy grunted with dismay. The parcel only contained two packets of twenty cigarettes. Forty cigarettes wasn't going to get her through to the end of the week! David held the note out to her; Daisy took it and read the message on the back.

"Cheeky bugger," Daisy muttered reading it. "She knows I'll pay her at weekend." More disappointment, life seemed to be filled with disappointments. She lit up and resumed her seat in the armchair. "Oh come on then."

David scrambled on her knee until she grew tired of his fidgeting. He just wouldn't sit quietly and let her have some peace. "Oh go on," Daisy said pushing him down in irritation. "If you can't keep still you'll have to go down and find something to do. Why don't you go and play. Go and fetch your bricks or something why don't you."

Teatime was approaching; that was something else. She didn't fancy anything; God knows what she was going to give him for his tea. He seemed to be living on bread and jam! Oh well...

The knock at the door startled her. Who could be calling? Quarter past five, nobody usually called at this time, it was far too early. She opened the door. "My God! What brings you here?"

Len was noncholantly surveying the weed ridden garden. He turned to Daisy and said, "You want to get something done about this lot."

"What do you think you want then?"

120

"Come to see you." He looked about him as though acknowledging unseen neighbours peering from behind windows. "Don't I even get a cup of tea then?"

Daisy stood aside and Len strolled past her into the living room. She turned to look at him. Bloody arrogant sod! Standing there all dressed up in his suit and shiny shoes, making her feel so… dowdy! She was always so careful to present herself at her best and he'd caught her on the hop.

"Well!"

"Thought you'd be pleased to see me." He looked around for somewhere to sit and thought better of it. Daisy fiddled with her hair to no effect.

"Why should I be pleased to see you? After all this time. After walking out like that."

"It was a shock," he said. "I mean, just coming out with it the way you did."

"Well what did you expect me to say?"

"Well I don't know. It was just a bit sudden that's all. Anyway, what about that cup of tea."

"Oh yes." Daisy went into the kitchen and Len looked at David under the table playing.

"Here," he said, "I've got something for you." He fished in his jacket pocket and pulled out a small lead aeroplane and making zooming noises he flew it between thumb and forefinger and landed it on the floor in front of David. "There you are," Len said, "Just like your daddy's."

Daisy paused in the kitchen doorway. "You spoil him. Tea won't be long."

"Cigarette?" Len produced a slim chrome cigarette case filled with Senior Service.

"Thanks." Daisy's cursory acceptance masked her gratitude. Let him provide the fags, it would eke out her meagre ration!

"Well, what you doing about it?" Len tossed the match into the grate.

"How d'you mean, what am I doing about it? I thought that's what you've come for?"

"Me! Nowt to do with me. Just thought if you needed any help." He let his gaze wander round the room. Daisy watched him and felt anger rising. The self satisfied bastard.

"Help? What would I need any help for?"

"Now then, don't get excited. I just thought…"

"If you'd anything about you, you'd be paying to get something done."

"Do you mean you haven't. The way you were talking I'd have thought you'd have got an abortion sorted straight away."

"I did. I mean, I tried. But its not as easy as that. I tried what our Mary said and nothing happened."

"Your Mary," Len scoffed. "What's she know about it?"

"Well she knows somebody who's, well… who knows about these things."

"Aye! Sounds like it."

"Well if you'd anything about you…"

"Wait a minute," Len protested. "It's nowt to do with me."

"How d'you mean, it's nowt to do with you?"

"You don't think it's mine do you?"

"Why you…" Daisy flew at him and tried to hit him but Len easily fended her off.

"Now calm down. Everybody knows you've been putting it about a bit. For all I know; for all you know for that matter it could be your husband's. He's been home since hasn't he?"

Daisy's face contorted with venom. "You're a cruel, conceited sod!"

"Aye, well. But it's not me that's in 'club is it!"

"What you come here for then?" Daisy subsided into her armchair. She felt tears rising but she wouldn't shed them in front of him. She turned her face towards the fireplace. Len looked at her. He wasn't a soft touch and tears would have made no difference but he remembered the nights with Daisy when she was on form, dressed up to go out and full of fun. And she'd been good fun in bed too! None of your open wide and stick it in and thank you very much. She knew how to play. God, she loved it. It was such a waste if she was going to get herself saddled with another kid. And she wasn't expensive either, always holding her hand out. Evening out, drinks, a laugh and a joke, a good time by all. He looked again around the place. Expensive? She certainly wasn't that!

"I just come to see if I could help, that's all." he said quietly.

Daisy felt a surge of hope. She turned and looked up at him. "You mean," she hardly dared say it, "you mean you'd pay for an abortion. Properly."

"Bloody likely," Len replied hastily. "I've told you, I'm not taking no responsibility. Not for what's not mine! And we don't know do we?"

"Well what then?"

Len took his wallet from inside his jacket and produced a fiver, unfolding it carefully and smoothing the creases. Daisy looked at the note with its discrete engraving. It was ages since she'd seen one; it was more money in one piece than she had dreamed possible. She battled with her pride.

"You can keep your money." But there was uncertainty in her voice.

"Come on Daisy. We can still be friends can't we? Eh? What's the harm in a bit of help from a friend? For old time's sake." He saw her hesitate. He saw how much she needed it. It was as much as he had been prepared to give when he'd decided to come and see her. But she'd been a good kid and Len decided on an impulse to save her face, to enable her to accept it.

"Look," he said, "why don't we go out tonight and have a good time? Eh? We can still go and have a night out can't we and forget about all this for a bit." He gestured round the room.

"What d'you mean?" Daisy was still uncertain.

"Come on," Len coaxed her. "Here, pick this up, first round's on you." He pressed the sheet of paper into Daisy's hand. Daisy took the fiver and gave a little shrug. Why not? Better than nothing and she wasn't so far gone that it'd make any difference. She didn't even show yet.

"Alright," she said. "Only it'll take me a bit to get ready. And we haven't had our tea yet." She hesitated, unsure. Christ if only she'd got something to give him in the larder. "What about you? Will you..?"

But that was where Len decided to draw the line. With any luck he might get Daisy between the sheets again but he would make other arrangements for eating.

"No," he said. "You don't want me hanging about while you're making yourself beautiful. Anyway I've got a couple of things to do first. I'll call back for you later. O.K."

Daisy smiled, a little wanly. "Thanks Len. I mean, you know... about." She gestured at the note. "And tonight I mean." She hesitated then said, "I'm sorry I went on a bit about... I wasn't trying to trick you, you know."

"You won't trick me," he said.

Three days previously Bill had reported sick again. The M.O. was having a busy time of it and was harassed. Rumours were circulating about a squadron posting. The gliders were moving south and there was even talk of the base being taken over by Yanks. Now he was having to deal with an unusually high number of complaints as the unit made ready to get up to 100% fitness or, as he secretly suspected of some of its members, to have solid medical grounds for remaining behind. The M.O. ignored the salute and waved Bill to the chair whilst he cast a cursory eye over the medical record.

"How's the tonsils? Should be healed up nicely now. Better take a

123

look. Open up." He reached for a spatula and came round to the front of the desk to where Bill was sitting. He tilted Bill's head back, inserted the spatula over his tongue and peered into his throat. "Seems alright. Mmmmm. Yes. Doing nicely." The M.O's manner became abrupt. "Well, what is it?"

"I got injured on excercises sir and it won't heal up."

"Injured! Where?" the M.O. returned to the desk. "Doesn't say so on your report." He gave Bill his piercing look, the one that sorted out the shirkers from the genuine cases.

"It's here sir." Bill indicated his groin, embarassed.

"Come on then, let's have a look. Get 'em off and stand over there."

Bill crossed over to the corner and began to remove his trousers.

"You'd better tell me what happened."

"Well we were crossing some wire sir and I got myself snagged on it. One of the wires sprang up and stabbed me. It's not much really only it won't heal up. It's a bit sore too."

The M.O. bent and examined the area Bill indicated. Then he took another spatula and moved Bill's genitals about, finally returning to examine the large inflamed spot at the base of Bill's groin and the swollen lumpish area around it.

"And you say you did this on the wire."

"Yes sir. It was just a little stab from one of the wire barbs. Only instead of getting better it's getting worse. I thought you could give me something to clear it up. It's a bit… tender…"

The M.O. was regarding Bill steadily. It was unnerving to be under that steady gaze and Bill felt he ought to say something more but he had nothing to add.

Finally the M.O. said, "You've got the pox lad."

"What!" Bill had a disbelieving urge to turn around to see if he was talking to someone else.

"The pox. Clap!" The M.O. removed his glasses and tossed the spatula into the bin. "You've got V.D."

"No!" The man must be a quack! "I got stabbed on the wire. I felt it happen." Inane statement. Of course you'd feel it happen if something stabbed you. "What I mean is, I felt a little prick where the wire barb stuck in me. It bled! Not a lot but, well, it didn't seem much so I didn't bother to report it."

The M.O's steady gaze was still on him. "Listen to me lad. You have got yourself a dose." He pointed at Bill's groin. "That's V.D. All right, get dressed." Bill pulled his trousers on, relieved to cover himself and what he regarded as a shameful affliction. The M.O. continued, "You may well have got yourself tangled in the wire but that's V.D.

124

you've got there. Who've you been around with?"

"Pardon?"

"Oh come on. Who've you been seeing?"

"Nobody sir."

The M.O. returned to the desk and examined Bill's record card. "So you're a married man eh?" Bill nodded. "And what's your wife going to say d'you think?" He gestured Bill back into the chair. Bill sat heavily.

"I've not been with anybody sir." He was almost pleading for the officer to believe him. "I get out when I can, we go for a pint but I haven't been with anybody. Nobody at all. You can ask the lads. Ask me mates. Ask 'em! They'll tell you."

"Well," the M.O. said, "you've got it from somewhere. It doesn't just happen on it's own you know. Not off lavatory seats despite what you might have heard."

Bill started to protest, "But I haven't..."

The M.O. raised his hand. "Now listen to me! We know it goes on. We're all broad minded. And whatever you say to me in here is in the strictest confidence. Between a doctor and his patient. Right?" Bill nodded in consternation. "Well," the M.O. continued, "can't have the whole bloody base going down now can I. If there's one of the girls in the village or over in Leominster sharing this around then we'd better get a grip of it hadn't we. No mess, no pack drill but I must know who she is!"

"There's nobody," Bill entreated the doctor earnestly. "Nobody. Nobody at all."

"All right, come on." The M.O. was conscious of the passing time and he had a queue of others waiting outside. "When did you last have sex?"

Bill stammered in his confusion. "Well... about a couple of weeks I think... three weeks. Or was it...?"

The M.O's patience was exquisite. He leaned back in his chair. "Who with?"

"My wife." Bill swallowed, his mouth was getting dry.

"Your wife."

"Yes sir. I'd had the sick leave after the tonsil op. And then afterwards..."

The M.O. leaned forward. "And then what?"

"Pardon?"

"Oh come on man. Who else? Who else have you been with? Since then? Or before?"

"I got a pass... well, she came down to Worcester. We met there for a few hours. You know. We..." Bill protested, confused. "There's been no-one else sir."

He fixed Bill with the gaze again. "You're sure?"

"Yes. Yes sir." Bill's mind was working furiously, retracing his visit, the conditions, Daisy…

"Well lad," the M.O. said, "it seems you've got yourself a little problem."

"Sir?"

"Your wife. It would appear she's given you a dose of the pox."

Bill declined to answer. He sat like a stoic avoiding the M.O's eyes, his mind elsewhere, evaluating other things.

"I can give you something for it, something that'll help to clear it up. I'll give you a note for the local hospital for you to go for some of their treatment. They have a clinic there. It's quite discreet. Not very pleasant I'm afraid but then, neither is the complaint. Now, if you'll just…"

Watching Bill's face the M.O. saw the shadows of conflicting passions flow across it. So many times he saw it with these young men, leaving homes and loved ones in trust while they came out to join the services; only to have their illusions shattered somewhere along the way.

Bill was rapidly alternating between blind anger and despair. What has she done to me? The bitch! The bitch! I'll kill her… Oh Daisy why? What for? There's only you, why did you do it? What have you done to yourself? What about us? What will we do…?

"Did you hear me? I said I'll talk to your C.O. and see if we can arrange for you to get 48 hours to sort it out. But meanwhile get yourself along to the hospital and get the treatment started."

And three days later Bill had set off once more for home.

CHAPTER 15

Crying in the night

Bill set off without a clear idea of what he was going to do. He wrote to
Daisy telling her why he was coming to see her but he was undecided
whether to post it or not. How could she do this to him; how would he
ever be able to trust her again? He wanted to find out the name of the
sod she'd been going with and give them both a pasting. Then he
checked his thoughts; he didn't want to catch them at it! No, no not that!
That wasn't what he wanted. Or was it? In the end Bill tore the letter
into shreds; he wanted the truth not some tale concocted in self defence.
He wanted everything clear and out in the open and no more secrets!

He still had to make two changes on the journey and didn't arrive at
Birmingham until late in the afternoon and then there was an hour to
wait. He went into the station buffet for a snack. It was crowded and he
queued for a cheese sandwich and tea in a mug bearing the insignia
'MR' in faded blue beneath the earthenware glaze. He ate standing,
wedged in a corner between the wall and the buffet door resentful of the
crowd that filled the room. Layers of dense bluegrey cigarette smoke
hung above the heads of the noisy, chattering people. Kitbags and
knapsacks lay in piles about the door and against the tables and
everywhere there were uniforms. Bill observed a few travelling alone
but most were with companions and whilst different regiments and
services mingled freely, officers stood with their counterparts whilst
groups of 'other ranks' engaged in lively chatter together.

The bustle and movement was constant; as fast as people left to join
their trains others entered to replace them, joining the never diminishing
line at the counter. And amongst all the activity were couples, standing
as Bill had once stood, intense and preoccupied, eking out their fleeting
time together in earnest conversation, hand in hand, heart to heart intent
upon their farewells. And then with minutes more still remaining before
their separation, saying their farewells again until the time to go finally
came. Bill watched it all with a strangely detached feeling. What were
they to him? Nothing but transient images.

His tea and sandwich finished, Bill checked his watch against the
station clock; another twenty minutes! He lit a fag and watched the
smoke rise to join the layers floating lazily above his head. Unheard, the

station announcements echoed their indistinct sing-song above the slamming carriage doors and steaming trains and whistles signalling departures into the smoking tunnels.

What was he to do? Again and again Bill asked himself the question and still he was no nearer the answer. She had said she loved him. Alone together they had companionship and that was precious too. His mind went back to afternoons in the park before they were married and Daisy's concern lest he should leave her. It was more than love. They had been friends too! He was a lucky man who contrived to marry his best friend. They had shared something unique; at least that was what Bill had thought; trust and confidence without fear of recrimination all bound up with the pleasure of each other. But Daisy had been resentful of his going away and leaving her. Bill knew that of course. And yet he believed that she had also been prepared to understand the restlessness and frustration that had made him take that fateful step and volunteer. How could she reproach him!

'For better or worse.' The words conjured the memory of their miserable wedding day. Had the drabness of that weeping day presaged what was to come? Homeward bound like this! Going home to what? Happiness, hope, love? Love! The word was bitter. Love had been different then. Love had been the look she gave him, inviting him with passion. The memory of Daisy's voice, 'Oh Bill, Billy I love you'. And breathless desire urgent and compelling, the touch of her skin, caressing, coming together with passion and kissing, always kissing... He remembered again the way she drew him to her, fulfilling her own needs, her own desires delighting him the way it always had, taking him to her and sighing in expectation as the first frisson of passion took her.

'Wanton.' Perhaps that was the word; perhaps that's what she was and what she needed? 'No! No! No! Not ever! She is mine! 'For better or worse!' But how can I love her now? What is left? What am I going home to? What for, what for...?

Bill's train arrived and he exerted himself to join the throngs at the carriage doors impatient to climb aboard. He made his way along the crowded corridor to the end where there was more room and lit a cigarette.

Fields of corn flashed by. Villages and trees, meadows full of cattle. 'That's what we are too! Herded here and herded there; pitched around and knocked about until the end of life.' He checked his watch again. Another half hour. Then what?

The train drew into Chesterfield and the passengers pointed out the crooked spire of the parish church to one another. Sheepbridge slipped by with its huge blast furnaces dominating the landscape and then once more the familiar suburbs of the city came into view and Bill was there, with all the rest, jostling to disembark against the impatient tide of travellers on the platform crowding close against the doors. Misgivings arose as he stepped out into the station. He wished he had sent the letter after all.

The shadows of night were lengthening as the last remnants of the summer day glowed in the strips of cloud high above the city. The journey had taken far too long and Bill had to wait in the city centre for a tram. He was hungry and tired of the journey, dishevelled from travelling. His greatcoat hung open and he felt tense and nervous but at last he was on the road to home. The houses were silent and remote within their gardens and from the valley of the Don the noise of the distant industry came fitfully on the breeze.

He came to the broken gate and made his way along the unkempt path. From the darkness of the window above him came a sound; the tired cry of an exhausted child calling, "Mummy... Mummy..." He put his hand to the back door latch but it was locked. The front door was the same. Bill took his key and entered the darkened house; without putting any lights on he checked the rooms downstairs. They were empty. The cries from above continued and Bill crept carefully upstairs. With his eyes accustomed to the gloom, in the twilight seeping through the thin curtains Bill made out the form of David, lying on a tangle of bedclothes in a fitful half sleep murmuring and crying, "Mummy... Mummy... Mummy..."

Bill sat by the cot and lay a gentle hand upon his son, soothing, calming, until the crying stopped and peaceful sleep came at last. He sat in silent contemplation, the distress of his son giving rise to growing anger. Not rage, uncontrolled and furious but a cold implacable angry sense of purpose.

When he was sure that David was sleeping calmly Bill returned downstairs to wait. He checked the time; it was quarter to ten. On an impulse he slipped out quietly so as not to disturb David by making any noise and went next door to Mrs. Mason's.

A querulous call, "Who is it?" came in answer to his insistent knocking. The door opened a careful inch or two. "Why," Mrs. Mason said, opening the door to him, "it's Bill." Then her face fell as though from guilty knowledge.

Bill affected noncholance. "I just got home unexpectedly. Only Daisy's not in," he said offhandedly.

"No." Mrs. Masons reply was hesitant and Bill sensed it. "She... she sometimes goes out for a drink."

"She say when she'd be back?" Again Bill put the question offhandedly. Mrs. Mason darted a glance along the path then she said quickly, "D'you want to come in a minute?"

"Just for a second then." Bill looked back over his shoulder to the house. "Only I've left David in there asleep."

"Yes," she said in a knowing sort of way. "Mester's in here."

Mr. Mason was sitting in his chair with his folded hands resting on the handle of his walking stick and his ear cocked to the wireless. "It's Billy Wilf. From next door. Come home unexpected. Got a bit of leave eh love?"

"Yes." Bill replied shortly.

"Turn that thing off." Mr. Mason gestured shortly at the radio with his stick.

"Any idea when she's coming back? Did she say?" Again the same light, non threatening tone of questioning.

"Well, we don't see much of her now really. Do we Wilf." But Mr. Mason remained silent and Mrs. Mason stood with her hands clasped before her. Bill sensed the end of conversation.

"Right. Well, sorry to have disturbed you." He paused for a second but there was just embarassed silence. "I'll be off then." He turned and made for the door.

Without shifting his position or raising his eyes to look at Bill Mr. Mason said, "It's a pity you're not home regular. Way she carries on."

"Shush Wilf." Mrs. Mason cast a worried glance at Bill but he stood still and made no response.

"It's a bloody disgrace her coming home at all hours. Carrying on in the street. Different bloke every night!"

Bill gave an imperceptible nod. Whether it was made as an acknowledgement to Mr. Mason or to himself was impossible to say. He turned and left to a worried, "Goodnight then Billy…" from Mrs. Mason and returned home.

In the darkness of the bedroom it was silent save for the gentle breathing of the child. Bill sat at rest keeping watch over the sleeping form. Now he was sure. How could he have been such a blind fool? Time slipped easily by as he sat in the darkness waiting.

But supposing Daisy came home alone? How would it look, to be discovered sitting here in darkness? Did it matter anyway? Perhaps not but Bill decided it would be better to wait unseen outside the house and see if she came home with anybody. She might be home any minute! He ran silently down the stairs and closed the door carefully behind him then slipped round to the back of the house, out of the garden and across the road, blending into shadow. His heart was pounding, it was past closing time, she must soon be here.

He heard her approach at last.

Along the blacked out road came the sound of unsteady footsteps, hers and a man's, and low chatter. He knew it was Daisy. So they were right all along; the Mason's, the M.O., everybody! Standing in the darkness and listening to them giggling and fumbling the key into the door Bill felt his anger dissolve into shame and a surprising sense of sadness. Oh how he had hoped that it wouldn't be so, that somehow this was all a great confusion and misunderstanding.

The door closed behind them and a downstair's light came on. The man appeared briefly at the window and pulled the curtains closed, and Bill felt his shame crystallise into anger again as he watched someone else with his wife in his home displaying such ownership. The kitchen light went on, briefly, and went off again. Bill paused. Should he march straight across now? – What? And find them sitting with mugs of cocoa? – Or should he wait to see how long the bloke stayed and then confront Daisy? The sitting room light went off and the house reverted back to darkness. Bill waited, watching the front door. Nothing happened. The house remained in darkness and no-one emerged. So this was the final betrayal and he would have to face it. He hesitated a few moments longer then crossed the road and quietly approached the house. With infinite care he inserted the key and stepped inside the lobby at the foot of the stairs, closing the door silently behind him. He could hear sounds from above. Movement and rustling, the low murmur of a voice but not the sounds of a child. Stealthily Bill started to climb the stairs.

Across the landing in the cot David lies awake in the darkness listening. His covers are kicked off in disarray at his feet and he is naked and afraid. He is afraid to be alone and afraid to make a sound. Just listening, as he always does when she returns, to the secret activity in the darkness beyond his door. The rasp of drawn breath, subdued grunting, and the whispering voice of mummy saying, 'Shhh… you'll wake him.' smothered in the darkness by the sounds of laboured gasping. But this time David is aware of something else. There is something silent and invisible coming for him on the stairs! This is worse than something you can hear. It is a presence coming with stealth, bringing retribution in the night. David's fear mounts. He needs her! Oh why doesn't she know and come to him? But in the bedroom across the landing the sounds continue unaware.

He scrambles into the corner of the cot in terror; he can feel the presence getting nearer and still the creaking, gasping sounds continue in the darkness. Now the child can bear it no longer. He betrays his fears in a terrifying scream, scrambling against the cot rails, desperately rattling and shaking them, screaming wildly now his presence is betrayed.

"Mummy! Mummy! Mummy! Mummy!"

The door crashes open and David waits for the fearful hand upon his back. But it isn't his door, it comes from the room across the landing

131

and the cries of the child are drowned by greater sounds, grown up shouts and screaming. And then, adding to the noise the crash of breaking and a scream, mummy screaming!! And voices shouting! Then grunting, and scrambling sounds and something crashing against his bedroom door and crashing against it again. David raises his voice in renewed terror, screaming, screaming. Now the fighting and shouting are moving rapidly down the stairs and mummy is shouting, "Bill, Bill, Len, Billy stop it…"

Downstairs the door slams as though it will tear the glass from every window in the house and the voice, a voice like daddy's voice, roaring, "Where are you?"

With his eyes still screwed tightly shut David senses his bedroom door open and hears footsteps running up the stairs and Daddy shouting, "No you don't. You leave him alone! Come on out of there!" David steals a glance, his mummy is in the doorway and then she is dragged back out again as though a mighty hand is pulling her.

"No Bill…" she cries desperately but her words are cut by the sharp sound of a slap and then another. There is fierce, intense and silent fighting on the landing whilst inside the door the child huddles and waits…

Muffled voices, straining against each other, "You dirty bitch, you've given me the bloody pox! D'you hear? I've got V.D. through you!" And the sounds of hitting, a slap and then another slap, hard and sharp, cloth tearing and mummy shrieking,

"No Bill don't! Stop it! I'm pregnant!!"

And all the noise stopped.

Only silence and the sound of laboured breathing. A figure in the doorway; sweating, gasping, stricken! Crossing towards the cot Bill gathers the child in his arms wrapping the blanket all about him. "Come on, let's get you out of here."

Weeping, both man and child.

And Daisy, crying and imploring, holding herself against the doorway, "No Billy no don't. Don't take him. Please. Please."

Bill pushes her roughly aside and carries the child downstairs and gathers up a few belongings, banging the door after him as he strides off into the night leaving the house in silence except for the echoes of crying from an upstairs room.

CHAPTER 16

Confessions of reality

"Who is it?"

Lilly called nervously into the blackness beyond the door and hesitated with her hand on the latch. Harold echoed her question from the gloom half way up the staircase. "Who is it? This time of night!"

She strained to hear the faint reply from the yard and said incredulously, "It's our Billy!" and opened the door carefully to peer at the figure standing in the darkness.

"Come on mother let me in."

"Bill! What's he doing back home this time of night!" Harold completed his descent into the kitchen, yawning, "Come on in. You'll have all the yard up."

Lilly and Harold received Bill with a mixture of solicitude and suppressed excitement. Then seeing David cradled in Bill's arms Lilly cried, "What's up? What's happened?"

"What's going on?" Harold demanded, following them into the living room. "What time is it?"

Lilly was bending over the sleeping child where Bill was laying him on the settee. "What's up with him? He's not poorly is he?" They never questioned the illogicality of their fears; if the child was ill why would Bill bring him across the city to them in the small hours of the night.

For the first time they studied Bill's face. He had a wild look about him that was beginning to sag into exhaustion. They took in his dishevelled appearance, his uniform beyond mere casual untidiness.

"Billy love. Here come on; what is it? What's happened? What you doing home? We didn't think you'd got any more leave for ages."

Bill had an awful sense of deja-vu. The same depression as he had felt three years before began to mount in him as it had on the morning following the first air raid and he began to cry, overcome with shame and ashamed of his tears. Harold went into the kitchen and the sound of the kettle being filled mingled with Bill's sobs.

"Come on Billy. Tell us what's up."

Harold re-entered. "I've put 'kettle on."

Bill bit his lip, snuffling and searching for words they would understand. He fiddled with his handkerchief about his eyes and said, "I found her with another man. She's been going with other men." He hung his head in shame.

They searched for something to say, a way to break through the embarrassment of his tears. Lilly reached out to him but Bill rejected her touch.

"How d'you know?" Harold said. "I mean…"

"I found 'em."

"What… you mean…?"

"Yes!" Bill cried. "What d'you think I bloody mean!"

"The dirty little tart." Lilly surveyed the dark sleek hair, the uniform. "How could she!" To her son who'd always been brought up so decent and respectable with his brother.

"Oh shut up mother." It was so unreasonable and he couldn't stand it if they were going to start calling her names. He'd married her for Gods sake; against their wishes and they had been right! He didn't want them telling him now; it was as though they were gloating over his misery. "I'm sorry. I didn't mean… It's just that…" He hung his head.

"Well what are you going to do?"

"I don't know." Bill wailed. "I've only got a forty-eight hour. I've got to go back tomorrow."

Lilly looked across at Harold. "What about David. I mean… he can't stop with her… Not if she's carrying on like that."

"I don't know mother. I've not had time to think properly."

"I'll make us a pot of tea. You having one Harold?"

Harold stood up, yawning and stretching. "Look at 'time. I've got to be up in four hours. We'll talk about it tomorrow."

Suddenly Bill was filled with alarm. He didn't have time to wait until they got home from work; tomorrow night he would be on the train and on his way back.

"Look," Bill began hesitantly, "I was wondering if you could have him. I mean, if I could leave him with you and mother. Just for a bit until I can get something worked out. I mean…"

"Well I don't know… I mean."

"Your mother's on war work."

"And then there's our George. It's a wonder he's not woke up as well."

"He couldn't sleep with your brother. He'd get squashed."

"Oh I don't know then." Bill resigned himself to his troubles, suddenly too exhausted to care. "I just thought. Just until I can get something sorted out. Oh what the hell."

"I wonder if his cot'd fit in our George's room," Lilly mused.

"But who'd look after him during the day? If you're at work?"

There was a brief glance between Lilly and Harold. "Your mother'll have to get some time off that's all. That's just as important as polishing machete handles, keeping the airforce flying."

"Just for a day or two. I won't be able to for very long. I mean I'd love to have him you know that. It's just that I don't know how we'd manage… They wouldn't let me take time off forever. Then perhaps we can get something worked out. Oh just look at him. Eh, I don't know."

Bill felt a surge of relief. "Thanks." he said. "God I'm tired. I'll fetch his cot down tomorrow." He looked down at David, still fast asleep against the arm of the couch. "Can you get me a blanket or something mother. I'll sleep down here on the settee with him tonight."

Lilly was back home by nine-thirty the next morning. Bill was sitting on the settee beneath the window with David on his knee and a pot of tea on the hob. He looked drawn and haggard through worry and lack of sleep. There was a ragged appearance to him. He looked up without much optimism at his mother's entrance and his eyes asked the unspoken question.

"I've seen the boss," she said. "He's given me the week off."

"Not much is it," Bill mumbled.

"Well what can I do?" she replied. "I had to beg and plead with him for that. I don't know. You had any breakfast yet?"

"I don't want anything…"

"Oh come on Billy. You must have something, you'll make yourself poorly."

"Give over mother! I'll get something in a bit."

"What about David? Has he had anything?"

"I did him some toast. He's alright."

"Well if you're sure. I'm going to make a fresh pot if you want some."

Waiting for the kettle to boil Lilly said, "Me and your dad was having a talk last night after we'd all gone to bed. We wondered if your Aunty Ame or our Rose'd have him for a bit until we can get some proper arrangements made. They've neither of 'em got kids of their own and they loves kids. 'Specially our Rose."

"Oh I don't know," Bill said morosely. "I mean, Worcester. It's so far away. I'd never see him."

"Well you're down in Leominster or wherever it is. You'd probably be even closer than you are now."

"But I mean, it's so far from everybody. You, me dad…" Bill let his arguments hang in the air. He was so beset by indecisions he didn't know what to do and had no suggestions of his own to offer.

"You'd know he was safely away from the air raids," Lilly

continued. "I'll write and ask her but I'll have to do it today. We haven't got much time. What d'you think?"

"They might not want him. If they've got no kids of their own. They won't know what to do with him. I mean... Oh I don't know. Do what you think best. I can't think straight. There's no time; I've got to catch 'train back to base again this afternoon."

CHAPTER 17

Borderland

It seemed as though the rain would never stop. It was pouring in ceaseless determination, flooding the spaces between the oily sleepers and spreading rivulet's onto the platforms where it dripped from the overhead canopy. Along the wall a drainpipe gushed into an overflowing gutter. Behind the platform buffers at the end of the line two porters stood disconsolately against the ticket barrier waiting for the next arrival. Outside, the distant hills of the Welsh border country could be seen indistinct and hazy through the rain. Beyond the platforms on the siding a solitary engine stood simmering on the gleaming rails.

Bill stood close against the red brick of the station buffet watching the barrier. There were few other travellers about; two, maybe three whiling away the time inside with tea. It was as though the rain had put a stop to travel for the day.

He had grown hungry waiting there and retired to the buffet but all he had been able to get was a cup of tea; sandwiches were off! With some irritation fuelled by a hunger that was now exaggerated by the fact that no food was available he'd carried the tea across to a table to watch the platform. Finally the train appeared, labouring down the line at the head of its three coaches beneath lowering clouds of smoke. Bill left the buffet and took up his position at the barrier.

The porters stirred themselves and began calling, "Birmingham train; Birmingham train," as it came to rest in a shroud of steam. "All change." One of them slipped down from the platform onto the rails between the engine and the leading coach and began to uncouple it as the passengers disembarked. There weren't many of them. Three servicemen – R.A.F. – a man in a trilby and fawn gaberdine raincoat whom Bill took to be a businessman, and Daisy. She lifted David from the carriage onto the platform beside her and turned to retrieve a small brown fibreboard suitcase from inside. Bill approached the barrier and addressed the ticket collector for confirmation. "Which platform's the Worcester train?"

"This is it." He indicated the train at the platform. "Leaves in twenty-five minutes."

"Thanks." Bill waited at the barrier as Daisy approached him.

David's face lit with a smile and he started for Bill but Daisy pulled him firmly to heel against her side and came through the barrier with David's hand firmly grasped in hers. Bill steered them to a corner of the station across by the deserted platform on the far side. He gestured to the small brown case that Daisy carried. "Is that all his things?" He was shocked to see how little of his son's life the suitcase represented in material worth.

"Yes." Daisy held the case close to her, resisting the reach of Bill's outstretched hand. "Billy, listen to me. We've got to talk about it."

"There's nothing to say." Bill gestured impatiently, endeavouring to force the issue. "Come on!" he lied, "train goes in a minute."

Daisy kept David close at her side and the child peered from beneath Daisy's protecting arm, looking up first at one, then at the other.

"Billy, listen to me. What about David? Think about…" But Daisy got no further.

"Don't you tell me to think about him!" He raised his voice to shame her. "You've never thought about him at all!" The porters glanced across in their direction and David began to cry, clinging to the skirts of Daisy's coat.

"Now look what you've done! You've set him off crying. You've upset him look." She stooped to David and fished out a handkerchief. "Come on, there's a good boy. Don't cry. There you are, dry your eyes." They were becoming the centre of attention for the small knot of passengers in the station. Bill looked about him desperately and pleaded earnestly with her.

"Look Daisy it's no good all this. You agreed! We said it would be for the best."

"I know we did but that was different Billy. You were angry. We were all upset. I might never see him again." She hugged David to her for comfort and Bill felt anger began to rise again. He had known all along it would be like this when it came to the time.

"Look," he said, "we're still upset! But it's finished Daisy. I want…" He paused, undecided. Was this the right time? But there was no other time! "There's another thing. I want a divorce. We're done. Come on Daisy! It's no good." He bent to pick up the suitcase and Daisy sprang to stop him.

"No Bill! No! Wait! Don't say that Bill." They grappled for possession of the case and David began crying again. One of the porters approached and halted at a discreet distance, demanding to know what was going on. Bill turned on him angrily but Daisy said, "Come on, come on we can't talk here." Reluctantly Bill allowed himself to be led away but there was nowhere for them to go. The waiting room was locked and the buffet lacked the privacy they needed. Briefly, silently they stood beneath the entrance canopy to the station watching the rain bounce into the puddles on the station forecourt. A blank row of shops faced them from across the empty road. For all they could see they might have been alone in the world but they had no privacy. Bill lit a cigarette and turned to Daisy.

"Look! It's all agreed. The divorce is going to go ahead; I'm starting the procedures, the arrangements..." Daisy looked at him in disbelief.

"You can't," she implored him.

"They're all made!" He bent and addressed himself to David, still sheltering in the folds of Daisy's coat and held out his hand to him. "Come here. Come on." Daisy stiffened her grip, holding David to her.

"Billy it can't end like this. Let's talk about it. Why don't we..."

"There's nothing to say!" Bill retorted. He gestured to David again. "Come here."

"Bill!" Daisy protested, "you can't take him just like that!"

"Right! That's it! Come on David. DAVID! Come here. Come along with me."

At the roar of Bill's voice David cowered deeper into the folds of Daisy's coat and she hugged him to her. Bill lunged at Daisy and pushed her off balance; gripping David's hand he wrenched him from her and made for the platform, dragging David with him.

"Wait!" Daisy screamed, "Wait Billy, David wait David, David!" Now David was struggling and screaming for her but Bill strode on, fending off her attempts to stop him. Suddenly Bill turned on her; as Daisy paused and before she realised what he intended Bill snatched the small case with David's belongings from her and set off again. By what mystery the child cried out for her is impossible to say. What did David know? He only saw the disintegration of his tiny world as Bill and Daisy battled, dragging him along to the platform towards the waiting train. They reached the barrier and with a struggle Bill got through.

"Get the police!" Daisy cried desperately. The porter raised his hand in a helpless gesture, his expression betraying conflict between interfering on behalf of... well, he wasn't quite sure, and concern for his personal safety made him act with discretion. This airman was clearly in no mood for listening to reason. Bill resolved the issue for him by delivering a glance of determined malice. "You bloody well keep out of this. He's my son and he's coming with me." The porter stood and looked around desperately for his colleague.

Bill reached an open carriage door; the compartment was empty and he tossed the suitcase inside and again Daisy turned, giving a look of desperate appeal to the porter who was now being joined at the barrier by the other one. She turned back to see Bill pushing David into the carriage between the seats, he was struggling against Bill's restraining hand, crying and reaching for her as Bill tried to slam the carriage door.

"Bill! Billy wait!" Daisy was screaming hysterically. "Don't take him away Bill. Please... wait... wait!"

The railwaymen began to approach along the platform together; Bill scrambled into the carriage and pushed David onto the seat across the compartment in the far corner, behind him and away from the platform door.

"What's going on then?" The porters came to the door and tried to take a tone of authority but failed. Daisy pushed them from her, pulled the door open and scrambled aboard leaving the porters once more in indecision. One of them checked his pocketwatch; departure time was getting close. In the doorway of the carriage Daisy was pleading with Bill.

"Please Billy, please. Let's give it one more try."

Bill was implacable.

"Billy. We can't end just like this. What about David?"

"Who the hell d'you think I'm thinking of!" He raised his voice so that it carried to the porters. "I'm not leaving him with you and your fancy men! I'm taking him with me. He's going where he'll be looked after. It's all arranged."

"Billy!"

"No! No! Now get off. Go on... off. Off!"

Daisy turned to the porters for support but their faces bore disapproval and her world dissolved like the teeming day around her, devoid of warmth or comfort. Through her tears she spoke his name, "David..." a long and anguished sigh between her sobs, smothered by the choking in her breast. She reached out for him where he huddled sobbing in the corner of the seat, held there by Bill's restraining hand..

"It's over Daisy. Come on. You've got to get off. Train's going in a minute." Was there a germ of its former tenderness in Bill's voice? She dared to hope even now, but in her heart she knew and her hopes were dashed with Bill calling to the porters who stood observing from a discreet distance on the platform, "Come on, get her off will you."

"No," she said, "It's alright. I'm... What time's it leave?" She dabbed at her eyes with a handkerchief. "Come on David. Give mummy a little kiss." Daisy reached across the space between them.

"No! leave him alone!"

"Just a kiss Billy," she pleaded, "Just a little kiss. Please." She stood with her arms outstretched. "Come on love. A kiss for mummy." Bill picked the child up, holding him firmly in his arms and Daisy took the small yearning face between her hands and kissed him, her own tears

140

mingling with the tears on David's cheeks.

"Come on Daisy. It's time. Train's going."

She kissed her child again and then stood glancing rapidly between them. The porter approached the carriage and stood behind her with his hand on the door.

"Billy." But for what she wanted to say she could not find the words except, "Goodbye." David began to cry and struggle for her again as she stepped down onto the platform. The porter stepped to one side to let her pass then slammed the door and Bill watched from the open window as she walked away from them with the discreet escort of the porters following, her back stiff with dignity. Not until she reached the barrier did she turn to look as the whistle blew and the carriages slowly began to move away until the only sound was the pattering of the rain upon the roof, the distant whistle of the train and the unheard echoes of her child crying, "Mummy…"

PART TWO
AMY – 1943

CHAPTER 18

Swans and fishes

A child has no conception of memory. But the things that happen are retained as experiences that colour and shape the child's character and ultimately, his life. 'Good' and 'Bad' as concepts are as yet unformed for he has no values against which to measure each experience. The child does not know; what happens, happens and that is the way of life. Just as a jungle indian whose sole knowledge of the world is the river bank has no concept of 'civilisation' as we know it, so a young child accepts as the norm the world in which he lives and the conditions which surround him.

So it was with David. You may look upon his circumstances and Daisy's amoral life, her neglect of him and the way it was evolving and feel pity for the child, exposed as he was to squalor. But your pity would be misplaced for if David could have reasoned at that age it would only have been to ask, 'Why did they take me from my mummy?' For life is what is, not what might have been.

Neither did the child have any concept of the future. The promise of tomorrow holds no promise within a mind where scales of time are undeveloped. A morning's play occupies a lifetime and the day is sufficient unto itself. There is no tomorrow when the whole of today extends beyond the limit of undeveloped imaginative vision. And the promises of good things to come hold no real value but are abstracts, to be dismissed in favour of the immediate. Tomorrow may be the pleasure dream of adults but for a child the whole of life is contained within today.

Thus it was with David, in the train on the way to Worcester. He could not have told you that his life was 'unhappy' for how could he know? Within the squalid house, sitting in the chill of the bare room with Daisy, stinking and dirty as he was he would still have sought to be in his mother's arms, bewildered when she ignored him but delighted and fulfilled when she did not. And in a strange, almost primitive way David understood that although he needed to be loved and cherished by her, she did not need him. But food came when he was hungry and sometimes it was hot and sometimes it was not and each day brought diversion and tears. Then night came and in his innocence David never

145

knew that each successive night would be the same and filled with lonely terrors. But at bedtime he was taken and imprisoned in the cot to face the night alone. And when the light went out and the familiar room vanished he knew he should not be standing there exposed and vulnerable in the darkness so he dropped into a tiny ball. He couldn't find the covers to hide in and if he reached out for them his hand might be seized by the terror that came in the night. So he waited, breathless and tightly curled in the corner with his arms and legs tucked beneath him and listened.

And sometimes in the dreadful silence of the room there came a noise from the world below. Dare he risk a tiny call? A little sound that would not betray his presence in the dark. But he waited and she didn't come and he called again, louder for he knew that it had heard him and begun to stir from where it lay unseen in the corner of the room. And now he screamed and screamed for her, louder and louder as it began to creep along the floor towards the cot and he must get his mummy to come before it got to him and so he screamed and waited for the dreadful thing in the room to find him in the darkness... And only the return of daylight brought blessed relief.

Daddy said it was over now. But what was over? And it was going to be alright! But it was alright. And we are going somewhere new but why isn't mummy coming too? Mummy can't come. Where is mummy? I want mummy! And daddy is getting angry and saying be quiet again and stop it! But David can't stop crying and daddy sits in silence glaring at him to stop. And David bows his head and tries to hold back the whimpering sounds of his distress. Slowly the train threads its way through the hills of Malvern, stopping at each wayside halt and country station and with every mile that slips reluctantly beneath the wheels David becomes more calm, alternatively looking nervously at Bill for approval, and gazing through the window at the unfamiliar landscape.

"Here, look at you. Come here, let's wipe your eyes. Come on, give your nose a blow, we'll be there soon."

The ground falls away and the train rumbles onto the bridge over the Severn. There are swans upon the river sheltering in the lee of the high bank, under the dripping trees that line the towpath in front of the cathedral gardens. Between the railway bridge and the elegant arches of the road bridge the Severn Belle and Duchess Doreen lay moored at the promenade, their varnished hulls and gleaming brass redundant in these austerity days. Silently they nurse memories of happier times and pleasure trips upon the river.

Below the train the far bank of the river is approaching and as they cross Bill has a fleeting image of Daisy lying beneath him in the darkness on the ground with her skirt above her thighs fumbling with

146

her knickers behind the high brick pier. He shivers with a momentary pang of sickness. Christ! When was that? In the spring. And now summer was over and that was over and everything was such a bloody mess. It was good of Aunty Ame to say she'd take David on; he just hoped it was the right thing to do. But what else could he do! Oh God! They were sliding into Foregate Street Station. Bill cast his musings aside.

"Come on then. Let's look at you." He surveyed David with misgiving. The child's mouth still had a ring of scurvy inflammation around it but at least his hair was clean and clear of infestation. God knows what they would think of him. He stood David on the seat and pulled his clothes straight. "Well; you'll have to do." He reached for the strap and lowered the compartment window, peering out along the platform. Nobody there! Ah well. "Come on then." They clambered out and took the lift down from the platform into Foregate Street and set off on the short walk to Aunty Ame's.

The rain had clearly set in for the day and Amy's kitchen windows were steaming up from the stew of cabbage stalk and bran simmering on the gas ring. The kitchen door opened and Rose entered calling, "Is they here yet Ame?" She paused and wrinkled her nose. "Gawd a'mighty Ame what's you got in there?" Rose was used to the concoctions that Amy cooked for the hens in the coop at the end of the garden but today's was particularly pungent. It wouldn't do for Rose and Bob to have their house filled with such odours. Rose was houseproud with everything in its appointed place and the furniture and ornaments regularly dusted and polished. She was younger than Amy by some five years but she and Amy were very close and had lived three doors apart in the same row of houses most of their married lives, which in Amy's case was twenty three years. Although neither Rose nor Amy had children of their own, neighbourhood children were always to be found at odd hours of the day in Rose's house, especially when Bob was home from work. Bob had the knack of being able to communicate with children and joke with them without being at all condescending. But when they had discussed the prospect of David coming to live at Worcester it was Amy who had said quite spontaneously that David should come to live with her. Now the day had arrived. Bill was due on the afternoon train and here was Amy filling the house with the smell of henfood. Rose went through to the living room where Amy was pinning up her hair in front of the fireplace mirror.

"Smells worse than usual Ame. What's you put in it?"

"It'll be alright. They loves it; you just watch when I gives it to 'em."

147

"I should think the poor kid'll want to run back up to Sheffield when he smells it. Anyway, where's Al? Thought he was supposed to be going up to the station to meet 'em."

"Had to go out," Amy replied. "He'll be back for tea."

Yes, Rose thought, he'll probably be back well before tea and fall asleep in the chair, heavy with beer and oblivious to Amy's reproaches. Albert supplemented his wage as caretaker of the grammar school by running an illicit street bookmaking business. It hardly seemed worth the risk. It didn't seem to make them much money and required Albert to spend an inordinate amount of time in pubs. Still, she and Bob enjoyed a drink themselves so she couldn't say anything and anyway Amy always seemed happy enough. "What time's they coming?" Rose asked.

"Don't really know. About half-past two I think." Amy glanced down at the clock. "What time's it now? I think this clock's a bit fast."

"Is you going for a quick one at the Wash?" Rose did enjoy a glass of beer before her dinner. "D'you think we've got the time?"

"Yes," Amy replied. "I'll just give the hens their dinner then we'll go. I've got 'em a nice piece of fish for their tea."

"Alright," Rose said. "Give us a shout when you'm ready." She departed to give the sideboard its weekly coat of Mansion.

Amy took the hens' mash off the cooker and left the lid off for it to cool. Then she rinsed the fish, two nice pieces of haddock, and put them in the pantry under a plate ready for teatime. She turned her attention to the fowls' dinner. Another liberal handful of bran went into the pan then she chopped it and stirred it vigorously until it was a stiff, dry stew of stalks, peelings and other leftovers. When it was cool she carried it down the garden to the hen run, checked the nesting boxes for eggs and returned to get herself ready to pop over to the Wash with Rose.

Powdering her face, Amy looked at herself appraisingly in the mirror. She was just turned forty, with striking good looks, dark hair and a vivacity that shone from her eyes. She was content with life. Oh, she sometimes lost patience with Al and his drinking and on the days when he overstepped the mark and came home too drunk to eat his meal she reproached him unmercifully. But for all that her life was content and she and Albert loved each other. Amy would not have called it love for life did not allow for romance. That belonged to the days before they were married and 'walking out' together, strolling hand in hand along the river in the sweet air of evening and dreaming their dreams beneath the chestnut trees. She applied a final dab of powder to her cheeks and went along the backs of the houses to call for Rose.

Twice during the afternoon Rose came down to 'see if they was here yet'. Albert had made the enquiries about the train times; perhaps he'd got it wrong, they were later than expected. Amy began to lay the table ready for tea. She set the best starched white linen table cloth, heavy with embroidered lace hanging stiffly round the edges and the cruet with the varnished plywood placemats that Bob had made them for Christmas. But with that done Amy couldn't settle. It was too soon to start cooking the fish and she went into the front room to see if there was any sign of 'em coming along the street through the bay window. A child of her own to look after! She was so excited. She heard St. Mary's chime quarter past three but the street was deserted and after two or three more minutes peering earnestly into the grey afternoon she returned to the living room. The fire could do with mending; they'd want it nice and warm when they arrived. She fetched a log from the coalshed adjacent to the toilet in the porch and supplemented it with a shovelful of coal. Right, that's done. What next? Amy decided to chop the parsley for the sauce. That'd be another job out of the way. Amy busied herself in the kitchen. The peeled potatoes in the pan could go on the gas ring ready to be lit when the time came, then she fetched sprigs of parsley and the chopping board from the pantry. Was that the sound of the gate at the back? No! Footsteps? A voice? A knock at the door? Excitement rushed upon her and with a quick wipe on her apron Amy opened the door. There was Bill with a little boy clinging to his side, eyes wide in bewilderment with golden hair and a flaming rash around his mouth. Amy's heart went out to him and ignoring Bill she bent and opened her arms to the child.

"Well there you is. We thought you was never coming. Come and say hello to your Aunty Ame." She drew David to her and hugged him but as soon as he was free he retreated once more to the shelter of Bill's greatcoat.

"Come on in then. Let's have a look at you." She led the way through into the living room. "Hello Billy, how are you? Here let's take your coat, I'll hang it in the bogey hole, how was your journey?"

David peered about him. He was overwhelmed and didn't like it much. It was strange, this lady who took hold of him straight away and did things so quickly. And it didn't smell very nice. He just wanted to stay by daddy's side until it was time to go.

"How long's you staying Bill? How much leave's you got this time?"

"I've got to get back tonight," Bill replied. "Train was later than it should have been."

"I know," Amy said. "Everything's upside down with this war. You can't rely on anything no more."

"Anyway," Bill continued, "it means I've only got a couple of hours then I've got to get back. I'm sorry aunt, just dropping him off on

149

you like this."

"That's alright ain't it David. We don't mind do we?"

David shook his head silently.

"And I've got you a nice tea. Won't be long. You likes fish don't you?"

David shook his head uncertainly. He wasn't sure what 'fish' was.

"Course you do," Bill said valiantly. David sat and searched his memory for some clue what 'fish' was that daddy said he liked.

Rose arrived. "I thought it was you. I seen you through my front room window. How are you Bill? Had a good journey? And who's this then?" She bent down to him. "Hello, is you David? My what a big boy you are." David sat looking wide eyed from one to the other. Rose turned her attention back to Bill. "He don't say much do he?"

"Well it's all a bit strange for him I suppose, ain't it David." Amy reached out and began to unfasten the buttons of David's coat. "Here let's have this off then you can sit nice and warm in front of the fire."

David withdrew as Amy tried to take his coat and Bill said, "Don't be silly. Let your aunty take your coat off." Reluctantly David complied.

"He'll be alright in a minute." Rose reassured Bill and gave David a big smile. "He's got to get used to us all, haven't you!"

"Anyway," Amy returned from the bogey hole beneath the stairs, "I'd better get tea under way if you ain't got much time. What time's your train leave Bill?"

"Quarter past seven. Foregate Street."

"Ain't you staying over?" Rose cried. "Bob was going to take you out for a drink."

"Sorry aunt. I've got to be back tonight."

"Never mind." Amy wasn't going to let a little thing like that put her out. It meant that she would have responsibility for David sooner and that was better. "Anyway," she continued, "I'll get this fish on."

Through the window they saw Albert arrive, parking his old pushbike for shelter under the creeper that covered the dividing wall between Amy's and Miss Fieldew, the old lady who lived next door. Albert was square set, dark haired and practical, a good looking man in a craggy sort of way but his drinking was beginning to make his features fleshy. As a youth he had trained as a boatbuilder in one of the boathouses on the Severn. But the river was bordered by the racecourse and Albert was seduced by the glamour of the jockeys, the trainers and their owners. So he gave up the boathouse and tried to make a living from bookmaking. But whilst he soon became a familiar figure round the Grandstand Hotel he was always on the fringes and never made the transition as an on-course bookie. But there was always a profit to be made from his discreet circle of illicit clients, always provided he placed his own bets wisely. It was a hit-and-miss existence and Albert needed the job as caretaker at the grammar school to provide security when he married Amy.

He shook the rain off his brown trilby in the kitchen and hung his cycle clips on the backdoor knob. "Is they here yet?" he asked and Amy nodded.

"They'm in there."

Albert headed for the fire in the living room. Seeing David in the chair beside Bill he adopted an expression of mock ferocity in what he imagined was an imitation of the characters in children's picture books and growled, "Who's this then? We got a boy in the house have we? Has he had his bread yet? 'As anybody fed him?"

Faced with such an unexpected greeting David burst into tears.

"Now look what you've done!" Amy cried, rushing in from the kitchen. "You've frightened him to death. You'm daft Al. You've been drinking again!"

"No I aint," Albert protested. "Just a quick one at the 'Lamb'. Before he opens. Had to take Ralph his winnings."

Amy glared at him. "You'll scare the kid out of his wits. Come here then, come to your Aunty Ame; take no notice of Uncle Al, he's just being silly."

"Well I'd better be off." Rose said, getting up from where she had been sitting at the table. "I got Bob's tea to get ready. He'll be home soon. We'll see you later then Billy. You won't go without coming to say goodbye will you?"

"No." Bill replied. "I'll see you both before I leave."

"Ta-ra then." She waved at David, sitting bemused and watching her. "He'll be alright in a bit when he gets used to things. I expect it's all a bit strange for him just at the moment." She turned to Amy. "Is you going up to the 'Sarry' later?"

Amy gestured at David, conscious of Bill's presence. "Don't know. We'll see you both later."

"See you after tea then." They heard Rose call from the kitchen as the door closed after her, "T.T.F.N."

"I think we'll have the light on. It's never cleared all day. Got a match Al?"

"Here aunt I've got one." Bill briskly offered a box of matches from his battledress pocket and Albert reached up and lit the mantle. The steady glow of gaslight gradually filled the room.

"That's better." Amy felt more relaxed. "Now I'll go and get your tea. You must be starving."

David sat impassively at the table looking at his plate. Even with

151

cushions on his chair he was barely high enough and his eyes were only just above the tablecloth.

"Come on then," Amy coaxed, offering a forkfull of potato. "There you is." David dutifully opened his mouth and swallowed it then sat as before. "Now another one. You do it."

"Come on David." Bill would let them see what a good boy David was. "Eat up this nice tea that Aunty Ame's made for you. You can do it. Come on, eat it up."

David sat with their expectant eyes on him. He didn't know what it was. He didn't know if he liked the taste. It was all white and strange.

"Here." Amy offered him another forkfull. "Now some fish. Fish is lovely. Make you grow up into a big tall man like your daddy. There we are." David chewed silently at the food. He didn't have the will to eat. "Now you do it. Come on, that's it," Amy said with encouragement, "there's a good boy. Now let's see you do it."

David took the fork from her and half heartedly pushed it into his food, nibbling at the edges. Now they could see that David was making an effort and the conversation turned to Bill. There were so many things that Amy and Albert wanted to ask Bill about. They had met Daisy of course earlier in the year when she had come to stay with them for that few days but they had no real idea that kind of thing was going on! Was she really carrying on the way that Lilly had said in her letter? But how could she? It was a wicked thing to do, they had no idea she was as bad as that. And dirty too…? David sat hearing the sound of conversation around him, the fall of the voices to a murmer when they thought he might be listening, the glances cast in his direction as each revelation was discreetly revealed. He sat in a languid world of dreaming, toying with the potato and building it into shapes around his plate… Bill turned to him, irritated at having to hold this conversation in front of the child. He wanted David to be able to forget her, but he was sitting there impassively, listening, showing him up instead of getting on with his tea.

"Come on, eat your tea before it gets cold. Sit up! Come on sit up properly and hold your knife and fork like a good boy. Now come on!"

"How long's the journey to Shobden?" Amy asked, trying to turn the conversation to safer ground.

"Have to change at Hereford," Bill replied. "Only if I don't get that last train I've had it."

"No you don't want to miss that," Albert said solicitously, "I'll go up with you if you likes."

"You're going up for a drink you mean."

Albert looked at Amy. "He want's seeing off properly. Can't let him just walk off up the road."

"Well if you likes. I shan't come. It'd be better if I stays here with David and gets him ready for bed."

"Thanks aunty," Bill said suddenly, "I don't know what I'd have done. Me mother'd have him but what with working... And I can't let him go to her family can I?"

"Course you can't," Albert said. "We'm glad to have him."

"He's better here anyway," Amy said. "You might be able to get across and see him a bit more regular."

"Anyway," Albert added, "He'll be out of the way of the air raids down here won't he."

David let out a cry. They turned to him; he was sitting with his fork poised, open mouthed and gaping full of food.

"Eat your tea there's a good boy." Amy tried to ignore the spectacle that David presented. She could sense Bill's embarrassment and turned to resume their conversation. David began to chew but in the attempt to swallow he cried out again and began spitting the food out.

"David stop that!" Bill was mortified. How dare he show him up like this! "Eat your tea like a good boy." he ordered.

Amy took David's fork from him. "He's alright Billy. I expect things is a bit strange for him. Here, have this." Amy held out some more mashed potato. "There's a good boy."

David took the food and was taken with another convulsive cry, spitting the food out onto the table. Bill rose angrily from his chair but Albert took Bill's arm. "Perhaps he's got a bone."

"But I thought I'd got all the bones out," Amy wailed. "I was ever so careful. Here, let's have a look then." She bent close to David. "Open wide. Come on, open up. Let's take a look inside."

David was afraid of further pain and he turned his head away, wriggling in his seat and grimacing with pain at each movement. They persuaded him to open his mouth and the pain stabbed at his throat. Amy stood aside and Bill held David's mouth open causing him to gag and heave. He gave an involuntary swallow, his throat convulsed and he shrieked. Amy was beside herself; David's face was getting red and he was choking, desperately fighting the need to swallow again and crying out with each spasm. He wriggled in Bill's grasp, desperate to be free.

Albert pushed Bill aside. "Here let's have a look." He thrust his little finger into David's mouth, pushing deep into his throat and holding him firmly to his side against David's struggles. There was something solid wedged across the opening of the throat, each end lodged into the soft tissue of the oesophagous. Curling the tip of his finger round it Albert pulled the bone up and over David's pallet. David gave a scream and struggled desperately; then it was gone and he sat whimpering with relief while Albert showed Amy and Bill the cause of all the trouble.

Amy picked it up from Albert's hand and held it up to David.

"There you are," she said, "it's just a little fish bone that's all. It's out now. Look." She lifted him up onto her knee. "There we are. You'm better now. Is that better?" David nodded and began to relax in Amy's arms. "Come on then, let's dry your eyes shall we." She took the hem of the tablecloth and began to wipe the tears from David's face. Then she hugged him to her as he ate reluctant forks full of potato until the anxiety and the panic of the day took its toll and he lay asleep in Amy's arms, to her deep satisfaction and Bill's relief.

CHAPTER 19

Hops and hopes

The factory hooters began their mourning dirge, hastening the streams of cyclists that filled the city streets into the factories to clock on. Then the cacophony died away and the streets became silent save for the pealing of church bells over the city.

David lay awake in his cot listening. Downstairs he could hear the faint sounds of Aunty Ame bustling about, interrupted by the last chimes of St. Mary's ringing the hour. Then silence followed by footsteps on the stairs. The bedroom door slowly began to open; David pulled the covers about him and thrust his face into the pillow.

On the tiny square of carpet at the head of the stairs Amy paused with the door of the bedroom half open. From the gloom inside came the sound of a suppressed giggle as David tried to squirm deeper into the pillow to hide. Amy crept over to the cot, pulled back the covers and tickled him. David screamed and kicked in delight. The smell of urine rose from the mattress. Inwardly she sighed, 'Oh God! he's wet again.'

"Come on then sleepy head let's be having you." Amy resigned herself to it and lowered the cot side with a smile. It was three weeks since Bill had brought David to her and every night since he had wet the bed. 'They didn't tell me about this when they asked me to have him,' she thought to herself. She had tried all sorts of strategies to stop it; strict toilet routine at bed-time; no drinks with his supper. Now she and Albert had resorted to keeping him up later at night. They took David with them to the pub, discreetly sitting him quietly between themselves and Bob and Rose. Amy shook her head gently at him.

"You'm wet again. Never mind, come on let's have you." She gathered him in her arms. "Let's see what we can see shall we?" She pulled the curtains aside then tugged at the cord to release the roller blind and David screwed up his eyes against the sudden brightness. From the window they could see right along Lowell Street directly opposite and at the far end of the street the high red brick railway bridge arching over the canal.

"It's not there yet," Amy said mischievously. "Perhaps we've missed it."

The child looked up at her; a shadow of disappointment crossed his

155

face and she hugged him to her.

"It'll be there; just you wait and see."

David looked back along the street in expectation and Amy wondered if she had left it too late this morning but then a small railway engine rolled slowly onto the bridge, paused, whistled and then trundled across the arch. The ritual over Amy took David downstairs and set him before the fire to keep warm until the kettle boiled to give him a good wash down in the sink.

"Now then," Amy said when she had finished dressing him, "how about a nice new laid egg for breakfast? Let's go and see if we can find one shall we?"

David took Amy's hand and followed her into the back garden. At the bottom, against the wall that divided the terrace gardens from the path running along the backs of the houses opposite Albert had built the hen run with a cockerel and eight pullets in it.

David was nervous of the birds. They pecked each other and they pecked his shoes. Amy shoo'd them away as they stepped into the run with its caked earth and empty food bowls; the hens cackled and ran in a flurry of wings and feathers and David clung to Amy's skirts as she closed the wireframe door behind them.

"Come on," she said, "they won't hurt you." They went into the low shed where the nesting boxes were. "Come on. You'm alright. Look." Amy reached into one of the boxes beneath the watchful hen sitting there. It made a desultory peck at the back of Amy's hand feeling in the straw beneath it and made another resentful peck. David remained at a discrete distance by the door and Amy drew her hand away from the box with a brown egg warm from the bird.

"Only one today." she said. "I'll have to tell Uncle Al they're still not laying. Never mind." She took David's hand and placed the egg in it. "You shall have it for your breakfast. Now be careful. Don't drop it."

After breakfast Rose came down on a pretext. "You aint got a couple of eggs has you Ame? Don't matter now. Bring 'em up when you comes for elevenses." Rose and Bob didn't keep hens themselves; their small well kept lawn was surrounded by a border of roses, paeonies and small border perennials.

"I aint got any." Amy turned from washing the breakfast pots in the sink. "They've stopped laying for some reason. Al's going to have to get 'em some more of that bran mixture. I got to buy some myself when we goes out. David's just had the last 'un for his breakfast."

"Oh well never mind. How is he anyway?"

"Wet again."

"Oh I don't know. What's you going to to do Ame?" It was a relief

156

to Rose that she wasn't faced with washing and changing his bedding every morning. She had been resentful when Amy had laid claim to David ahead of her, and not a little angry. Now she was secretly relieved.

Amy took the tea-towel off the rail and began drying the pots. "Dunno. He'll grow out of it I expect."

"Makes you a hell of a lot of washing though don't it."

"He's alright during the day," Amy confided. "It's just at night. He gets so upset."

"Is he still shouting downstairs for you?"

"It's not so bad if he falls asleep before we puts him to bed. But if he wakes up he's terrible. He's terrified of the dark."

Rose shook her head in sympathy. "Makes you wonder what really happened to make him like that don't it. Well I'll see you in a bit then. Is we having elevenses or d'you want to go up to the shops?"

"Oh I don't want to go up town unless you do. I'm just popping down to the co-op for some eggs if they got any."

"Alright then." said Rose. "See you in a bit. TTFN."

Late summer was hop-picking time. Mabel Cooper round in Chestnut Street made the arrangements to go out to the farm at Leigh Sinton as usual and set about confirming names of those who wanted to go for the short season of picking. First come first served and as usual there was fierce competition to go.

"Wish I was going with you," Amy complained to Rose. "I don't want to lose my place next year. Besides I could really do with the money. I mean, I know it's not a lot but it does help with the extras." She bit her lip wistfully. It wasn't just for things like coal for the coming winter but occasionally the pickers were favoured with a bit of produce from the fields like spuds or a cabbage, at better prices than you'd pay in the shops. "Only he's a bit young to take out hop picking all day in the fields," she continued. "I mean you can't keep your eye on him while you're picking can you? And in the back of the lorry, there and back every day…"

So during September Amy hardly saw Rose at all.

The twenty or so women gathered on the pavement outside Mabel Cooper's house were shivering in the early morning damp.

"Time's he coming?" Rose demanded for the umpteenth time. She had seen to Bob's breakfast before coming down the road to wait for the lorry; Rose normally saw him off to work but on hop picking days she was the one who was out of the house first. She didn't want to miss it; hop picking was the best time of the year so she was here nice and early.

157

Just in case..

"Seven o-clock," Irene said. "'Least that's what I was told. That's right ain't it?"

There was common assent amongst the group and the bells of St. Mary's began to chime the hour, blending with the distant pealing from the cathedral.

"Well he's late!" someone said triumphantly.

"I bin here quarter of an hour now. He could have come early then we'd all have been on our way. Nobody missing is there?"

"Only Mabel. She'll be in there having a cup of tea."

As though on cue Mabel's door opened and she appeared on the doorstep, glancing quickly up and down the street. "He's not here yet then?"

"Don't look like it." Irene responded. "He is coming ain't he? You did book him didn't you?"

"He's here." someone called, to the general relief of the waiting women and Mabel grabbed her basket and flask from just inside, slammed the door shut and pushed her way through the crowd to 'have a word' with the driver.

Once they were on their way, crammed standing on the back of the open lorry the women fell silent as it jolted through the town. The need for another hours sleep fell upon them and they resented the keen wind blowing through them now they were on the move. Cat calls and whistles came from other workers on the pavements or cyclists that they passed and one or two of the women responded with bravado. But for the most part they were occupied with their own thoughts, braced against the morning chill. They crossed the misty Severn and left the city behind. At Powick they crossed the Teme, another misty river and then it cleared and the Malverns reared into view, bright in the morning sun.

Now they were in the fields and the sun was warming the air and they shook off the morning lethargy, striding through the dewy grass to collect their cribs, hessian bags slung like deep hammocks between poles into which they would pick their hops. Rose and Irene had teamed up together to share a crib and they carried it, sedan chair fashion into a row of hop bines.

"God there'll be none left for us," Irene said as they raced as quickly as they could over the uneven earth, carrying it across the mounds strewn with the bare foliage and bines dangling from the wires above where the row had already been picked. Along the rows ahead of them were pickers already at work, their cribs bulging. A farm overseer appeared and directed them ahead of the pickers with an admonition not to begin another row until this one had been cleared.

"They must have been here hours already."

"They sleeps here," Irene replied. "It'll be them that comes from Dudley. They'm here every year. I wouldn't want to sleep in them barracks though."

"Nor me." The barracks were brick outhouses near the farm buildings devoid of anything save electric light. The toilets were communal, fresh water came from the stand pipe and they slept on straw. But they had an advantage over the pickers who came in from town every day; their day in the fields began at six.

Rose and Irene set the crib down and began. They tugged at a bine festooning the wires above them with bunches of hops hanging like grapes from its branches. It resisted and the women got the first of the painful little cuts from its leaves. "Careful, we'll have the whole lot down on top of us." Other women set up their cribs adjacent to them and began tugging at their bines; suddenly it gave up its hold on the wires above and crashed down on them. Rose and Irene set to and disengaged themselves, draping it across the edge of the crib. Now the picking began, plucking the hops cleanly off the branch without the leaves. Any leaves and the overseer would deduct it from their pay. They worked happily together. Rose was a dexterous picker and she was glad that Irene had agreed to share a crib. Between them they could make a bit of money and perhaps get a bonus. But that meant keeping hard at it and whilst not as good a picker as Amy, Irene was no shirker.

They worked steadily down the row leaving the stripped bines in their wake and the crib slowly filled and began to bulge. At periodic intervals one of them would take a break and straighten up and stretch from leaning against the crib then thrust her hands deep into the hops and turn them, searching for the leaves that inevitably got picked in with them. By eleven o'clock the overseer had begun to move down the line with the bushellers to count and tally what the pickers had achieved.

"I'll get kettle on while he does that," Irene volunteered. Rose had brought some dry newspaper and sticks and Irene got a little fire going within a circular hearth of earthen clods whilst Rose went and filled the kettle from a standpipe.

The busheller arrived with his labourer and began scooping the hops from the crib into his bushel basket whilst Rose and Irene sipped their tea and carefully watched in case he tried to overfill it at their expense.

"One." The overseer noted Rose and Irene's tally into his book and their first bushel of hops went into the huge hessian sack held open for him by the labourer.

"Two." The crib steadily emptied into the labourer's sack. When it was full he drew a length of twine and a needle from his pocket and

159

deftly sewed the mouth closed, tossed it to one side to be collected by the tractor following him down the rows and opened another sack.

"Five bushels." The overseer turned to a fresh page and moved on. Irene and Rose finished the tea and turned once again to the crib that now hung empty. They hoisted the half picked bine across it and began again and slowly the crib began to fill once more.

It was hot and the sweat mingled with the sap and their hands became discoloured and the insects rose and buzzed but they dared not wipe their brow with their hands for fear of the irritation it would cause, the streaming eyes, blinking and itching to drive them mad. Only their forearms or a piece of cloth or handkerchief, if they could keep it clean, to keep the sweat off their brow.

Dinner was a welcome picnic sitting on the ridged earth with their back to the bulging crib and a mug of tea with the special flavour of tea made over a wood fire in the open air and the chatter that rose all around in the fields, the smell of woodsmoke mingled with the vapour of methylated spirit from primus stoves and over it all the smell of fresh picked hops. Groans and laughter as the women began to raise themselves from where they sat. "Oh gawd my back, it don't half ache. I must be getting too old for this lark." Figures dispersed discreetly into the gloom of unpicked bines where no-one had been and no-one could see, bobbed briefly and then returned once more to the cribs and the picking began again.

Returning home from the fields was in contrast to the morning. There was tiredness again but this time it was the tiredness of fulfilment and they sang as they crossed the bridge into the city, the envy of those who had spent their day in offices and factories. They glowed with weariness but they were without care and happy. And even when it was wet their enjoyment was undimmed. They complained about the rain and wrapped themselves in plastic and gaberdine whilst the mud crept over their shoes until they were caked and their legs and feet were soaked. They contrived inadequate makeshift covers to eat their soggy dinners with nowhere to sit except on paper or plastic or mats of twigs on the glistening earth. But still they picked on steadily and put up with the chidings of the overseers and labourers and returned home defiant of the weather in anticipation of a better day tomorrow.

"Last day tomorrow Ame." Rose took a sip of her beer and looked across at David amusing himself with another child in the yard of the 'George and Dragon'. "Haven't half missed you though. Irene's alright but she aint as quick as you. How's he been?"

"He's alright."

"You might be able to take him next year. He'd be alright. I'm sure he would."

"Next year." Amy echoed Rose's words enigmatically. Rose looked up at her sister.

"You alright Ame?"

"I had a letter from our Billy today. You'll never guess." Amy paused briefly for effect. "He's going abroad. They're sending him to Gibralter."

"Get away." Rose's surprised echoed Amy's own surprise when she had read the letter that morning.

"In fact he might be there already," Amy continued. "It don't make it very clear."

"Well they has to be careful. What they says I mean. They can't tell you too much can they."

"Well anyway," Amy continued, "that's where he's gone."

She was faced with a new perspective on caring for David. Not that it filled her with dismay but she had thought, up until then that the child was going to be with her just 'until other arrangements could be made'. Whatever that had meant. Now, with no end to the war in sight and Bill posted abroad her responsibility for the child was much more long term. And secretly that thought filled her with delight tempered with more than a little apprehension.

CHAPTER 20

Bloodsports and April showers

"Come on slowcoach."

"My shoes is loose." David stared with dismay at his feet whilst Amy and Rose looked at each other in exasperation.

"What again. They can't be. You've only just had 'em retied," Rose admonished him. "We aint ever going to get our shopping done at this rate Ame."

It was the third time David had stopped to have his shoes retied. The shoes he brought with him were too small and he was developing hammer toes. At first Amy hadn't noticed, but the shoes she bought to replace them had room in the toe to allow David's feet to develop normally. As a consequence David felt uncomfortable in them; they were 'too loose' and he was afraid of them coming off. Amy bent once more to retie them.

"Look," she said, "I'm tying them ever so tight. See, I'm putting a knot in them so they can't come undone. Come on now David or we'll never get the shopping done at this rate. Is you ready now?"

David nodded and set off reluctantly. Rose and Amy took a hand each and swung him along between them.

"I wants to have his photo took soon." Amy had been applying a cream to the rash around David's mouth and the inflammation was almost gone. "It'd be nice to send one to our Billy for Christmas."

"Where's you going to go?" Rose asked. "You aint buying a camera are you?"

"Well I thought I might next year. For the spring. There's that photo shop up on The Tything. You knows."

"Be expensive won't it Ame?"

"Be worth it though to get a nice picture of him to send to Bill. Then we can keep one for ourselves can't we."

A lorry trundled slowly past them and they paused to watch it go by. It was an open farm lorry with the sides extending upwards with wooden lattices and filled to capacity with green bananas. People stopped what they were doing as it passed them and turned to watch it.

"Not very ripe though is they," Amy commented.

"Aint seen a banana for years," a shopper lamented to them.

"Wonder where it's off too."

"Bet we won't see 'em in the shops anyway," Rose commented. "Poor kid." She looked down at David. "At this rate kids like him won't know what fresh fruits like."

Someone called from across the road, "I'm going to try and follow it; see where it goes. Coming?"

"No," the shopper replied. "You'll never catch it anyway."

"Anyway," Rose said resignedly, "I'm going to see if the butchers got any sausage for Bob's tea. Come on Ame."

"Wonder somebody don't kidnap the driver next time it stops and share 'em all round," Amy said with resignation. "Come on then David. Let's see what we can find for our tea shall we?"

They continued on their way with David between them.

"Has you thought about Christmas, you know, what's you getting him?" Rose nodded down in David's direction.

"Picture book. He'd like that," Amy replied. "He loves his Rupert you know." One of Amy's morning routines with David was to find the Rupert pictures in the Daily Express and read them to him. Then she mixed a little flour and water paste, cut the pictures out and stuck them in an exercise book. "And a little toy. Perhaps an aeroplane or something," she added. "Something to remind him of his daddy."

"I think Bob's going to make him something," Rose said.

"Ah," Amy replied. "That'd be nice."

Miss Fieldew had a crocodile and David loved to go next door to play with it. He was only allowed in at certain times because Miss Fieldew was very old and set in her ways. She didn't encourage David to come and go as he pleased; he had to knock first and only if she was 'at home' did Miss Fieldew let David come in to play. But to David it was fascinating to gaze upon the array of trinkets and ornaments that filled Miss Fieldew's parlour. There were beads and brooches and cut glass and pins adorning her sideboard and tables. Lace hung from the mantelpiece and pictures decorated the walls. The room was always dark, even on the brightest days. Not gloomy, for Miss Fieldew was not a gloomy person, but dark through antiquity. The room belonged to another age. Invariably Miss Fieldew dressed in a white blouse decorated with lace or embroidery, and a dark ankle length skirt. Her small back garden was filled with flowers, all perennials from which she took sprays and bunches but from which David was strictly barred. Under any other circumstances Miss Fieldew would not have encouraged David at all but she and Amy had been very good neighbours for the twenty three years since Amy and Albert had moved next door after their wedding and she was in sympathy with Amy taking

163

David under her wing. So, adhering to the principle that children should be seen and not heard Miss Fieldew allowed David into her cloistered life.

His chatter fascinated her. She didn't reply to his questions in baby talk and maybe because of the great difference between their ages they became friends. His visits provided her with spontaneous stimulation and David respected her wishes. He knew what was allowed and what was not and if he transgressed the bounds then Miss Fieldew made him leave and the visit would be over there and then. Miss Fieldew's' will was not to be flouted!

Under Miss Fieldew's supervision David was allowed to inspect Miss Fieldew's treasures. She allowed him to handle them, told him what they were for and sometimes even allowed him to try on modest pieces of jewellery so long as they were carefully and properly returned to their rightful place in the display. The most fascinating piece was the crocodile.

On a side table beneath the parlour window Miss Fieldew kept her collection of spectacles and glasses. A magnifying glass with an onyx handle; another one that hinged and folded back into a silver case. David loved to hold them and look at pictures through them. And then there were Miss Fieldew's reading spectacles within their individual case. But what fascinated David most of all was not the spectacles with tiny round lenses and soft, springy wire arms that wrapped around your ears; it was the case that contained them; a red leather case with a hinge at one end that opened up like a crocodile's mouth from which the glasses could be withdrawn.

"Be careful of them." Miss Fieldew admonished him as David opened it up and took the glasses out. "Put them down carefully there's a good boy."

David's game was very simple. It consisted of him lining up the smaller items on the floor length chenile cloth which covered Miss Fieldew's dining table while Miss Fieldew told him the story of how savage the crocodile was and how it ate up everything it could find. Then David simply moved the crocodile across the surface of the table and pushed the trinkets into the crocodile's mouth as they came within reach, snapping the mouth closed upon each victim.

"Be careful. Don't force them or they'll break." Miss Fieldew always kept a watchful eye on these proceedings. The game didn't usually last very long and as always David began to look around for other stimulation at which point Miss Fieldew would draw the visit to a close. "Time to go now. I've got to get ready."

"Where's you going?"

"I've got to go out."

David recalled never actually seeing Miss Fieldew ever go out but on subsequently returning and knocking to see if he could go back in again to play he invariably received no reply so Miss Fieldew must have gone out somewhere. In reality Miss Fieldew hardly ever went out at all except for very brief trips to the local shops; she simply ignored his knocking until he went away.

"Where's you going to?"

"Never you mind. Off you go now. Aunty Ame'll be waiting for you. There's a good boy."

"Do I have to?"

"Yes. See you tomorrow. Bye bye."

Miss Fieldew carefully closed and locked the door behind him leaving David standing in the porch. He was perfectly safe; he couldn't get out onto the street because the two houses, Miss Fieldew's and Aunty Ame's were in the middle of the terrace with a gate at each side enclosing their backs.

What to do now? David sat on Miss Fieldew's back step. He didn't want to go in to Aunty Ame's yet. He went to the corner of the outhouse and looked across beyond the wall that screened the two houses from each other, wondering whether to see if he could find some snails in the garden to play with, when he saw Uncle Al coming up the garden path from the henhouse carrying a chicken. David was about to run up to ask Uncle Al what he was going to do but immediately stopped and crouched down behind the wall. Uncle Al hadn't seen him and by some intuition David guessed that if Uncle Al did see him he wouldn't be allowed to watch what Uncle Al was up to. For instead of cradling the chicken and talking to it as he normally did when he handled them – for Al was a compassionate man despite his air of gruffness – this time Uncle Al was carrying the bird by its feet dangling upside down and wildly fluttering as he walked up the path with it.

David remained where he was, crouching behind Miss Fieldew's side of the wall, waiting for Uncle Al to go inside. But the sounds of fluttering continued to come from the yard beyond the wall. David peered round cautiously, afraid to be seen. Uncle Al had tied the hens feet together and was bent to the drainpipe over the grate, tying the bird to it about three feet from the ground so that it hung head downwards struggling wildly. As David watched Uncle Al took a penknife from his pocket, opened it and laid it on the ground. Now he tried to gather the bird up and enfold his arms about the wings to stop them beating. He was talking to it, cooing it to calm its wild flutterings. Finally he had it under control, first one wing then the other folded back against the bird's side. He reached down and David dodged back into hiding behind the wall. A moment's silence and then the hen could be heard again but this time it was a different sound, nothing like the sound it was making before. David peered fearfully around the wall; Uncle Al had the birds body imprisoned beneath his arm, holding its head firmly with his thumb and forefinger at the corners of the bird's beak, forcing its mouth open. His other hand held the penknife, forcing the blade down into the birds throat and he was working it, cutting it on the inside. A trickle of blood appeared at the beak and the bird squawked and spluttered. It choked and coughed a gout of blood, a great red clot spattering on Uncle Albert's wrist but its cry was smothered as more blood rose into its mouth and Uncle Albert stepped smartly back releasing the bird which immediately began desperately beating its wings, flying up against the wall to which it was tethered then falling back, swinging in a wild arc, a pendulum of wings and blood. Uncle Al went inside the house, leaving the bird to die and, unseen, David watched as a wide area around the grate turned red, appalled and fascinated by the bird's agony. It went on interminably until the fluttering became weak and spasmodic and the blood, instead of flowing started to congeal about the hen's beak, hanging in a long glistening clot that swung and dripped as its struggles weakened into reflex twitching. The back door opened and Uncle Albert came back out. David withdrew quickly behind Miss Fieldew's wall but not quickly enough and the small movement caught Uncle Albert's attention.

"What's you doing there?" he demanded.

"I've just been round to Miss Fieldew's." David answered tremulously. He knew he should not have been witness to the slaughter. Uncle Albert considered briefly.

"Well you shouldn't be out here," he said gruffly. "Come on inside. Your Aunty Ame's got something for you."

The image never left David and neither did the sounds of the hen choking. There was a lesson to be borne here, that even those who give you comfort and caress you might be plotting your murder just as Uncle Al had been reaching for his penknife even as he cooed and attempted to soothe the bird. David's self confidence took a setback from the death of the chicken.

Later he watched Aunty Ame pluck it, filling the kitchen with feathers and he wrinkled his nose in disgust as she withdrew her hand from the bird's inside drawing the glistening, stinking entrails out. When she wrapped them in newspaper and put them on the fire to burn, stinking the house out he went with her up the yard to Aunty Rose's. But when it came round to dinner time when the chicken was carved and served David ate the meal with as much enjoyment as any other and never for one moment equated the horror he had witnessed with the meat he had eaten.

"Uncle Al's taking you for a haircut then you'm going to have your picture taken. That'll be nice won't it?"

David was nonplussed. What did 'picture taken' mean? But there was a lot of fuss and attention all of a sudden. The usual routine of shopping was interrupted by a visit to the children's department at Russell and Dorrells, causing David infinite boredom whilst his two aunts pored interminably over different items, checking their clothing coupons and assuring him, "We shan't be long now."

Pausing at The Reindeer for their customary glass of mild before returning home from town with the shopping Amy couldn't wait to open the parcel and hold up David's new clothes in admiration.

"They'm lovely." Rose fingered the soft texture of the wool and they bathed themselves in mutual congratulation on the purchase. "It's just right ain't it. He'll look lovely in it. Is you going to let him wear it?"

Amy held the woollen brown trousers up against the jersey, fingering the buttons at the collar. "Not until he's had his picture taken. I'm saving it for then. I wants our Billy to see how much better he looks. Nice shade of green ain't it?"

"That'll go nice with his new shoes as well." Rose turned to David, sucking noisily at his Vimto. "You'm going to look lovely aintcha?" David nodded dutifully, his attention fixed on the flattened end of his straw and the drought of Vimto this had produced.

"Al's taking him for his haircut this afternoon." Amy ruffled David's head. "Then you'll be all set for your photo taking." David tried to open up the straw by blowing and a froth of bubbles erupted. "Careful," Amy cried, "you'll have it all down you."

"Better put them clothes away Ame before he gets 'em all wet."

"We thought we might take him to the pictures later this week. There's that new picture at the Gaumont. They says it's lovely."

"Is you sure he's old enough?" Rose was mildly surprised at Amy's suggestion. "He won't sit still long enough will he?"

"Well they says it's a kids' film." Amy responded.

"But he won't be able to see. 'Specially if he gets a big 'un like Bob in front of him."

But Amy was determined to give David another kind of treat. And anyway she wanted to see the film herself. She poo-poo'd Rose's doubts. "He'll be alright and he can sit on my knee if he wants to."

Rose busied herself with her handbag. "Has you heard from the Welfare yet Ame?" She produced a packet of cigarettes and took a delicate sip of her beer. "Want one?" Amy declined the open packet as Rose knew she would but politeness demanded the offer. She pushed the

167

pack in front of David. "Do you want one? Yes you would wouldn't you." as David reached across for it. "You'm too young to smoke."

"I'm still waiting for a letter back," Amy answered.

"You should get something you know. After all you'm looking after him full time now while our Bill's in the forces. You should get some help. I mean, shoe's ain't cheap. Then there's them other things you bought today."

"Still we don't mind do we?" Amy put an arm around David and hugged him. "He's worth a guinea a box." She picked her glass up. "You having another Rose?"

"No ta." Rose drained the remnants from her bottle into the glass. "This'll do me. I'll have to be getting back for Bob's dinner."

The photographic session was booked for Thursday afternoon and David, freshly scrubbed and dressed in the pale green woollen jersey and the new brown trousers was ready to go and have his picture taken. The rash around his mouth was almost gone and his hair shone; it was brushed down with a parting at the side; Albert had taken David to have it cut specially for the photograph.

David hadn't liked the experience much. The barber kept gripping his head and turning it this way and that whilst he used the clippers, unlike Aunty Ame who only used the scissors to briefly trim the ends. The clippers buzzed and tickled and that made David squirm and the barber gripped him tighter, forcing David to hold his head still. He was beginning to get exasperated with the kid. Kids were all the same; they took more time and you had to charge less. Hardly worth doing the little kids at all, it was more trouble than it was worth. And this kid Albert had brought in was worse than most. Despite the fact that Albert was one of his regulars the barber turned to him between the clippers and the scissors and told him that he wasn't going to do the kid again if he was going to wriggle about like that, at which Albert took umbrage and said he'd go somewhere else for his own haircut next time; he wasn't the only barber in town.

"I was only saying Albert that's all." The barber protested. "You've seen for yourself what he's been like. It's taken twice as long as usual. And it keeps people waiting." He took the line of reconciliation. "Next time you brings him don't make it teatime. It's when everybody comes in. Can't you make it in the morning?"

"If there is a next time," Albert grumbled. But he had to admit that he'd done a good job and David's hair looked much better.

But it was the same in the photographic studio. Rose waited at the front in the shop on The Tything whilst Amy followed the photographer into the back with David. "There's not too much room and besides we don't want too many distractions do we?" The photographer smiled weakly; he'd had experience of children's portraits before!

They set David up on a dark oak table with spindly barley sugar legs and as the photographer turned to his camera David climbed off and made for Aunty Ame sitting against the far wall. Patiently they re-sat him and he climbed down again. After three attempts Amy sat with David beside her on the table whilst the photographer disappeared beneath the black cloth to focus the shot. He emerged and went to David and posed him with his ankles crossed at which David immediately began swinging his legs to and fro beneath the table.

"Keep your legs still there's a good boy." Amy rose from the seat to which she had returned and made a step towards him. David's legs stopped swinging; the photographer raised his hand and said,

"Just like that. Don't move. Right."

He disappeared beneath the cloth again and David began to turn on the table to look about him. Amy rose again but the photographer emerged and forestalled her. "It's alright. I'll see to him." There was the beginning of tension in his voice. He set David back in his pose and retreated carefully and slowly to the camera, like a hunter suddenly confronted by his prey. With sudden inspiration he said, "Watch the birdie," and gestured vaguely to the ceiling behind him. Obediently David looked up as the photographer disappeared once more beneath the cloth. But David turned his attention to Amy and said in a petulant voice,

"I can't see nothing."

He looked up again in the confident hope of seeing a bird materialise from somewhere behind the camera but nothing happened. Once more David turned his attention to Amy and began to climb off the table. Amy sprang forward to prevent him falling and the photographer emerged again exhibiting signs of exasperation.

"Well what are we going to do?" he demanded. "Perhaps it'd be better if you brought him back another day. When he's a little less… fidgety."

But Amy was adamant; it had to be today. She had prepared David and herself for it and she wasn't going to be disappointed.

The photographer had another brainwave. "Sit him back up there," he commanded, "And stay with him while I refocus the camera." Once more he busied himself beneath the sheet. "Right," he said, "I think we're ready this time. When I say 'go' I want you to step from David's side. But first of all…"

He went to a cupboard and produced a coloured ball the size of a goldfish bowl and placed it in David's hands. Then he smartly retreated to the camera, grasped the shutter lead, called 'now' to attract David's attention and as Amy stepped away from the table he pressed the shutter with relief. After that the second shot was easy but it left David wondering what had taken place; as far as he could see there had been no point to the proceedings. But Aunty Ame seemed pleased with herself.

There was bread and lemon curd for tea, one of David's favourites.

"Would you like some more?" Amy asked as David finished off the last slice on his plate. David nodded vigorously with his mouth full of bread.

"He likes his cakey jam don't he." Albert made a face at David, an ogre's face intended as play and growled, "We'll have to put this boy on bread and water. He's going to get fat eating like this. Fetch us a cup of water for him." Albert fondly imagined it was fun for them both but David merely gazed up at him in incomprehension, unsure whether his uncle really meant it or not. His Uncle Al could be so unpredictable at times and he began to feel nervous.

"Leave him alone you great daft thing," Amy admonished Albert. "Pulling faces like that you'll frighten the kid half to death. No wonder he can't sleep at night for crying. It's you." She turned her attention to David and gave him some more bread. "Take no notice of your Uncle Al. He gets daft sometimes. Hurry up and eat that and then we've got a treat for you. Would you like to go to the pictures?"

"What's that?"

"Oh you'll like it, you'll see," Amy replied, "But we won't let Uncle Al come with us shall we. Not if he keeps pulling faces at you like that we won't."

"Bread and water. That's the best thing for hungry boys," Albert growled but Amy silenced him with a look.

"Come on David, hurry up and eat that then we'll wash your hands and face ready to go shall we…"

Walking into the darkness of the cinema with his hand safely in Aunty Ame's and Ruff, his little woollen dog clutched in the other, David was almost unafraid. The usherette shone a pencil of light ahead to show them where to sit and Aunty Ame and Uncle Al perched him up on the edge of the upturned seat so that he could see. Between the two of them David felt secure. Rising smoke wove patterns in the beam of light flickering above and then the lights came up and looking about him David could see that they were not alone. The huge red curtains covering the wall in front of them began to open as the lights went down again and the screen lit up with the newsreel. Images of aeroplanes flying in formation; figures tumbling from them like spent cartridges ejected from the breech of a gun, streaming down until the parachutes opened, then a gentle descent from view. Bombers landing and rolling forward, their propellers shuddering to a stop before the camera.

Aunty Ame bent to David and whispered, "That's your daddy."

"Where? Where?" David cried jumping forward off his perch and gripping the back of the seat in front of him, craning to see.

Amy was dismayed. She had only said it from a desire to keep the image of his father fresh in David's mind. She had not anticipated the spontenaiety of his reaction.

"One of them airmen," she whispered in half hearted reply.

"Shush." "Be quiet," came from the darkness.

"Come on," she said, "sit back up here like a good boy."

"Where is he?" David pleaded anxiously. "Which one?"

Now she wished she'd never said anything and shushed him into silence but before the newsreel was over David was restless and beginning to chatter once more. In the brief interval that followed and before the lights dimmed again Amy took David on her knee. Now he could see without craning and he settled down in the darkness to watch.

A coloured picture rose before him; a forest, blue birds swooping in the trees and the leaves of a thicket parting to reveal a deer with a newborn faun.

A cry, "The new prince!" from wide eyed animals scurrying forward and then drops of water splashing onto the leaves and running into crystal droplet's; peals of thunder, lightning, and the voices of the forest singing the song of the April shower.

The faun's mother gently coaxing him out to play, joyfully bounding across the open meadow, a look of alarm, panic, flight and a sudden noise, clear and sharp, fearful in its finality. Silence, except for the deer's child wandering alone crying, "Mother... mother..." And a sudden presence in the forest, waiting to emerge and save him from the dark...

Amy carried David sleeping from the cinema and nursed him whilst Albert descended into the cellars of the grammar school to stoke the boilers. Then briskly home. David remained asleep whilst Amy undressed him and tucked him into his cot then went downstairs to a supper of chicken broth in front of the fire leaving David dreaming of daddy waiting for him somewhere in a woodland with aeroplanes and raindrops parachuting down into the forest.

But for all the love and patience Amy bestowed upon him, David's fear of the dark was absolute. It had shown itself in the cries and protests rising from his cot when Amy switched off the light at bedtime although, with every week that passed the crying was becoming less intense. But even the transition from daylight to darkness in familiar surroundings had a profound effect.

171

On two or three occasions after Albert had been home for his dinner he took David back with him to the grammar school when the quadrangle lawn needed to be cut. David's job was to collect the grass clippings in discrete heaps about the lawn. It wasn't a job that the child could undertake with proficiency but that didn't matter; it was an excuse for an afternoon walk and Amy kept David well out of harm's way. They walked to the school together, only six or seven minutes walk with David's hand in theirs beneath the high brick wall with the trees above which skirted the playing fields beyond, happily chatting. But at night it was different, en route from pub to school for Albert's final job for the day. Now the sunlight was gone and the road was gloomy in the moonlight. The wall was pierced at intervals by disused doors which at one time had given access to the school grounds. During the day they were unremarkable but at night, who knows what might be lurking in the darkness of the shallow recess to draw an unwary child from the pavement into what lay beyond under the trees. Amy and Albert were aware of David's nervousness. They saw how he paused from skipping along ahead of them when he reached each doorway and look discreetly over his shoulder, just to check they were still there with him. Then bracing himself, run past the door, always careful to veer to the edge of the pavement as far from the wall as possible. Each night without fail the doorways produced this ritual and sometimes walking along that road during the day, on his way to or from the school with Albert, David looked keenly into the doorways for reassurance as they passed. And the doors were always the same. Begrimed from the weather and neglect with accumulating dust building into the corners and small weeds struggling to grow in the cracks at the base of the wall. Inside the school grounds too at night the same transition was wrought. Now the old school buildings loomed faceless in the dark and the trees rustled and whispered about them. Only Albert's long familiarity enabled him to march with confidence along the drive without stumbling with Amy and David following close alongside.

The boilerhouse was situated in a small enclosed yard adjacent to the main buildings and entry to the yard was through a locked gate. Amy and David stood close against the wall as the keys scraped in the lock and Albert went inside.

"We'll wait out here," Amy whispered drawing David close into the folds of her coat. "Come on, keep warm." But it wasn't just for warmth that David snuggled close. All around was darkness with soft unseen sounds and a wind that probed and touched his neck and ears and made his face cold. From inside the boilerhouse yard came the sound of keys again and a low squeak as the door to the cellar opened. Then an age of silence until Albert found the switch at the foot of the stairs and

172

the soft glow of light from below leaked into the yard. Now came the terrible sound of clanging to disturb the silence and this was the worst of all for it told whatever was beyond the darkness that they were here and alone. How David wished that Aunty Ame would take him down into the light with Uncle Al. Amy felt him push against her, burying his face against her coat.

"Is you cold?"

David whimpered quietly in reply. She hugged him to her again. "You'm alright. There you is, you keep nice and warm with me. Uncle Al won't be long."

Then the resounding clang of the furnace door slamming shut with the shovel. David silently pleaded for the sounds to stop. The small glow of light went out. David stiffened and waited, listening to Uncle Al's footsteps on the cellar stairs and the sound of locks being turned again and then the sudden voice, unexpectedly close. "That's it then. Come on let's go."

Ahead of them and oh! so far away, the gateway at the end of the drive and the welcoming road; behind, the great mass of buildings, brooding in the darkness. David wanted to run, to escape as fast as his legs would carry him but Aunty Ame and Uncle Al would only walk.

"What's the matter? Is you tired then? Come on. Let's carry you home."

"Can you manage him all that way Al? He's heavy."

David snuggled gratefully against Al's shoulder. "No he's alright. You'm tired ain't you?"

David nodded drowsily, his arms round Uncle Al's neck. Now he could relax. No more dark gates to negotiate and they were nearly at the end of the drive and back onto the road.

"There," Albert said proudly. "He's asleep already."

CHAPTER 21

Lost and found

Christmas was approaching and with it came winter and bitterly cold weather. Amy sat so close up against the fire that her legs became criss-crossed in blotches of heat rash.

"Don't matter Rose," she said. "Got to keep warm somehow."

She was admiring the photograph of David, ready to send to Bill with a card for Christmas. "It don't look much though do it?"

"He'll love it. Here let's take another look." Amy passed the postcard across. David sitting with his ankles crossed, clutching a ball and open mouthed with a slightly surprised expression. But there was a spontaneous charm about it and Amy was pleased with the result. It showed David well cared for. There was no trace of his anxieties or the other afflictions which had shocked her when he first arrived. "I mean, you've only got to look to see he's alright. Aintcha? Did you say you've got one for our Lill as well?"

"Yes. D'you think she'll like it?"

"'Course she will. I likes mine anyway. I'm having it framed."

Amy put the photograph inside the card together with the letter and sealed it.

"Hope it gets there in time. It's such a long way ain't it. Anyway I'm posting it when we goes up town today. Remind me won't you Rose."

"You got to see that bloke up at the ministry today as well don't forget. You got all your papers and forms?"

"Behind the clock." Amy glanced at the time. "Better get ready to go I suppose. Don't want to be late."

The waiting room at the Ministry of Food was full and Amy was dismayed to see how crowded it was. The packed rows of chairs were all taken and a queue had formed around the walls. The low murmur of discontented chatter was heightened by the crying of bored infants and toddlers straining for freedom to run about. The room had an air of chill brought about by the inadequacy of the heating and the frostiness of war weary and overworked officials striving to provide from resources they hadn't got.

"Can't you keep those kids under control!" The intolerant demand came from a clerk at one of the desks lined up across the far end of the room.

A mother made a half hearted grab at a child's arm. "Come here and do as you're told," she cried, without much conviction that she would be obeyed and dragged it protesting to stand by her in the line. A second woman pulled her child on to her knee but it immediately wriggled free again. She sighed in hopeless resignation and turned to the woman next to her. "Well what can you do? I mean, if only they'd get a move on! I've been here almost an hour now."

"I been here longer than that," chimed another.

"Think they'd get a move on wouldn't you," she repeated sadly.

The murmurs of resentment increased about the room and the clerk dropped his forehead into his hand in a vain attempt to block them out and focused with renewed concentration on the papers which the next claimant placed on the desk.

Rose sighed, despondent at the length of wait before them. "How long d'you think you'm going to be Ame."

"Gawd knows. Hours by the sounds of it."

"I'd better get down to the Home and Colonial before they sells out. Do you want anything?"

"See if they've got any brawn," Amy said. "And some faggots. We nearly had some last week but they'd all gone."

"I was going to get some for me and Bob anyway."

"You got enough coupons? Only I better keep my ration book with me. They'll want to see it here I expect."

"Shan't be long." Rose was glad to have an excuse to escape the queue. It was bad enough waiting at the shops but this was even worse! "Oh, give us that card. I'll post that while I'm out."

Amy pulled Bill's card from her bag. "See it goes safe won't you," she called.

The queue shuffled a few feet forward with the cry of "Next," from two of the clerks simultaneously and for a moment everyone's spirits in the room lifted but quickly evaporated again into despondent grumbling as the waiting resumed. David tugged at Amy's hand. He wanted to be free to run about like the other kids but Amy held him firmly to her. "No. You've got to stay close to Aunty Ame there's a good boy. Ought to have let you gone with Aunty Rose didn't I. Never mind. She'll be quicker on her own."

David swung and pirouetted in boredom at Amy's side, pulling at her arm until she was pushed to the limit of her tolerance. "Keep still," she admonished him, "You'll have me over." She gave David a sharp tug and he began to cry in frustration and surprise at the rebuke for Aunty Ame had never done anything like that before.

The voice of petulant authority raised itself in protest at the sounds of discontent. "Can't you keep that child quiet! You'll have to leave if you can't control it," he snapped. In the sudden hush the clerk addressed a comment to the room in general. "You shouldn't bring your children here anyway."

Amy refused to be cowed. "I got an appointment." She brandished her letter. "It says to be here by half past ten. What's the point of coming here then if you ain't got time to see us!"

"He's kept me waiting an hour," someone else put in. "I was supposed to see him an hour ago." A general cry of assent rose and the clerks looked up in dismay. Couldn't these people see they were coping as best they could. It wasn't their fault there were so many claims to be dealt with.

With cries of protest rising all her around Amy renewed her attack on the clerks. "What are we supposed to do with our kids? Leave 'em at home all alone?" Amy looked around at the roomful of expectant faces. The clerks were momentarily nonplussed. "And don't you tell me to keep the kid quiet. Keeping 'em hanging about all day. What d'you expect the kid to do while you sits there. You'm nothing but a little Hitler. It's people like you we're supposed to be fighting against."

Here was a diversion and the waiting room erupted with joy, with cries and catcalls coming from those who until then had been waiting in sullen resentment. The clerks raised their voices with demands for calm to be restored otherwise no more claimants would be seen and the uproar subsided as quickly as it had arisen. But it had been a welcome protest, warming the blood and raising everyone's spirits. It was something to talk about when they got home, something to tell the neighbours with suitable embellishments. And David, whose crying had begun it but who had stopped when the turmoil began, treasured the image of Aunty Ame, an adult in an adult world standing up for him.

"Anyway I got some coupons for him and he'll get welfare orange too."

"You'm lucky though Ame." Rose shared a deep seated respect, in common with the rest of the general population for the authority invested in 'officials'; even if they were the meanest of clerks she believed they held the sanction of yea or nay on all decisions likely to affect her. "I mean, speaking back at 'em like that. They might have stopped your claim."

"Well anyway I've got it now." Amy beamed down at David. "And it wouldn't have made any difference even if I hadn't would it." She tousled David's hair. "He's worth a guinea a box."

"You still thinking of having a party Ame?"

"I ain't done anything about it yet. But, you know, we ain't had a party at home for years. Not a real 'un I mean. Anyway things is so short you can't have a party like we used to have. But we thought it'd be nice for him." Amy glanced down at David, busy with trinkets from her sewing box on the hearthrug. "Just have a couple of the neighbours round, you and Bob; perhaps Mrs Wales from up the top, she might like to bring their Anne down to play with him. She's old enough ain't she?"

"About the same age I think," Rose replied. She changed the subject. "You should see the…" and here Rose dropped her voice and mimed 'set of animals' – she resumed her normal voice again, "that Bob's making him. They'm lovely. All made out of fretwork."

"Be nice to have Christmas with a kid in the house."

"Soon be here," Rose said. "It's December already. I don't know where this year's gone."

Albert viewed the forthcoming school holidays with mixed feelings. The break over the two days of Christmas would be welcome but it also meant lots of additional work as well. All the maintenance which couldn't be done during the school term was undertaken during holidays and Christmas was no exception.

He paused from brushing leaves from beneath the beech tree on the playing field and leaned on the besom. It was never ending, what with the boilers and keeping the grounds tidy and all the jobs inside as well. But this was thankless, trying to wage a winning war against nature and keep the lawns clear of leaves. He wished it would rain, then he could go inside with a clear conscience but although the day was cold and the low clouds were leaden there was only this cold, raw dampness. His back ached from sweeping but at least it was keeping him warm. As Albert gazed about him a gowned figure came into view across the playing field. Pullinger! He set too once more, flicking the leaves across the grass towards the pile that was accumulating. Thank God there was no wind to blow them all about again and they were so wet they lay where they fell.

From the corner of his eye Albert could see that Pullinger was making directly across the grass towards him. What is it this time? Another list of jobs to be done during the holiday no doubt! Pullinger paused a few feet away. As headmaster he normally avoided familiarity with his staff but seeing Albert out on the playing field he had deliberately chosen this opportunity to speak to him. Albert looked up. "Thought I'd get the lawns tidied up a bit while I had the chance."

Pullinger smiled to try to put Albert at ease. He liked Albert. Oh he was well aware of Albert's extra source of income and he turned a blind eye to Albert's unofficial little absences when he was late back after a drink, paying out or taking bets. For he was also deeply conscious of Albert's loyalty to the school and his dedication to seeing that practical matters like stoking the school boilers last thing at night were attended to. For virtues like loyalty and dedication were important to Pullinger. That was what he endeavoured to inculcate into the boys and having someone like Albert who, no matter how lowly in the school hierarchy, practised and demonstrated those virtues unselfconsciously, then he was an asset to be valued.

"Yes," Pullinger replied. "At least it's keeping dry for you." He shivered. He was slightly built and already beginning to feel the cold. He turned and looked back across at the buildings. On summer days Pullinger loved to be out on the playing fields with the red brick buildings forming a backdrop to games and competition. Today they looked grey; days like this took the colour from everything. He directed Albert's gaze to follow his own. "I'm getting concerned about all the creeper on the walls. Especially out here at the back of the school. It gets the sun all day and the stuff's getting rampant. I wonder if you'd arrange to get it cut back a bit."

"It's a big job," Albert retorted. "It'd mean either cutting it through at the base, and then it'd all have to be stripped back off the walls. Once it's dead. It'd look awful while it was…"

"No, no," Pullinger interrupted him. "I don't mean that. No, just to cut it back from where it's getting too high. Into the gutters. And," he pointed, "do you see up there. Where it's obscuring part of the windows."

Albert could see that what was, to Pullinger, merely a small case of 'cutting back' was in reality a major task. "It's going to take ages," he protested. "I mean, it's a job for the long ladders ands then moving them around the walls into the right positions and going up… You can't reach over too far at that height either. It'd be a terribly slow job."

"I know, I know," Pullinger temporised. "I don't mean it's to be completed all at once. Perhaps it's something that could be done over a period. Before the growing season begins again in the spring. When you have the chance."

"I'll have to see," Albert said reluctantly. "We've got a lot on this holiday you know."

"Yes." Pullinger agreed. "We've a lot to get through."

'We' thought Albert. I'm glad you said 'we'. You mean 'me' more like. "Well, I'll see how I can fit it in. See if I can get a start made on it anyway."

"Thank you. Just so that we can prevent it getting completely out of hand." Pullinger half turned to go, paused and then said almost as an afterthought, "I hear you've got a boy staying with you."

"Yes. My nephew's son. Amy and me's looking after him. For the duration if you see what I mean." Albert didn't care to share all the details leading up to it with Pullinger.

"I thought so. Was that the little fellow I've seen sometimes. I think he's been here with you hasn't he? In the afternoon?"

"Not lately. I mean, earlier in the year, when it was nice Amy brought him over for a walk. It was just…"

And then Pullinger surprised him by saying, "Perhaps we'll see him here as a pupil some day." Albert was lost for an answer, unused to this level of familiarity. "Anyway," Pullinger continued, "as it's Christmas Mrs. Pullinger and I thought you might appreciate a little gift for him. Perhaps you'd care to bring him round this afternoon. To the house."

"I… Thank you," Albert stammered his thanks. "Any special time?"

"No that's alright. Whenever it's convenient. My wife and I are going away for the holiday tomorrow. Oh by the way, what is his name?"

"David," Albert replied.

"David," the headmaster repeated. "Yes. Good. Well we'll see you this afternoon then." A moments pause to look over the grounds and the school buildings. "Let's hope that nineteen fortyfive is a better year for him." He suddenly became conscious of Albert looking at him. "I'm sorry, I didn't mean to infer that…" For the first time Albert saw the headmaster discomfited. Pullinger drew his gown about him and muttered, "Yes," in a satisfied sort of way, then, "getting cold." and strode off.

Albert shook his head and gazed briefly at the departing headmaster's back. 'Just goes to show', he thought and returned to sweeping the leaves with renewed vigour.

He called in at the 'Lamb and Flag' for a quick one and to see if Lenny was there to pay him his winnings from yesterdays bet. Behind the bar Tom looked up and laid his newspaper to one side.

"Usual Albert?" He began pulling Albert's pint. "Len's not in yet. 'Spect he'll not be long. Bit early for him."

"It's quiet ain't it." Albert sipped at the beer looking round at the empty bar.

"Not much money about. 'Specially middle of the week," Tom said miserably, reaching for his paper again. "Lenny had a touch?" Tom knew Albert's habits. If there were bets to be placed there would have been a discrete gathering of customers in the bar; it must mean someone was due to some winnings for Albert to arrive.

Albert nodded, "Outsider. Come in at eight to one."

Tom renewed his perusal of the racing page. "Any tips for

Wincanton this afternoon?" he asked with feigned casualness.

Albert replied offhandedly, "Grounds too hard. Could be anybody's." Then as a sop to Tom for past favours, "You might like to look at Razzle Dazzle. Not very well priced but she might give a showing."

"Oh." Tom rescanned the field and began to re-appraise his previous fancy.

The bar door opened and Lenny, a builder's labourer in a grimy gaberdine mac and clay covered boots walked in blowing on his hands. "Bloody cold."

Tom looked up sharply. "I've told you before about coming in with them boots all covered in mud. They're ruining my carpet."

Lenny looked down at the well worn, stained carpet covering the approach to the bar, ignored Tom and nodded a greeting to Albert. "You having another?"

Albert nodded and reached for his pint, drinking a third of it down at a draft. "You'll soon have finished that job in the market won't you?" he said.

"Two or three more weeks to go yet," Lenny replied. He took his pint from Tom, said, "Cheers," and he too took a huge swig of beer. "Ah, that's better. Might be going on that County Hall job when this one's finished. Could be working with your Bob."

"That'll be nice for him," Tom put in facetiously.

"At least it'll be inside," Lenny said.

Half way down the second pint Albert left the bar and went to the toilet's in the yard. He started to pee against the wall and within a minute Lenny came and started to pee alongside him. When he had finished, Albert fastened up and in the act of smoothing down and fastening his jacket, extracted a small wad of money with Lenny's betting slip wrapped around it and deftly passed it into Lenny's hand without a word. Lenny took it without comment, slipped it into his pocket and waited, giving Albert a few moments discretion before following him back into the pub.

Albert and Tom looked up as Lenny entered the bar. "Another?" Lenny asked, his eyes flicking to them both. "Had a bit of luck today," he added innocently.

"That's very kind Lenny," Tom replied. "Same again Albert?"

"Quick one," Albert replied. "Got to be getting back for my dinner." And with that the charade was over. Tom pulled the pints with satisfaction. He could always rely on Albert to be absolutely discreet. Even when there was nobody about, Albert never took any chances; he always observed the fiction. And on a day as deadly as this dinner time had been so far, Albert's little business had resulted in six pints being sold.

"You'll have your dinner ruined," Amy admonished Albert when he walked through the door. "I don't know why I bothers cooking it for you. Has you paid Lenny?"

"Yes. Here, Tom's having a bet on Razzle Dazzle at Wincanton." He placed Tom's betting slip on the table.

"Put it away; don't leave it there. I'll do it this afternoon. What odds you give him?"

"I've written it on," Albert replied, and opening the top drawer in the sideboard he reached beneath it and pulled at the narrow veneered decorative panel between the sideboard drawers. It slid forward half an inch revealing a shallow drawer. Albert gripped it and pulled the drawer open. It was filled with betting slips and Albert added Tom's to the pile inside then pushed it closed again. To all appearances there were no other drawers in the sideboard except the three obvious ones with the cutlery, tablecloths and personal bric-a-brac in them.

"Where's the boy?" Albert asked.

"Round at Miss Fieldew's," Amy replied.

"Good. Here you'll never guess what Pullinger said to me this morning." Albert glanced up at the window but the yard was empty. "He's not coming in is he?"

"No." Amy said, placing Albert's dinner on the table. "Here come on eat this before it gets cold."

Albert sat appreciatively at the table. "He's got David a little present. He must have seen him when we took him along to the school."

"There wasn't any trouble about it was there?"

"No," Albert replied generously. "He was as good as gold about it. Even said we might see him as a pupil there one day."

Amy let this pass.

"Anyway," Albert continued, "he wants us to call in this afternoon and pick it up."

"What! Up at the school?"

"At the house," Albert said proudly.

Amy felt a mixture of pleasure and apprehension. Not that she felt herself to be anyone's inferior but even so, to be invited to the headmaster's home!

"When?" she asked. "What time? I needs to get ready. And our David. Is he to come along too?"

"I think so. I think he wants to meet him. Anyway why don't you come over about three o'clock. Just before school finishes. That should be a good time."

Albert finished his meal and got up from the table. "Anyway I'd better be getting back. You knows where to find me."

Amy looked at the clock. It was already a quarter to two. She decided to get herself ready first without interruption whilst David was next door and she put the kettle back on to boil some water for herself while she washed the dinner pots. Then she went upstairs and changed into her best frock and went along the back to tell Rose.

"We'm going up to the school this afternoon. Mr. and Mrs. Pullinger's got him a Christmas present. They wants us to take him up with us to fetch it this afternoon."

Rose was impressed. "That's nice. What's they got him, d'you know?"

"Haven't got a clue. They never said. Anyway I just thought I'd come and let you know. 'Time is it now? I'd better fetch him and get him ready to go. See you later Rose. TTFN." And Amy went happily back down the path to collect David to have his face washed.

There was no response from Miss Fieldew's. Amy waited then knocked again but the house remained silent. She tried the door but it was locked. Returning home she called as she entered, "David where is you. I've got a nice surprise for you. Come and get ready we'm going out." He wasn't in the living room, or in the front room either. Amy went upstairs to see if he was there; she didn't really expect to find David in the bedrooms because he very seldom went up there except to accompany Amy when she went up herself to make the beds. "Come on David," she called. "Let's have you. I knows you're hiding." But David's bedroom was empty as was hers and Alberts room at the back. Amy looked under the beds feeling slightly ridiculous as she did so and called him again but her voice sounded hollow in the empty rooms. After checking the junk room above the kitchen Amy began to get angry and frightened. Once again she checked downstairs, dashing from the living room to the front, calling David's name and telling him to come out from wherever he was hiding and stop being so silly. In the pantry? No! Surely he's not hiding in the coalhouse! She checked that and the toilet in the porch. Both were empty. She put her hands to her head and tried to think. Had she closed the back gate when she went up to Rose's? She was sure that she did. What about Albert? Had he left it open when he left to go back to work after dinner? But the gate was closed; Amy was sure she distinctly remembered having to open it to go up to Rose's. But then…? The canal was only just at the end of the street. Ten houses away. She'd always told David whenever they were out together to keep away from the edge… It didn't bear thinking about! She dashed round to Miss Fieldew's again and again there was no response to her frantic knocking. She went along the backyard and peered into the kitchen window then the parlour window and rapped on the pane. But Miss Fieldew's house was silent and empty. Amy's head was spinning.

What...? She couldn't think, only that something awful must have happened. She dashed up the yard to Rose's and burst in crying, "Rose... Rose... I've lost David. Rose! Something terrible's happened to David."

"Ame what is it?" Rose cried. "What's gone on? Whatever's the matter?"

Amy was crying hysterically and now she couldn't get the words out. Rose picked up 'David', 'awful', 'canal' and 'drowned'. She shook Amy to try to make her coherent. "You've got to come and help me to look for him," Amy sobbed. "Quick! Quickly! Before it's too late."

"I thought he was in Miss Fieldew's."

"He was," Amy cried, "but now he's not there."

They dashed from the house together. "The henhouse! Has you looked in the henhouse?" Rose demanded.

"He won't be in there. The hens frighten him." An instant's pause. "You go and look there Rose, I'm going up to the cut. Oh my God, if anything's happened..."

Amy ran down the entry between the houses into the street calling, "David! David..." There was a solitary fisherman on the towpath sitting on his basket with his rod drooping over the water. Further along a woman walking her dog was heading in the direction of the railway bridge over the canal. "Has you seen a little boy?" Amy called. The fisherman turned and looked at Amy without comprehension. She ran up to him, breathless. "Has you seen a little boy up here. About four, that's all he is. Not even four! Just now, on his own. Has you seen him?"

The fisherman ruminated briefly. "Ain't seen nobody. O-oh, not for the last ten minutes, quarter of an hour. Except her of course." He nodded towards the woman with the dog slowly ambling along the canal bank. Amy ran along the path and caught up with her. "Has you seen a little boy? On his own, playing by the canal?"

The woman looked at Amy with some concern. "I ain't seen nobody. Has he got lost?"

"He was in the house playing. I... I only turned my back for a minute... You sure you've not seen him?"

"There's been nobody like him at all. And I been on the canal with our Blackie all the time. Only him." She gestured back towards the fisherman observing them with interest. Amy ran back along the bank to the head of the street. "Any luck?" he called as she passed him.

"No," Amy sobbed.

Rose was waiting in the street at the bottom of the entry. She went forward to Amy as her sister ran towards her. "Any..."

"Nobody's seen him," Amy wailed.

"He ain't in the henhouse. I've looked in the gardens. I don't know

183

where to look next."

"Has you looked in your house?" Amy cried.

"He can't be in there." Rose protested. "He couldn't have got through the gate. Anyway I'd have seen him. He wouldn't come in without saying something. Would he?"

"We'll have to get the police." Amy was beside herself with anxiety. "What are we going to tell our Bill? And Lilly?"

"Come on." Rose pulled Amy back along the entry to the back of the houses. "He couldn't have got out. Not if the gates was properly shut. Let's go and have another look."

Together they searched every room in Amy's house. Then they went together up to Rose's and searched there but there was no sign of David.

"We'll have to get the police," Amy sobbed. "Whatever's I going to say to Al? He's expecting us up at the school…"

Stricken they looked at each other. Neither wanted to say what they thought; neither wanted to hear what the other was thinking.

"Better go and call the police," Amy said quietly. "Is you coming Rose?" Amy's nose began to run and tears welled into her eyes. "You got a hanky Rose?"

Rose snuffled; she was close to breaking down herself. "Here you are Ame. It's a clean 'un." She dabbed at her own eyes and passed the handkerchief across. "Has you got some money for the phone?"

Amy shook her head. "In my purse. At home."

"I think I've got some." Rose went into the living room and took her purse from her handbag. "Here, I've got some pennies here." A thought struck her. "We don't need any pennies for a nine nine nine call do we?"

Quietly weeping, Amy shook her head. "I don't know. I don't think so."

They left the house together and set off for the bottom of the road.

The telephone box was next to the co-op and slowly emerging, leaning on her walking cane and carrying a small string bag of groceries they saw Miss Fieldew. She looked up as Amy and Rose came running along the street and her look of pleasant greeting changed immediately to concern.

"Amy." She paused in consternation. "Whatever can be the matter?"

"It's David. We've lost him."

Miss Fieldew looked from Rose to Amy. They were so distressed – Amy was unable to speak for the trembling of her chin; her mouth tried to form words but the sound was incoherent – and Miss Fieldew immediately felt the pangs of her own responsibility. "But I thought he'd come straight home to you when he finished playing Amy. I went into the kitchen to have a wash. He... he'd come home by then. Oh dear. Oh dear," she wailed.

"We'm just going to phone for the police." Rose continued. "We don't know what else to do. We've looked everywhere for him. In the gardens. Ame's been up to the canal."

Amy burst again into tears and went into the telephone box with Rose. Miss Fieldew waited outside whilst they made the call and in her mind she went back through David's visit. After playing, and when Miss Fieldew decided it was time to get ready to go down to the co-op for a few things, she had made David tidy away all the trinkets he had been playing with and return them to where they belonged. He had been reluctant to leave even when she had begun loosening the ribbons of her blouse in preparation for a brief ablution at the sink and had tried to linger. He had a precocious curiosity to see what Miss Fieldew was going to do that involved starting to undress in the middle of the day.

"I'm only going to have a wash," she told him. "Off you go there's a good boy."

"Aunty Ame say's I can stay," he protested.

"I know, but it's time for you to go. I've got to get ready." The kettle began to boil and she turned to the sink, poured the water into the bowl and cooled it from the tap. Then she put the kettle back onto the gas ring and turned to usher David outside but he had gone. She gave a little shake of her head. He was like quicksilver she thought to herself. One minute arguing to be allowed to stay, the next minute off to play somewhere else...

She filled up with guilt. If only she had seen him safely back next door instead of just shooing him away. And she never ever checked to see that the backyard gates were properly shut. Oh, if he's gone and wandered up to the canal. The thought gave her distress. Years ago she had seen a drowned pageboy from the Star Hotel dragged from the River Severn. He had still been wearing the short crimson tunic with the close row of buttons up the front and trousers with a gold stripe up the leg that was the popular uniform of hotel staff in those days. There must have been a pillbox hat set at a jaunty angle too, she mused inconsequentially, but that was missing and was never found. She had been crossing Worcester Bridge from Cripplegate into the city when they dragged him onto the towpath below the hop warehouse. Peering over the bridge parapet she had seen the waterlogged figure hauled on shore and the sudden recoil of the circle of curious bystanders as he was landed. A whiff of decomposition had risen on the wind. No-one knew how long he had been in the river but the hotel had posted him missing over a week before. The body was so bloated that the tunic was stretched to bursting, straining at the buttons. They had to resort to cutting it off him, the buttons were so tight and then the body, freed of constraint expanded further like a balloon. Oh! Miss Fieldew's head reeled with the recollection. David! She couldn't bear to think of it but now the resurrected image refused to go away. Miss Fieldew turned to Rose and Amy ashen faced as they came out of the box. "Help me home." She leaned on Amy's arm and Rose took Miss Fieldew's bag of shopping. "Oh dear. Oh dear..." she wailed.

They took her to the door and saw her safely inside.

"Let me get you a cup of tea," Rose offered.

"Oh yes," Miss Fieldew said tremulously. "Do. I think we could all do with one."

Amy sat Miss Fieldew in her armchair under the window and Rose called from the kitchen, "Where d'you keep the tea caddy?"

"In the pantry. Next to the bread bin. Will you go and show her Amy?" Her voice was weak with anxiety.

"I'll just make this then I'll have to get back next door. The police'll be coming."

"I'll stay with you for a bit if you likes," Rose offered and Miss Fieldew smiled faintly. She wanted to be left alone but it was too much effort to argue.

Amy made the tea and brought in on a tray. A long chenille cloth covered the table. "It'll be alright on here won't it?" she asked, conscious of the antiquity of Miss Fieldew's possessions.

Miss Fieldew nodded and made a small gesture of assent. Rose pulled a dining chair forward to the table. "I'll pour it. Just let it mash a minute." she said. "You stopping for one Ame? You could do with one."

"It's just if the police comes," Amy replied anxiously.

Rose sat down and her feet came in contact with a cushion or something beneath the table. Like Amy, Rose didn't want to spoil any of Miss Fieldew's things and she bent to move it to one side. As she lifted the tablecloth to reach beneath she saw a movement and recoiled with a cry and jumped up from her chair.

"What is it? What's the matter?" Amy and Miss Fieldew cried simultaneously. They were so overwrought and on edge that Rose's sudden reaction made them nervous. Rose's hand was to her mouth and she was standing looking down at the table.

"There's something under there! I felt it move!" She shuddered with the recollection and as they watched, to their dismay the fringe of the tablecloth began to sway and lift. David crawled out rubbing his eyes. He stopped, crouching on the floor with his mouth open in surprise at the sight of his aunts and Miss Fieldew staring down at him with looks of fearful expectancy.

The policeman was very good about it. He lectured David about going straight home and always telling people where he was. And then he told Amy and Rose that he understood how these things happen with young children falling asleep in the most unexpected places. David could not understand why there was so much fuss. He had stolen back into Miss Fieldew's parlour whilst her back was turned at the sink because he didn't want to go home. He wanted to stay and play a bit longer. So he had crawled underneath the table, hidden from sight by the long tablecloth, curled up into a little ball so that she wouldn't see him and gone to sleep. And Aunty Ame was angry and happy all at the same time and it made him feel so confused that he wanted to cry as well. And then when Uncle Al came home from work Aunty Ame had to tell him all about it too.

That night the temperature dropped and frost appeared on the ground, a biting frost that coated the sodden leaves on the playing field with a brittle shell of ice crystals. The sky was clear and cold and the rooftops of the empty school buildings gleamed in the reflection of the pale moonlight. Down in the boilerhouse David and Amy, standing discreetly in the corner but far enough from the wall to avoid getting coal dust on their clothes observed as Albert checked the water glasses. They were grateful for the warmth that radiated from the fireboxes of the great boilers. There was a reassuring cosiness about the warmth down here; it was far better than standing in the cold yard outside, huddled together in the gateway.

"Stand clear a bit," Albert ordered. Amy shuffled away to one side as Albert reached for a shovel hanging from the wall above the mountain of coke and then unlatched one of the boiler firedoors and swung it open. A blast of heat roared at them and made them blink as it momentarily seared their eyes. Suddenly David understood what made the clanging that he heard night after night in the darkness with Aunty Ame. Albert thrust the shovel into the base of the coke, grating it along the floor and then swung it into the flaring mouth of the furnace, clanging it onto the rim so that the coke shot onto the firebed inside. The noise seemed immense to David, as though it would echo out through the school grounds and wake everyone in the street beyond. Then Albert added a greater, more violent sound as he pushed the furnace door shut, clanging it home with the shovel before repeating it again with the other furnace. When the job was over he watched Amy and David up the cellar steps and when Amy called from the top, "We'm alright now." Albert closed the boilerhouse door below and switched off the light to join them. But tonight, instead of turning to the right and retracing their steps back along the drive to the school gate and the safety of the road beyond they turned left into the deeper blackness of the quad and the looming ivy covered buildings standing all around the softly gleaming lawn. Amy whispered to David and it seemed strange to him that she should be whispering out here in the vast darkness when just a moment ago there had been so much violent noise in the confines of the cellar. "We've got a surprise for you."

David didn't reply. He could not understand what she meant for the night wasn't following its usual pattern and he was unsure what was going to happen only, he was with Aunty Ame and Uncle Al so it must be alright.

"They've gone away now for the holidays," Albert was saying in answer to Amy's repeated query. "They were disappointed to miss him. Still, couldn't be helped I suppose," he added grudgingly. "Of course it's alright. I told you. There's nobody here only us."

The words echoed in David's mind. 'There's nobody here'. And instead of giving comfort it increased his unease. Nobody here! Only the three of them alone in the vast darkness. And meanwhile unseen things lay in the secret corners of the high buildings all around, watching them from the shadows. Unbidden, a vague recollection arose in his mind, a half heard conversation, Aunty Ame telling somebody about Uncle Al, how he wasn't afraid of anything, not even a ghost. And the White Lady he had seen and followed on a dark night across the school grounds until she vanished, passing through an old locked door in the garden wall. And an underground passage linking these old buildings with the Cathedral through which the hooded figures of persecuted monks would silently pass. David shuddered and glanced fearfully about him but there was nothing to be seen. Now they turned towards a dark doorway set deep in a wall and David's fear increased. Albert produced a key and the sound of it turning in the lock betrayed their presence. Amy sensed David's unease. "You'm alright," she said hugging him close against her. "We'll soon be inside then we've got a surprise for you. You'll see."

Again the words 'A surprise.' What did it mean? Was it good? Why was it in the dark, in the secret darkness of the night?

"Is you sure it's in here Al?" Amy ventured. This was the first time she had been inside the school house and even though Albert had assured her that it was empty and he was entrusted with the key she still felt like a trespasser.

"Yes. Come on. I knows where it is." He switched a light on and led the way across the hall with portraits hanging above the panelling towards a door marked with a discreet brass plate; 'Headmasters Study'.

High windows behind the desk let a faint glow of moonlight into

188

the room and despite the coldness of the night a residue of warmth still remained even though the fire, which burned during Pullingers residence, had been cleared. Albert hesitated and declining to switch on the light, relied instead on the glow spilling through the doorway from the hall. He led them across the room and they stepped in carefully as though afraid their intrusion would disturb the residual presence of the headmaster. Albert took them to the fireplace and picked David up so that he could see. "Mr. and Mrs. Pullinger's left you a Christmas box," he whispered. "Look."

David looked, not knowing what he was looking for. He saw his face, pale and wondering reflected in the mirror on the wall, and behind him a big room with an empty window with its curtains open wide to the night. He cried out and wriggled to be put down. He didn't want to be held up here to be seen. He wanted to be at Aunty Ame's side down on the floor again. Aunty Ame reached up her hand beside him and said, "Look. Here you are then. A Christmas box. Look. It's for you." She picked up a parcel which lay on the mantelpiece It was wrapped in coloured paper and neatly tied with string and she placed it in David's hands. "It's a present. For you. From the headmaster."

David took it, not knowing what it was for. It didn't look like a 'box'; slim and rectangular, it was the size that a picture book might be, but when David attempted to tear at the wrapping paper they quickly took it from him saying, "Not now, you're not to open it now. It's for Christmas."

He was nonplussed and couldn't understand why they had brought him to this room and given him something he couldn't have. Then tiredness overcame him and he drooped against Alberts shoulder.

"Come here Al. Give him to me." David felt the softness of Aunty Ame's hair on his face and the smell of her powder lingering on her coat. He snuggled against her and heard faintly the sounds of keys as they carried him from the moonlit room. By the time the last door was locked behind them David was fast asleep and oblivious to darkness and ghosts and shadows.

CHAPTER 22

Copper bottoms and citrus delight

Christmas week was upon them. The cold weather brought sleet and biting frosts. They huddled round their fires and grumbled when they had to leave them but the pub still attracted them at night and it was worth braving the weather with scarves and overcoats for the warmth of the smoky bars and crowded friendships.

Winter made washday a nightmare and Rose and Amy, along with everyone else, struggled to get their washing dry. They hung it in damp spare bedrooms or draped it on makeshift lines across sitting rooms and kitchens, putting up with the inconvenience and finally relying on the ironing to get it dry enough to put away.

But for Amy actually doing the wash wasn't a problem. She had a copper boiler built into the corner of the kitchen between the back door and the sink. There was a round wooden board which, when David was old enough he likened to a viking shield, covering the deep copper bowl. The bowl itself was encased in bricks with a small firegrate underneath. On wash days Amy filled the bowl with water and lit the fire. An hour later the washing was in the boiling water with soap flakes and Amy gave each item a good scrubbing over the sink on the washboard. The water overflowed everywhere but that didn't matter; the floor was tiled so it would mop up later with no harm done, and the water running down the face of the bricks couldn't affect the fire which was set back deep within the bricks and underneath the bowl. It was a messy business but on winter days Amy didn't mind. It made the house steamy and warm.

Albert's betting activities slowed down during the days when frost and hard going made racing impossible but still he made the rounds and commiserated with his clientele. And he took the opportunity to accept orders for Christmas poultry.

"They'm about ready this year." he told Amy. "They'll be too old next year. I'll get some pullet's off Sam over at Ombersley next spring."

So the Christmas slaughter began. One by one the birds were brought up from the henhouse to be tied struggling to the drainpipe. And each semi-circle of blood was washed away with disinfectant into the kitchen grate, ready for the next one to choke and vomit its life away to the accompaniment of distressed flutterings from the coop at the bottom of the garden. Then there was a frenzy of plucking and drawing their entrails to get the birds dressed and ready to be collected in the short run up to Christmas day. The house retained the permanent odour of their innards and newspaper parcels filled with offal burned and sizzled and smoked on the fire. Amy tried to burn the feathers when there were too many for the dustbin to hold and these, some with bloody quills where they had been particularly tough to pluck, flared up the chimney until Rose, who had arrived to choose her Christmas dinner took alarm and said, "You'll have the chimney on fire Ame." But Amy only gave the fire a token stirring with the poker and said, "It's a lovely blaze though ain't it?"

David normally had his bath after tea in an oval galvanized tub in front of the fire in the living room. But on this Monday of Christmas week when the weather was particularly miserable with a raw wind carrying sleet from the north Amy finished the washing and then a thought struck her. There was the copper, still full of hot water. It seemed such a shame to ladle it out and throw it away into the sink. She called David into the kitchen from the living room where he was playing.

"Here David, how'd you like to have a bath in the copper?"

David paddled into the wet kitchen. The walls were running from the condensed steam but it was warm and the water in the boiler was nice and soapy. His eyes lit in expectation.

Amy checked to make sure the fire beneath the copper was out; she didn't want to risk putting him in with the flames licking the bottom of the copper beneath his feet. No, the fire was safe and she plunged her arm up to the elbow into the water. That felt cool enough too.

"Come on then let's try it shall we? It's a shame to waste all these lovely suds."

She undressed him and lifted him onto the copper top. "Come on," she coaxed him, "dip your toes in. See, it ain't too hot is it?"

David did as he was bid and the water felt lovely and warm compared to sitting out where Aunty Ame had perched him for he was already beginning to feel cold despite the steamy warmth lingering in the room. With Amy's help David lowered himself into the copper and the water surged out and flooded across the top, splashing over the edge onto Amy and soaking her completely down the front. She shrieked and David cried out too, startled by Amy's scream and because the bottom of the bowl was unexpectedly hot and was burning his feet. He jumped up. Another wave poured over Amy.

"What's the matter?" she cried in sudden discomfort. Her wet clothes were clinging to her and she was aware they were rapidly getting very cold.

"Hot," David cried, hopping from one foot to the other and trying to scramble out. More water splashed over the side.

Amy looked into the bowl. To her surprise it was almost empty with just two or three inches remaining in the basin, all the rest having been displaced when David lowered himself to crouch inside it. Cold and wet with the kitchen floor awash and her clammy dress clinging about her legs Amy lifted David, naked and shivering onto the kitchen side. She grabbed the towel off the mangle, wrapped him in it and carried him through into the living room.

"Here." She drew a chair up close to the fire. "You sit here for a minute nice and warm while I goes and gets out of these wet things. Then we'll get you nice and dry and warm again."

The back door opened and Rose walked in and stopped, on the point of asking if her sister was planning to go up town for anything. She looked aghast at the water running across the floor.

"Gawd Ame! What's you been up to?" Rose cried. "Is you alright? Where are you?"

She heard Amy's muffled reply and paddled gingerly across the kitchen. Amy was standing at the open door at the foot of the stairs, dripping water onto the carpet. She appeared to be completely wet from head to foot. David sat shivering in a towel in front of the fire. Rose stopped dumbstruck.

"I'm just going to get out of these wet things," Amy muttered, and dashed upstairs, her clothes flapping uncomfortably about her legs. 'Shan't do that again,' she vowed to herself. She called down to Rose, "His clothes is airing on the fireplace." But Rose was already towelling David dry and reaching for his vest.

Amy looked with irritation at the pile of wet clothing on the bedroom floor. 'More washing!' And just when she thought she was on top of it and ready for Christmas. Well, it would have to be done! She couldn't leave them wet until next week, they'd go mildewy and smelly. Besides, there were things she wanted to wear. Perhaps she could get away with washing them in the sink; save having to light the copper again. She felt such a fool.

Rose called up from below. "There's somebody a'knocking at your front door Ame. I'll go and see who it is shall I?"

"I'll be down in a minute." Amy gathered up the bundle of clothing and carried it down to the kitchen. David was dressed and had resumed his game by the hearth. "Is you alright now?" David nodded. "Well Aunty Ame was daft trying that wasn't she. We'll have a proper bath in front of the fire next time eh?"

192

Rose came through from the front room carrying a big square parcel wrapped in brown paper with double bindings of string and bright red patches of sealing wax on the knots where the string criss-crossed.

"Postman!" she said, placing it with some relief on the centre of the table. "He brought you this. It ain't half a weight."

"Whatever is it?"

"Open it and find out," Rose replied laconically.

"Who's it from?" Amy checked the label. It was addressed to her but beyond the address it was blackened with official looking imprints stamped all over it. "Can't make it out." The postage stamps bore the King's head but the franking was unclear.

"Well ain't you going to open it then!"

Amy fetched the scissors and cut the string carefully from the knots of sealing wax, rolled it into little balls and placed it on the sideboard to be put away later. She peered again at the writing.

"Come on Ame!" Rose was in an agony of curiosity to see what was in it. "Oh come here. Let's get it undone."

"No hang on, don't tear it." The paper was also completely sealed down with heavy brown tape. There was nowhere open for them to get at.

"You'll have to cut it to get the paper undone," Rose cried.

Amy inserted the point of the scissors and began to cut it carefully along the top edge of the parcel. Rose was in an anxiety of impatience. "Come on Ame. You takes all day."

Amy placed the paper to one side to be folded up later and they looked in dismay at a brown wooden box a foot square and nine inches deep with a plywood lid securely nailed all around the top.

"Whatever is it?" Rose demanded.

"Dunno," Amy replied, perplexed. "Has your Bob got a screwdriver or something to get these nails out with?"

"He'll not be back for ages," Rose replied. "It's not something your Al's sent for is it?"

"No," Amy mused.

"Ain't you got anything in your bogey hole?"

"All his tools is over at the grammar school."

"Here, let's have a look at that paper. See if we can work out where it's from."

Rose pulled the brown wrapping paper across and straightened it out. They peered again at the writing and the fuzzy black ink rubber stampings. "Pity it's got these marks all over it."

"Here, what's that say?" Amy held the paper at an angle to catch the light. "Here Rose, is that... RAF... or what?" She pointed at indistinct letters framed inside a heavy black outline.

"Could be," Rose agreed carefully. Suddenly recognition hit them both.

"Oh God!" Amy cried. "It's from our Billy."

"'S'have a look!" Rose grabbed the paper from Amy. "It is look. Don't that say Gibralter or something? If it ain't it's something very like it!"

"Oh my God whatever can it be?" Amy picked up the box and began turning it about.

"Careful Ame," Rose pleaded. "It might be something fragile. You don't want to break it."

With a cry of impatience Amy tried the point of the scissors between the lid and the rim.

"Steady Ame, don't cut yourself!"

With careful prising a tiny gap began to open up.

"Careful you don't break your scissors Ame. Here, let me have a go for a bit."

Amy stood aside for Rose to carry on the attempt. "Gawd we'll be here all day."

Gradually the lid began to lift but it was still held over the box by the row of nails all around the rim.

"Whatever's in it they certainly didn't want it getting out."

Rose paused and they peered beneath the lid to see what was inside but could see nothing.

"Ain't you got no pliers?" Rose tossed her head in exasperation. "You ain't got nothing has you!"

Amy inserted the scissors again. Suddenly she had the first nail free and the lid began to come away with relative ease. "Mind these nails. They'm sharp." Amy admonished David whose interest was aroused and was now standing looking over the edge of the table and reaching out.

Now that the lid was off they were faced with a membrane of greaseproof paper securely pinned across the top.

"He's packed this up well ain't he?" Rose chivvied Amy along. "Come on Ame. Let's see what's inside."

Amy pierced the membrane and tore it to one side. There was an envelope lying on top of curls of wood wool packing.

Peering across the table top, David watched his aunts' excitement with interest. Perhaps this was the 'box' they had been talking to him about. Whatever it was, he had never seen his aunties quite like this. He heard them say, "It's from your daddy look. I wonder what's in it?"

"Here Ame, get him a chair so's he can see."

"Daddy!!" David's eyes opened as wide as his mouth and he began to jump up and down, as excited as Amy and Rose.

Amy lifted him onto the chair and began pulling the wood shavings out with cries of joy. "Oh Rose look!" and her shouts were echoed by Rose and caught by David who, leaning forward on the table began dancing on the chair yelling "Daddy, daddy, daddy."

Amy began emptying the contents of the box.

"Oranges!" she exclaimed placing them carefully on the table. More packing was removed. "Look, there's bananas." she cried. "And what's this?"

"Ain't seen one of them before," Rose declared. "Funny looking orange." She examined the pomegranate briefly then turned her attention back to the other things Amy was pulling from the packing. The table was becoming a litter of wood shavings and fruit. Two slim packs emerged. "What's them Ame? They ain't..." Rose reached out in disbelief as Amy opened one of the packs and carefully drew out a pair of silk stockings. "Oh Gawd." She caught her breath, unable to speak and stood momentarily silenced in a turmoil of feelings, confronted by the luxury, the sheer indulgence the box contained.

"There's something here for our David too." Amy's voice was quiet. Now the excitement was subdued, overcome by a great welling of gratitude. "What d'you think Rose? Shall we give it him now or d'you think he ought to wait?"

Rose peered inside. "Oh let him have it now. Go on."

Amy lifted the aeroplane, a toy bomber from the box and presented it to David whose eyes grew even wider. He scrambled from the chair with it and began to taxi it across the hearthrug, zooming it around and landing it again.

All the wood shavings were out and they looked carefully inside. Now the box was empty and they began to take stock again of the fruit and gifts that lay upon the table.

"What's the letter say Ame?"

"Oh!" Amy exclaimed. "I'd forgot about that." She rummaged in the debris that littered the table and found it. The envelope simply said 'Aunty Ame'

"Ain't you going to open it? Gawd Ame, you ain't half slow." Rose peered over Amy's shoulder to read as Amy unfolded it.

'Dear Aunty Ame and Uncle Al,

I hope this reaches you safe. You'd be surprised how many things you can get here that you can't get back home. And the weather's a lot better too. Here's a few things for Christmas. I thought you might like the fruit. The oranges grow on trees out here and you can just reach out and pick them.'

A cry of wonderment rose from both women. "Imagine that Ame. Just picking oranges off the trees whenever you feels like it." Rose

195

conjured up images in her mind of the films they had seen. Ronald Colman; exotic locations with palm trees, lives free from anxiety. Did such places really exist? Did people really live like that? Only if you were a film star! Outside in the yard the mean grey drizzle was turning to sleet. She turned her attention back to the letter.

'I managed to get hold of a couple of pairs of silk stockings so there is a pair for you and a pair for Aunty Rose. I hope they are O.K.'

"Here you are Rose." Amy picked up the unopened packet and handed it to Rose. "They'm yours."

"Is you sure?"

"Course I am." Amy brandished the letter. "Says so here. Come on, don't be daft."

"Oh ain't he good." Rose took the stockings and put them safely in her apron pocket. "Here come on, what else does he say?"

'I hope David is alright and being a good boy. There is a little present inside for him as well. Give him a big hug and a kiss for me and tell him I am thinking about him. I've enclosed a photograph of the squadron.'

Rose gave a cry of anxiety. "Where? Where is it?"

Amy examined the envelope. Inside were two Christmas cards with the photograph between them. 'See if you can pick me out. Anyway I've got to go. I'm on duty in half an hour and I want to get this all wrapped up safe. Hope it reaches you in time. Remember me to Aunty Rose and Uncle Bob.

Wishing you a Merry Christmas,
Bill'

"Lovely card ain't it," Rose said admiringly. They were both the same, a small grey card with a borderline in maroon surrounding the RAF eagle and inside a simple message, 'Merry Christmas. RAF Gibraltar.' And Bill's signature.

"We'd better divide all this up." Amy began sharing out the fruit on the table.

"Them looks like apricots. And what's this?" Rose picked up the large green fruit. "Looks like a melon. You'll never eat all that Ame."

"We'm going to share it all up anyway," Amy replied.

They divided everything between them; the oranges, a couple of banana's each, apricots, even grapes.

"He did well to get that lot here safe didn't he! Gawd, we'm going to have a fine Christmas."

On Christmas Eve there was a party at The Star Hotel. The drink flowed and they sang carols and admired the fairy up on top of the tree in the hotel lobby. David had never heard such a cacophony of noise but

196

Aunty Ame and Aunty Rose kept him close by them and showed him off to their friends together with the squadron photograph of Bill in Gibraltar. "There he is look," they pointed to a smiling figure standing in line on the wings of a Lancaster bomber above other rows of airmen posed in ranks beneath. They had found Bill with the aid of a magnifying glass, a small face among so many others and marked him with a cross. "That's his daddy." They tousled David's head amidst the ahs of approval. "We'm looking after him for the duration."

Before the party broke up there was more singing, a mixture of carols and popular sentimental songs spiced with unsteady kisses and beery promises that, 'You'll be alright little'un. Salt of the earth,' and 'You couldn't do better than you are with Al... Albert... pardon!' He was lifted high to 'see the pretty fairy on the tree.'

"And," David was accosted by a florid man pushing forward with a brightly made up, determined woman on his arm. "How d'you think she got up there then? Who put her up there?" David was too tired and bemused to answer. He looked around at the sea of well wishing faces around him. "Ask him how she keeps up? Eh," the man continued. A knowing grin at the woman accompanied this suggestion together with her laughter. "I wish I was where the top of that tree is. Eh... Maureen." He pulled the woman close. "Come here," and she rubbed herself against him. "You could tell us how that fairy keeps up that tree. You know. Don't you," he leered at her.

"Shut up you dirty beggar," Bob intervened. "Leave the kid alone. He's too young for you and your mucky jokes." The crowd eddied round, edging the man and his woman away as the voice persisted, "Aye, but ask him how she does. Just ask him. He's got to... find out someti..." But the crowd closed about them and the voice was drowned in more singing, and a final hearty rendition of 'Silent Night'.

Christmas morning was no different to any other except in one respect. David was woken by both Amy and Albert which was unusual. And it was earlier than on other days.

David rubbed his eyes sleepily as Albert drew the curtains. A cold daylight filled the room and Amy shivered. "Fetch us my coat Al." She pulled the bedcovers up around David. "Come on. Let's keep you nice and warm." Then she slipped her coat round her shoulders and pulled it close about her. "Ooh that's better ain't it. Now, come on, let's see what Father Christmas has brought you."

Father Christmas! It didn't mean anything to David. They kept talking about Father Christmas and something called Santa but it was a mystery.

"Here he is look." Uncle Albert was pointing to something hanging from the corner of the cot. David vaguely remembered what it was. It was from last night. They had taken an old stocking of Aunty Ame's but he had been so tired and sleepy he couldn't remember what they said it was for. Only now it was a funny shape with corners protruding from it at funny angles all down its length. Uncle Albert unhooked it from the rail and lifted it inside. "Here you is David. See! It's full of presents. All for you." David stared at it motionless and didn't know what was expected of him. Aunty Ame reached inside it and drew forth a brightly wrapped parcel, leaving it protruding from the stocking's mouth. "There you is. Pull it out and open it." With a bit of help from his Aunty and Uncle, David began to see the point, and soon he was reaching in and pulling each gift out, ripping the paper off and throwing it about. In no time the cot was littered with little presents; a tin car, Bill's aeroplane which they had re-wrapped, some coins stuck to a length of sticky tape, an orange, books. They seemed more excited about it than David was and it was their excitement that animated him, more than the presents. "Here look. I think these is what Uncle Bob's made for you." A series of small parcels revealed a range of toy animals, each one cut and painted in the shape of a giraffe; rhinoceros; zebra; elephant; with legs that moved to and fro so they could be made to walk. "Ain't that nice of him. To make you all these animals then. If you asks him nicely perhaps he'll make you a zoo."

Now they were approaching their own piece de resistance. "Is that everything?" They held up the stocking and it was amazing that such a slender, flimsy garment could have held the amount of gifts that littered the cot. But, satisfied that it was empty they said, "Come and see what we've got you then." Lifting David from the cot, under some protest, for having just been given his toys he was quite content to sit there oblivious to the chill in the room and play with them, they guided him across the bedroom to the door of the boxroom in the corner. "There," they said, "open the door and see what's inside."

A spasm of apprehension gripped him. "Go on, open it," they urged. David hesitated. There might be something ready to seize him. He hung back. "Go on David. See what's inside." But the more they coaxed, the more reluctant he became. What had been a vague fear began to become a reality. Albert and Amy felt their own pleasure diminish. "Go on Albert," Amy said, sensing David's fear. "You open it and let's see what's inside."

Albert opened the door and cautiously David peered within. It was filled with accumulated bric-a-brac, suitcases, parcels, an old chair. "There! Go on David." But the child could not recognise anything. Albert reached over him and retrieved a parcel, oddly shaped with protruberances wrapped in bright paper. He placed it in front of David and they stood back to watch him. "Open it. It's yours."

He hesitated. They seemed very pleased with it and something told him they didn't want him to spoil it so he hesitated, not tearing the paper as he had just been doing in his cot. Amy reached over and helped him by tearing at a corner. "Here. Like this look." David took the corner she had torn and pulled it. They beamed their approval and he tore it all away. Then more and more until he could see the tricycle. It was bigger than all the rest! With bright red wheels and a seat all red as well. Amy lifted him on it while Albert beamed at David's obvious delight. "Put your feet on it then. Like this look." She placed his feet on the pedals and gave it a little push; the pedals went round and David's feet fell off. But that didn't matter; he could push along with his feet on the floor, gingerly at first, then with more confidence all around the room with Albert and Amy looking on with delight.

Bob and Rose came down to share Christmas dinner with them and afterwards they sat around and dozed. The drinks they'd had across at 'The Wash' with the dinner on top made them drowsy. "That was a nice bird," Rose commented with lazy satisfaction over the washing up. "Hope ours is as good. We'm saving it to have at New Year. It'll be alright won't it."

Then Albert fetched a bottle of brandy out and he and Bob had a glass or two over the rest of the afternoon. Aunty Rose had David on her knee and looked at his presents. "Tell me a story," he begged her, seeking some stimulation whilst all around their eyelids drooped. He pressed his new book on her. "'Bob the Dog'. Where's you got this from then?" she asked.

"It's what Pullinger got him. That was nice of 'em wasn't it. Another drop of port Rose?"

Rose reached for her glass and drained it. "Ta. Not a lot! That's it." She replaced the refill daintily on the hearth. "Now," she said to David, "you tell me what this story's all about."

In the evening some of the neighbours came round. Bob pitched in with Albert to provide an additional crate of ale and David and the neighbours children admired each others presents and played under the table, getting under everybody's feet but for once the adults were tolerant and didn't seem to mind. As the night got later and the children grew more exhausted and the games began to pall there were tantrums and imagined slights, and crying followed by consolations and cajoling. Eventually the evening began to come to an end. "Come on David, it's time to get your 'jama's on."

"But they're not going to bed," he protested.

"They will be soon. They're going to go home to go to bed as well. Come on, say 'night night' and give everybody a kiss."

They called goodnight to him and waved and David raised a reluctant arm and waved back. Despite his protests he was asleep by the time Amy had carried him to the top of the clanking stairs.

CHAPTER 23

'We'll build a sweet little nest...'

Winter gave way to spring and the hedgerows began to display new buds, just the faintest haze of green on the bare brown branches. The nights were drawing out and there was warmth in the sun. In the Ardennes the German counter-offensive had failed and Allied troops were making steady progress in the liberation of mainland Europe. It was the beginning of a bright new year.

For Amy and Rose it was time to resume their regular fortnightly pilgrimages to the cemetery to tend the family graves. Armed with a trowel and shears and flowers from the shop opposite the cemetery gates they cut back the grass around 'our dad's' and 'mam's' and took special care over the grave of 'our Nell', their sister who had died of consumption within a year of her marriage. They removed the debris from the urns and washed them out and arranged fresh cut flowers in their place. It wasn't a sombre duty. There was a cheerful bonhomie between Amy and Rose as they chattered and preserved their memories. And then, the obligation fulfilled to their satisfaction, home again across the white bridge and along the canal towpath to a welcome cup of tea.

Once a month on Sundays Bob and Rose went for tea with Bob's mother. She lived in the country with Molly, Bob's older sister, a gaunt spinster with wisps of beard and round bottle lensed glasses. Now that winter was over they decided to take David with them for a visit. He was dressed up specially for his first visit and then they walked into town to catch the Midland Red to Malvern. David found it very exciting to be going out on a bus ride.

"You'll like it there," Aunty Rose told him. "Uncle Bob's mother is a very old lady. She has a lovely big garden with lots of fruit in summer and if you'm a very good boy you'll be able to come again and pick it."

They crossed Powick Bridge and the Malvern Hills suddenly seemed to rise ahead of them. At the outskirts of the town they alighted, crossed the road and turned into a country lane.

"There it is. We'm nearly there, look." A brick cottage, whitewashed, with a roof of heavy thatch and a wooden fence stood with a path of red bricks leading from the gate to the dark brown weathered door. Inside it was small with a mismatch of furniture

201

arranged wherever space would allow. Embroidered antimacassers covered the top of the armchairs and there were assorted brasses and porcelain ornaments on the window sills and on the mantelpiece over the bright fire. The faint smell of camphor and mothballs hung in the air as they entered and then it was gone, overtaken by the aroma of burning applewood.

"Is this him then?" The greeting was not unwelcoming but it carried a critical edge. David felt that he was undergoing some form of inspection. He stood very still, hung onto Aunty Rose's hand and averted his eyes to avoid challenging the old lady's stare. She was very old with gaps between her long, crooked teeth and her face was brown and deeply wrinkled, giving her a gnarled appearance which David found repellent. But despite her abrupt manner she had a kind disposition. David wanted to look at her and found himself staring in fascination from a distance, but whenever she looked across at him he immediately looked away. Molly came in from the kitchen with a bowl of beetroot.

"Hello," she lisped at him. "How is ya?"

Although affecting jollity and friendship towards David, he found her unapproachable too. "Alright thank you," he mumbled.

The table was laid for tea and after pleasantries and catching up with gossip they set too and reorganised the places at the table whilst Bob fetched a stool in from the tiny kitchen at the back for David to sit on. Tea was formal and the conversation centred around mutual acquaintances and events of which David had no knowledge. David felt he was expected to eat little so he said, "No thank you," when they pressed him to have more, and sat fidgeting until the formality of tea was over. After tea Uncle Bob took him outside to see the garden. It extended an inordinate length at the back of the cottage and its rows of fruit bushes and carefully prepared beds was entirely given over to produce. It was Molly's province now that Bob's mother was too old to take an active part in it.

Then Bob and Rose took David a short walk across the adjacent meadow. They stood briefly and lifted David onto the stile by the railway crossing in the cool of the spring evening and as the local train passed the driver gave them a wave. Then they began to shiver in the breeze and returned to the warmth of the cottage.

After further brief conversation, accompanied by a cup of tea during which David grew restless, Molly walked back with them along the lane to the bus stop. They left the hills in shadow with the faint glow of the cold sunset beyond, and crossed Worcester Bridge into the city in time to catch up with Amy and Albert for a last couple of drinks.

David awoke to find an air of excitement in the house and brief, half heard conversations that he couldn't understand. It was the excitement that had been building over the past week. Rose came down to Amy's half a dozen times in the course of the morning and then, unexpectedly Albert was home at dinner time earlier than usual. Then Bob arrived home briefly too and all four of them had a hurried conversation in the same tone of high excitement that had characterised the morning, before Bob and Albert swung onto their 'bikes and pedalled off to work again.

David found his aunties looking at him in an odd sort of way, in a mixture of pity and extreme benevolence. He couldn't understand that either. It unsettled him so he went off to see Miss Fieldew and even she was excited in her small fluttery way. But nothing happened for the rest of the afternoon. He had his favourite tea of bread and lemon curd and then after washing up Aunty Ame said she was going to get ready and vanished into the kitchen for a wash.

"Put us the kettle back on will you," Albert called. Then David watched with his usual fascination as Albert brought his mug of piping hot water and razor onto the mantelpiece, draped a towel round his neck in front of the mirror, lathered up and attacked the days growth with rasping strokes of the razor. Then he stuck little pieces of newspaper over the cuts, changed his collar and tie, and David watched with interest as the newspaper turned red.

Uncle Bob walked in and said, "How long's you going to be?" He was wearing his best suit.

"Her's upstairs; just getting ready."

"Ah. Won't be long then. Rose's just finishing her makeup."

"We'll come up when we'm ready," Albert said and Bob left.

Amy came back downstairs and David thought he had never seen her look so nice in her best dress and discreet lipstick. "Now let's have a look at you," she said. She fetched the flannel from the kitchen and wiped his face while David squirmed and wriggled. "Come on. Let's put this on." She changed him into a clean jersey and smoothed his clothes and looked at him critically. "You'll do," she said and then, "D'you think I'll need my big coat Al? What's it like out?"

"Not too bad," he replied. "Anyway it'll be warm on Arthur's. You know how warm it used to get. And there's bound to be a crowd tonight."

"I'll take it anyway. You never know what it'll be like coming home."

"Come on then, let's go if you'm ready. It's nearly half past seven now. They'll not be able to wait for us!"

This wasn't like their usual going out. David could sense that it was something special, something that had been building up with increasing

203

expectation. They collected Bob and Rose and stepped out along the street with David's hands in Amy and Rose's as they swung him along. A loud bang startled him but they didn't seem to mind, only laughed as though it was expected. Then there came another accompanied by a flash in the sky which startled him again. "It's alright," they said, "it's only fireworks."

They passed the usual pubs and headed down Castle Street towards Pitchcroft and the river. Nearing the railway bridge high above the Severn, the one that David and Bill had crossed all those months before, the road became more crowded and noisy with people milling about and calling, laughing at one another as they hurried along towards the embankment.

Albert took the lead. "Come on. Never mind the queues." He began to weave his way through the crowd, ignoring the remonstrances and reluctance of people to make way for him.

"Which 'un's we on?" Rose asked.

"Severn Belle," Amy replied.

To their joy the promenade was brightly lit for the first time in years, the way it used to be with lights dancing on the surface of the river, just as they remembered it in the days before the war had plunged them into darkness. Now the crowds became more animated and dense as they neared the landing stages where the Severn Belle and Duchess Doreen were moored. A straggling line, three or four deep lined the railings, and around the ticket kiosks which had opened at the head of the gangways on the quay, crowds were milling, with those in front jealously guarding their places from those jostling in from behind. But the protests were, in the main, good humoured and people were laughing and calling to friends, "We're here, over here. Come on, we've saved you a place." Everywhere David looked there were flags; sticking out on poles from windows in the Old Rectifying House, draping the lamp posts, and the people themselves waving them and cheering.

"Oy where d'you think you'm going then?" The protest came from a group near the head of a gangway running down from the quay to the floating pontoons. Albert ignored the protest as he craned to see across to the Severn Belle and into her wheelhouse. There were already crowds filing on board but he could see no sign of his brother. Down on the pontoon a crewman with a sweater and peaked cap was inspecting tickets as the passengers filed down before motioning them to board.

"Hang on a bit Al," Amy called. She bent to pick David up but Bob forestalled her.

"Here; I've got him." He hoisted David into his arms. "There," he said, "you'm better up here anyway ain't you. Now you can see where we'm going. See that big ship down there?" He held David higher so that he could see above the crowd. "We'm going for a sail. That'll be nice won't it."

"Is he there?" Amy said anxiously with a glance at the growing throng. "We ain't got a ticket and it'll have gone without us by the time we gets one."

"Don't worry," Albert replied. "He'll get us on." He craned again. "Where's Bob and Rose? Is they keeping up with us?"

"We'm here!" Rose cried laughing. "We'm all here! Ain't we eh? Go on Bob, you go on ahead o' me."

Albert gave a sudden start, craned again and called out above the noise, "Arthur! Arthur!" He waved, tried a whistle which was drowned in the crowds hubbub, and called again. Heads turned and the crowd, sensing that he was trying to jump ahead, closed around him but Albert, undaunted called and waved again. "Arthur! We'm here."

The figure in the wheelhouse turned, stared and searched the sea of faces lining the promenade and lit up with recognition of his brother. 'Come on down' he mouthed in exaggerated pantomime. Then he left the wheelhouse and crossed the gangplank to the crewman admitting the passengers on the pontoon. He pointed up to Albert and the rest of the family trying to make their way to the head of the gangway through the reluctant crowd which now began catcalling them. But at last they were safely down and heard Arthur say as they approached the boat, "It's my brother and his family. They're alright."

Albert briefly greeted Arthur and Bob and Rose thanked him, then Arthur said, "You'd better get down into the saloon, it's filling up and you'll finish up here on deck if you're not careful. It'll be a bit cool when we gets out on the river."

"Bet you'm glad to be afloat again?" Bob said.

"Been a long time," Arthur replied. "Been much longer I'd have had to sell it. You can't keep a boat like this idle. Never mind." He looked around him at the passengers already on board. Then he turned back to the man at the gangway. "How many more d'you think?"

"We'm nearly there," the man replied.

"Better get on board then."

They followed Arthur up the gangplank and David became conscious of the gentle motion of the boat against the jetty as Bob put him onto the deck and took his hand. "Now you keep close to me and your Aunty Ame and Aunty Rose. We don't want you falling overboard do we?"

"Uncle Arthur's the captain," Amy said proudly. David watched Arthur proceed along the crowded deck and shortly afterwards the back of his head appeared in the window of the wheelhouse above them.

"Come on then." Albert led the way and they descended the

companionway into the saloon below.

It was smoky and crowded and on first entering the noise was almost overwhelming with cheers and calling from one side of the saloon to the other. Drinks were already in full flow and Amy said, "Now you hold tight onto Aunty."

They spotted some friends on the bench against the wood panelled bulkhead and with a bit of miming were invited to 'come and sit down with the kiddy.'

"Thanks Alice," Amy said.

"Here, come on," Alice continued, shuffling from side to side on the bench and addressing the people around her, "Hutch up a bit more. Make room for Rose. There's plenty of room."

"Ta," Rose said gratefully.

"Your Bob and Albert with you?"

"Trying to fight their way through that lot for the drinks." Amy gestured towards the bar and the crowds milling round it.

"What a blessing now the war's over though ain't it it!"

Severn Belle's horn blared out above them and a great shout went out from everyone on the boat, echoed by the crowds on the promenade.

"We're moving!" They felt a shudder as the boat began to move away from the jetty, then the deck swayed as she turned into the current and the drinkers swayed and spilled, made sudden grabs at the walls, the brass pillars and each other; and then they got their sea legs and the carefree mirth resumed once more. In their wake the Duchess Doreen swung out into the channel to join them. With cheers ringing out from both boats, they set off in line ahead, away from the brightly lit shore into the darkness of midstream and the revellers on the quay watched the illuminations reflecting on the water recede upstream beyond the dark, high bridge.

In the saloon of the Severn Belle David was kneeling up to a window where a space had been made for him. The lights from the windows illuminated the water and he was watching the bow wave as it slid by and broke into foam, rippling out into the darkness towards the riverbank. And almost immediately another one followed it. As they turned into the bend behind the grandstand he pressed against the window and looked downstream. Reflected in the rippling water he could see the lights of their companion following behind as Duchess Doreen approached the bend.

"Look!" he cried in excitement, "I can see the other. It's following us!"

Looking on benignly from their seat against the panelling, Amy and Rose smiled at him and sipped delicately at their drinks. On the shore beyond they saw periodic flashes in the city and heard the sound of fireworks above the din. A roar of laughter erupted from a group across the saloon and a man brandishing a cigar and brandy approached them, delivered an unsteady imitation of Churchill to Bob and Albert, staggered, and brandished two fingers to all and sundry. There was another roar of approval and glasses were raised, spilling beer on all and sundry to cries of 'Good old Winnie'. Then a chorus of 'Land of Hope and Glory' began and the hard pressed stewards behind the bar dragged more crates out and began tapping another barrel. And so the two boats made their noisy and triumphal way along the river to the cheers of revellers on the bank.

Much later, when the boats returned, they slipped down the peaceful river on the current to the sound of tranquil lullabies and nostalgic ballads. At the quayside the revellers unsteadily disembarked, swaying on the solid ground and gripping one another in incoherent friendships. The sounds of distant jollity came down to them from the city. It continued through the night and some went off to join in that. But David was asleep in Amy's arms and they prepared to set off for home. From the wheelhouse of the Severn Belle, Arthur gave them a wave and shouted a promise to 'see you soon'. Albert, leaning against the railing to exchange yet another final farewell staggered some yards sideways along the promenade in the effort of focusing on his brother.

"Come on Al. You've had enough for one night!" Amy admonished him and Albert turned and fixed her with a drunken eye. Then he nodded, gave a final dismissive wave at the boats, now lying in darkness on the river, and braced himself stiffly to follow her with Bob, who was equally drunk, in mutual support.

Unsteadily home beneath the stars, softly crooning snatches of a wistful song they felt the weight of war lifting and dreamed of an imagined peace.

"It'll mean no more rationing though won't it." Amy cuddled David to her and gently hummed to him, "We'll build a sweet little nest, somewhere out in the west, and let the rest of the world go by…"

"Shouldn't think so Ame. Not yet anyway," Rose replied. "We ain't licked the Japs yet."

"They won't last long… not now the Germans is beat," Albert added bravely from the darkness behind them. "Now we can turn all our att… attention to them… We'll soon have 'em licked. Won't we Bob? We will… won't we."

But Bob's reply was incoherent.

"Still," said Amy, "it's peace and that's all that matters ain't it!"

They continued along the moonlit streets in companionship, each in thoughtful search of the future.

"You sure you're alright Ame? He ain't too heavy is he?"

"No," Amy replied. She gave David a tiny lift in her arms and the sleeping child wound his arms closer about her and snuggled into Amy's shoulder.

"I'll have him a bit if you gets tired." Rose looked sidelong at Amy and gave her sister a wistful glance.

"No he's alright." Amy nuzzled her cheek against the sleeping head. "You'm alright aint'cha."

Rose paused and turned to look back along the road. Bob and Albert had fallen some way behind. Having lurched off the pavement they were making unsteady progress along the gutter, trying and failing to remount the kerb onto the pavement again. "Just look at them two! They'll never be up in the morning."

But Amy didn't reply. She was holding David close and quietly singing to herself, "'I'll be your sweetheart, if you will be mine. All my life I'll be your valentine. Bluebells we'll gather, I'll always be true...'" The song tailed off. "Come on Rose. They'll catch us up."

Rose turned and quickened her pace. "'Let him go, let him tarry, let him sink or let him swim. I'm going to marry a better man than him...' What's that other song you were singing Ame?"

"Which 'un d'you mean?"

"On the boat. Just before we got off. You know...'With someone like you, la, la, la, la, la, la.' Forgot the words."

"Wonder if our Billy'll have to go," Amy mused.

"Oh I hope not! He's been lucky so far."

At the entry between their two rows of houses they paused to wait in the silence, in the still night shadows.

"Come on you two," Rose called gently. She turned to Amy. "I know what it was. 'All my life, I'll be your valentine. Bluebells we'll gather, I'll always be true...' What time is it Ame?"

"Dunno," Amy replied. "Must be well after one though."

Rose yawned. "Good night though wasn't it."

"Mmm. Wish them two'd hurry up. Time this little 'un was in his bed."

"And me."

CHAPTER 24

Pork chop ill!

The street party, long planned, was put into effect. Rationing! What did they care for that! The kids must have a party too. Safe in the shadow of the spire of St. Mary's, beneath the blossoming trees, in the schoolyard of St. Mary's school they set up trestle tables covered with sheets and made jellies, sandwiches, tarts and blancmanges for all the local children. The red sandstone walls were draped with an enormous Union Jack and red white and blue rosettes were framed in the windows. Now the tables were set the kids were forbidden to touch the food until they had posed all around it with the proud helpers and mothers beaming in the background to have their photographs taken. It was a glorious sunny end of April day; a novelty for the children and adults alike.

"Smile," the photographer called, and the kids dutifully turned to face him. "Are you ready then?" The mothers and helpers beamed again, there was a barely audible 'click', and the party began…

"Well they made short work of that!" Amy said, looking at the debris of the table as the final bowls of blancmange and custard went the rounds for second helpings and thirds. A relay of women collected the plates for washing and began wiping the creamed and jellied hands of the children. Then there were games in which the adults had to intervene when the older children began racing round out of control and knocking the little ones down. The school piano was brought out for a singsong and passers by entered the schoolyard and joined in and more photographs were taken and then, before anyone had time to think about it, the afternoon was wearing into evening. The tables were cleared away and the schoolyard gradually emptied of all except the last few dedicated helpers. But the party went on into the night in the pubs with the kids running in and out and joining in impromptu games in the pub yards and clustering about doorways and around the streets.

Once the euphoria of victory evaporated life quickly returned to normal but with a retained sense that a weight had been lifted from them. The shortages continued; rationing was just as intense, the queues just as long. But the streets remained festooned with bunting and flags, interspersed with pictures of the King and Queen and Winston Churchill, who had broadcast to the nation, "The war in Europe is at an end."

Amy and Rose planned a picnic in June for David's fourth birthday.

"We'll take him on a bus ride out to Upton and have an afternoon in the country on the meadows down by the Severn. If the weather's alright." Amy and Rose were out shopping.

"What's you getting him Ame?" Rose asked.

"I've seen a," and here Amy leaned close and whispered, aware that David was looking up at them and listening, "red indian's feathered head-dress. What d'you think?"

"He'll like that."

"Will you have him for a minute or two while I goes and has another look at it? It's only down the High Street. I'll see you back at the Home and Colonial then we can pop over to The Reindeer."

"Come on then," Rose said taking David's hand. "You can come and help me with my bit of shopping. See you in about twenty minutes Ame."

"Where's Aunty Ame going?" David asked, turning to look after her.

"She's just got to go and get something," Rose said. "Come on, we goes this way."

"I want to go with Aunty Ame," David protested, tugging at Rose's hand.

"No, come on, this way." Rose set off towards Woolworths. "Tell you what, it's your birthday soon. Let's go and look at the toys shall we."

"When's my birthday?"

"Next month. Let's go and see what you'd like for your birthday."

Rose bought David a small lead aeroplane, for having taken him to see the toys with a promise that it was 'for his birthday, she had to come away with something. It was only a small thing to keep him happy; she knew that what he was really going to get was the railway engine Bob was making for him. For weeks Bob had been collecting different items for his project. An empty dried egg tin for the funnel; a plywood drum that had once contained dye from the tip would be just the right size for the engines boiler. Wheels off a pushchair that no-one wanted. Discarded blocks of wood from the joiner's shop could be shaped into buffers. For Bob was making a railway engine big enough for David to sit in. He was making it in the small back room over the kitchen that he used as a workshop and she knew that he was putting his heart and soul into it. It was already starting to look like the real thing. She couldn't wait to see David's face when they gave it to him...

On board the aircraft carrier HMS Queen, Bill lay in his bunk and prayed for death. The huge ship was caught in a spring gale in the Bay of Biscay and heading westward into the Atlantic, sailing into the storm to try to minimise the beating she was taking. Her escort had dispersed, seeking sea room and all that her lookouts could see was a close horizon and a sea that seemed to be boiling as the wind whipped the tops off the waves that pounded the ship, leaving the surface boiling, streaked with seething foam and spray. This was one of the worst that many of the crew had experienced and seasickness was affecting officers and crew alike. For the squadron confined below decks it was appalling. There was no predictability to the ship's motion. As she climbed each wave 'Queen' seemed to shudder in indecision as the crest passed beneath her before pitching forward to meet the wall of water following, slamming into it with a violence that almost stopped the ship in motion. And she was rolling as well in the most unpredictable manner. Rising, rolling to port or starboard then skewing round again and falling, twisting almost in her endeavour to breast the next wave in the storm. The squadron was in transit from Gibraltar to England for regrouping before posting to the Far East. This was a rude awakening from the lazy winter they had spent on The Rock, remote from the closing stages of the war in Europe. Almost without exception they remained in their bunks and prayed for death.

The smell of vomit which had permeated the quarters for the past thirty six hours was almost commonplace and failed to produce further retching which the first bouts had induced, for the men's stomachs were voided; they had nothing further to give. But the nausea persisted. They couldn't predict the movement as the ship seemed to swirl about them, dropping away beneath them and stopping almost with a jarring that they feared would smash the ships hull and consign them to panic stricken drowning.

Bill tried to close his eyes and sleep through it but the sickness kept sleep at bay. With malicious perversity the thoughts that came into his mind only added to his discomfort. Embroidered memories of binges in the mess back at Shobden; foaming pints, the sea a foaming mass of beer. Oh God!

The V.E. party! That had dissolved into a night of oblivion. God! But they had drunk some stuff! He had managed a pass with Mako and some of the others. Go away! I don't want to think of it! Bill's bunk sank beneath him, he rolled his eyes again, his head ached and his mind swam. There was a little neglected garden with engraved memorials beneath the small unkempt trees. Stillness and silence after the storm of battle. Trafalgar. Forgotten heroes. Dead! And the dying, brought to Gibralter to die of appalling injuries. Buried in neglected peace. Young men like those groaning and calling out around him, drowning, tossed into the heaving sea. The bar in the square above the dockyard. Dervish grinning and shouting and the memory of iced beer and swilling foam. Clattering boots, chattering girls calling for them, their breasts jiggling inside cotton. Freedom and thoughts of touching them, caressing and... But the laughing girls moved on into the distance, seen through the fogging eyes. And Mako and Bill reached for another drink. What is it this time? Something strange and untried but tonight is the night for the fear of death is lifted. The war is over and we drink to our triumph! Gin... Bill staggered and reached for another. Never mind the glass give me the bloody bottle! What's Mako got? He's holding his bottle to the girls mouth and fondling her as she drinks and splutters, laughing, her eyes scanning the bar for others. No recollection of dazzling lights, clambering about the town from bar to seedy bar, falling painlessly down stone flights of steps. Waking slowly, painfully with hurt behind his eyes and a searing pain inside his head. Sleeping fitfully and waking again inside a spinning room. Staggering for water to the sink, barely able to support himself against its rim to slurp water from the tap and falling as a result back into drunkenness. The ship lurched and the nauseating memory faded rapidly from the nauseating present and Bill groaned and prayed for some relief...

Presently he began to stir. His stomach ached and felt bruised, as if he had sustained an unremitting series of heavy punches. And there was sourness inside as though something foul and stagnant was sloshing about in the pit of his bowel. He suddenly longed for air to clear his mind. Down here it was stale. He recalled hearing from somewhere that food was an essential to combating seasickness. Your stomach needed something to work on, they said, otherwise you are condemned to retching on an empty stomach with no way of gaining any relief. Food! He couldn't bear the thought of it. He sank back onto the bunk in despair and listened to the moans of distress from all around. He closed his eyes and his head began to swim again; he opened them and his eyes ached intolerably. Perhaps he could find something bland to fill the aching emptiness.

It took a great effort, but he finally raised himself, paused to allow his balance to establish itself and gingerly lowered his feet onto the deck. He felt as though he ached everywhere from holding himself rigid; he daren't relax his stomach muscles and as the ship lurched and pitched around again he clenched his muscles tighter, staggered and gripped the bunk for support. Oh God! He stood in indecision but, tempting as it seemed to collapse back onto his bunk, now that he was upright he rebelled at the thought of the exertion needed to haul himself up onto it. He took a step and his head reeled. He took another and the deck swayed beneath him. He dared not think of anything, just focus with his eyes screwed painfully, concentrating on getting to the companionway ahead. The ship flung herself against him, bruising his fragile arms but gradually he staggered with more assurance until he began to smell food as he approached the galley. Pausing and gasping, unable to draw the deep draughts of air that he sought Bill wondered if he should turn back. But forward or back, neither way was the right way. Perhaps just a drink of water now that he had come this far. Cold water! He braced himself and continued to falter ahead.

The ship's mess was aptly named. Chairs were strewn in disarray and on the tables there was a litter of cutlery and used plates. A couple of the tables were occupied by crew but Bill's was the only RAF uniform. How Bill wished he could be like those unfeeling souls, oblivious to the elements. They looked up from their plates at his entrance, noted his delicate condition and began to laugh. Bill ignored them and made his way to the servery. The chefs raised the lids and displayed steaming pork chops, cabbage, potatoes – boiled and mashed, potato's roasted, sausages submerged in gravy, onions, steamed sponge, custard. Bill's mouth went dry and he turned his head as the smell of the food rose about him.

"Potatoes. Mashed," he croaked. "And a drop of gravy." He shook his head at the offer of tea. "Just water. I'll just have a drink of water."

He braced himself with his meagre tray, judged the moment and moved quickly and unevenly to a table a discrete distance from the others who were so obviously enjoying eating. He sat down with relief, nursed his head in his hands and stared without enthusiasm at his plate. The sound of suppressed laughter came from across the mess. He ignored it and tentatively took a small amount of potato onto his fork, paused, braced himself and then passed it into his mouth. It was alright. He allowed himself a gentle swallow, paused, and tried another. That was alright too. Bill took a sip of water. His stomach still felt delicate and the water reawoke it. But, he didn't feel sick! He began eating with more confidence. Small amounts of potato punctuated with sips of water. They were right! Whoever had said it knew what they were talking about; the food did help and he began to feel wholesome normality pervade his system. The tension slowly ebbed away and relaxation took its place. He became aware of sounds around him and didn't feel the need to close out the smell of cooking from the servery. Renewed laughter broke out from the table where the crewmen were sitting and now Bill felt composed enough to raise his head and acknowledge them. He looked across with a self depracating smile to see them all looking at him and laughing. Bill gave a little toss of his head and shrugged as he joined in the laughter with them. They kept their eyes on him and Bill dug into the potato, raised a forkful and doffed it with a confident grin. Then as he scanned the faces of the group he saw what was the cause of their laughter. A seaman – he could have been a stoker by his appearance – in a grimy vest and with a patina of oily sweat glowing on his face and arms, was holding centre stage at the head of the table. The rest of them were staring intently at Bill, with alternating glances at the stoker then back to Bill and laughing in expectation. But Bill's eyes were now fixed on the stoker's face and his grin was gone. The stoker was leering at Bill in comic malevolence with two strips of fat from the pork chops dangling glistening from his nose. He shook his head at Bill and the fat jiggled against his lips. Then he poked his tongue through them, licking and sucking at them noisily. Bill wanted to look away but he was transfixed. He put the fork, uneaten, back onto his plate and reached for the water as sweat broke out on his brow.

"Watch this then," one of the sailors called to him and they all turned to the stoker in expectation.

"Go on then." They began to call, "Go on, do it."

The stoker leaned across the table and half rose to his feet. "Are you ready?" he taunted.

Bill felt the water at his lips and continued gazing steadfastly. The stoker gave a snort and the fat rose up inside his nostrils. With finger and thumb he reached and delicately pulled one of the strips out, raised his head with his mouth agape and dropped the strip of fat in, chewed it ostentatiously and swallowed it. His companions roared approval then went quiet as the stoker put his finger and thumb to his nose again, pinched it then released it with a snort and the second strip of fat vanished up into his nostril. Once more the table roared its approval and turned to savour Bill's reaction. But they were too late; Bill was already half way along the companionway, staggering and retching back to his berth.

CHAPTER 25

Re-union

Amy went into David's room and threw back the curtains letting the morning sunlight illuminate the room with the promise of another warm June day. The child stirred and yawned then immediately threw his arms up for Amy to lift him from the cot. She lifted him to the window for the ritual of the train.

"Do you know what today is?" She gave him a delighted cuddle and he yawned again and answered,

"It's my birthday Aunty Ame."

"That's right."

The small engine on the bridge sent a burst of steam shooting into the air and they heard its whistle, two short hoots of impatience and then, after a pause, it slowly rolled forward off the bridge and out of sight.

"Come on then. Let's get you ready then we've got a big surprise for you."

"What's my surprise?"

"You'll see. We've got to get you ready first."

There was an air of excitement about her that filled David with expectation. Aunty Ame was always smiley in the mornings when she came to wake him but today she seemed specially pleased with herself. He had his face washed as usual and, as usual his breakfast was a boiled egg fresh from the hens with his bread cut into soldiers and lovely runny dip. And all the while Aunty Ame was sort of humming to herself as though the humming was running the time along.

"How's your egg? Is it nice then?"

David nodded and Aunty Ame nodded and then she carried on humming with a glance through the window and David noticed it was the third time she had done that since he started breakfast.

"What's you looking for Aunty Ame?"

"Just to see if the bread man's coming yet. He's late this morning. Come on, eat your egg up. Here's another soldier look."

After breakfast Aunty Ame cleared away and put the pots in the sink. "We'll leave them 'till later shall we?" That was different to her usual routine and she hadn't begun to make the hens feed either but

David didn't remark on it and Aunty Ame spread the Daily Express on the table and turned the pages to find Rupert. Then she read him the Rupert story but it was as though her mind was elsewhere this morning. She fetched the scissors and began to cut the pictures out.

"What's my surprise Aunty Ame?"

"You'll see." Her reply was accompanied by another glance at the window. "It won't be a surprise if I tells you will it?" she smiled.

She fetched the exercise book out from the sideboard drawer with the Rupert story in it and they set to with the newspaper clippings and paste. When it was done she said, "Come on, let's read it and see how far we've got shall we?" But barely had she begun when the back door opened and Aunty Rose came through all breathless and excited.

"You'll never guess Ame," she cried with her eye firmly fixed on David.

Amy turned David on her knee so that she could face him. "I don't know Rose. What's happened?" and now she too was smiling at David with a heightened air of expectation. "What d'you think can have happened David?"

"I don't know." David felt a stirring of misgiving. Perhaps he wasn't going to get Aunty Ame's surprise after all.

"Up at our house," Rose continued. "I couldn't believe my eyes when I saw it. There's a great big parachute in our garden."

"What!" Amy cried. "Where's it come from?"

"I don't know." Rose's voice held wonder and disbelief and they both looked at David as though he might be able to provide the answer. "You'd better come and look."

"Oh yes. Let's go and see shall we David." He began to scramble off her knee, bewildered by the sudden excitement of his aunts and the advent of the parachute. Whoever could have put it there?

"Come on then. Off we goes."

They bustled out of the kitchen door and up the path along the backs of the houses. In vain David looked over the small fence into Rose's garden to see the parachute but it wasn't there.

"Perhaps somebody's tidied it away," Aunty Ame offered.

"They must have," Aunty Rose replied. "Anyway come on in here." She opened the back door. "We've got a surprise for you."

"Where is it?" David peered about the kitchen with expectation but everything looked normal. There was nothing different and nothing waiting for him as far as he could see. Aunty Rose paused and opened the door into the living room and Aunty Ame ushered David ahead of her. "Come on then David. It's in here. Your surprise."

Behind the living room door there was someone sitting in Uncle Bob's chair. David saw black polished boots and slate blue trousers. He

216

peered round the door and his gaze wandered up the legs and beyond the blue greatcoat slung over the chair arm. "Who's this then David?" his aunts cried in excitement.

A forage cap, dark wavy hair and arms reaching for him! David's face creased in tears of joy.

"Daddy!"

Rose and Amy stood and watched the joyful reunion as David leaped up onto Bill's knees and threw his arms about him. They smiled down in benevolence and with satisfaction that their trust had been honourably discharged.

Rose gave a small, almost inaudible sigh. "Well, I'll go and put the kettle on. You'll have that cup of tea now won't you Bill?"

Bill emerged from the ecstasy of hugs and childish chatter. "Yes please aunt. I will if you don't mind." His tanned face beamed at her and she thought how much better he looked since the last time she had seen him. Service life seemed to have done him good.

"You'll have one won't you Ame?"

"Yes ta."

Rose went through to the kitchen happily la'ing the tune of Housewives Choice. David's reaction had been spontaneous; they had preserved his relationship with his father whilst giving him their own love and security. But there was another thought in Amy's mind and it dimmed the sparkle in her eyes and froze her smile. She loved the child. He filled a need that she hadn't known existed. He had created a space for himself within their lives, a space that she had not been aware of. Content in her marriage to Albert and with no children of their own, she and Albert had accepted that it was the way of things and ordered their lives accordingly. And so it had been, happily so until David came into her life. It wasn't that they felt he had been foisted on them. But Lilly had asked and Bill's plight was so desperate that they found it in their heart to say yes without reservation. After all, he was only a small child and it was only for the duration. She could not have foreseen, looking at Bill with David on his knee, that she could have grown to love him so. And she watched them, so happy together and she felt as though her heart would break. For with the image came the realisation that, at some indefinable time in the future David would leave to go back home with Bill. And she could not imagine the emptiness in her home that his leaving would create. Bill glanced up at her staring at him and Amy switched life back into her smile.

"How long's you here for Bill?"

"Got to be back today," he replied. "Only got a twentyfour hour pass I'm afraid."

"They don't give you long do they? You'd think you could get

217

more time. I mean with David and all."

"They don't think like that." Bill pushed his forage cap down on David's head and pulled it over one ear at a jaunty angle.

David chortled with glee and called, "Look at me Aunty Ame. I'm an airman."

"Anyway," Bill continued, "we're not forced to be over here for long. It's just for regrouping before we get another posting."

"Oh you're not going away again?" Amy felt a mixture of anxiety and hope. It was irrational. But Bill being here somehow came between her and David, even though it was only a few hour's visit.

"Who's going away?" Rose came in with the teapot. "They're not sending you overseas again is they?"

"War's still on aunt. Might be," and here Bill's bravado was tempered by the careful indoctrination; he lowered his voice involuntarily and gave a slight inclination of his head, as though about to peer around to see who might be listening, which he immediately checked, "Far East. Burma. Who knows." Then he basked in the sensation his careless words produced.

"Oh no! That's right across the other side of the world."

"They won't send you there will they Billy?"

He gave David a tickle which sent him rolling off Bill's knee screaming.

"Can't say," he replied archly.

"Where's your parachute Daddy? Can I see it?"

"Isn't it…" Bill looked for inspiration to his aunts.

"Oh!" Rose cried. She turned to Amy. "Wasn't it in the garden when you came up? That's where he landed."

David looked with concern at all three and his jaw dropped. He didn't want his daddy to get into trouble for losing his parachute.

"No!" Amy exclaimed. "Oh what shall we do if it's gone missing?"

But Bill picked up the story. "I expect it's been collected and folded up ready for repacking so's I can use it next time I get a chance to come and see you." He hugged David to him. "And if it hasn't I can always get another."

"They won't really send you away again though will they?"

Amy watched carefully, measuring how Bill replied to Rose's question. David was scrambling over the arm of Bill's chair and, "Here mind my tea," Bill admonished. "You'll have it all over me if you're not careful." He lifted his arm, raising his cup to safety. David shrank at the unexpected rebuke, as though all his spontenaiety had suddenly evaporated. "Have to go where they send us." Bill continued. "Never mind," he added. "They've not said anything about it yet and I'm pretty certain I can get some more leave before then. And I'll be able to come

218

and see you again, won't I?" He wrapped his arm about David and drew him onto the chair. David snuggled close, careful this time not to spill tea onto his daddy's nice blue uniform.

"He looks better don't you think Bill?" Amy said brightly. "That rash has gone nearly."

Bill looked down at David then gave Amy and Rose a smile of approval. "He looks a lot better aunt. It's done him a world of good. It's such a relief to know he's being so well looked after. Especially when... well you know, you have your mind on so many other things." And they nodded in sympathy.

CHAPTER 26

The hops of war

Bill managed one more visit a week later on a twenty four hour and then all leave was cancelled as the squadron prepared for posting to Burma. He arrived at Worcester during mid-morning, just as before and went through the make believe of parachuting into the garden, watching with satisfaction the effect the story had on David, who listened again open mouthed. But by mid afternoon his aunt's chatter bored him. It was all bound up in domestic inconveniences and he was not sorry to have an excuse to leave.

"Only if I don't get this train the next one'll make me late and I might not get another pass."

"Oh no don't do that Billy." Amy lifted David to her and kissed him. "Daddy's got to go again. But he's coming back. Soon." She replaced David on Bill's knee. "I'll get my coat and then we'll come and see you off. That'll be nice won't it David. Go to the station and see daddy go off in the train?"

Rose joined them and they walked in the heat of the July afternoon through the quiet streets past the hop warehouses and the small barrack yard where tanks had waited to be deployed up until two years ago. Then they climbed up onto the sleepy platform spanning the bridge across Foregate Street and the shops below.

"Any idea when you'll be coming again Bill?"

"Difficult to say really. I was lucky to get this one. You know… What I said about posting…" This time, on the open station platform Bill was less melodramatic and more careful.

A small engine and two coaches appeared and the station announcer intoned the stops and changes; Malvern Link, Great Malvern, Ledbury, all the way to Hereford.

"Only if I don't get this and miss my connection…"

"Don't worry Bill. We understand. Don't we David." Amy reached and took David from him. "Go on then Bill, jump in. You might get a seat."

"Write and let us know won't you Bill." Rose reached and gave him a brief hug. "Any time. You'm welcome, you know's that."

"Thanks aunt. Both of you." He slammed the door and pulled the strap to drop the window.

"Do you think you'll get a seat?" Small inconsequential matters filled their brief parting. Anything to fill the time; anything but just standing, waiting for him to go. Then the peremptory blast of the guards whistle and a small 'pop' of the train whistle and Rose and Amy between them urging David to 'Give a wave' in answer to the waving of Bill's raised arm.

It was a shame it was so short but, they consoled themselves, it was better than nothing. But with all that on his mind, the prospect of having to go abroad again it was good of him to come all that way just for a few hours. And in all this heat too. No wonder he seemed preoccupied. Not as relaxed as he had been before. Ah well. War'll soon be over.

And the train chugged through the lazy countryside into the afternoon sun and Bill, his duty done, contemplated the hours remaining. With luck he'd make that train in Hereford and be back in time for a few hours with Mako and the boys, back up into the village. The prospect of an evening's drinking, relaxed, in the open air, in the garden behind the pub. The war'd soon be over. All the signs were that this year would be the last and then what...?

Perhaps he'd get something off that barmaid tonight. He felt good. Really good! And the way she'd been looking at him... Been ages since he'd had it! He watched the fields, the ripening corn, the orchards replete with opportunities for earthy passion on a summer's night... Hmmm...

And then the war ended in a flash of blinding light. A people gazing up and wondering at the audacious aircraft alone and high above their city, beyond their recognition, beyond their ability to see Fat Boy falling from the 'plane. And not a sound, before or after. Only a dimming of sound before their world became searing white and the city and its people vanished. Away from Hiroshima they ran in panic, unable to comprehend what it was or what they had to do while their enemy paused and waited. But no sound came. And the people waited and searched for the elusive way to end it but too late! Another aircraft, alone and high cruised over them again. And again, soundless white, the searing, blinding sunflash. And sound returned from beyond the horizon and filled the desolation of Nagasaki. And the war came to an end.

The end of the war brought a relaxation in the regime of prisoners of war. Relationships started to be transformed. Was this really our enemy? This person who, on reflection, now the threat we thought he posed has gone away, looks remarkably like that bloke down the street? Enemies began to be viewed as citizens awaiting repatriation.

So it was that the women at the cribs in the hopfields, enjoying the carefree warmth of early morning sunshine and the lightness of heart that an end to war had blessed them with, saw a line of men walking in file along the perimeter of the field. The word passed along the rows of cribs and penetrated into the other rows deeper beneath the overhanging bines. The lighthearted chatter ceased and the women were joined by others who stood and watched as the men passed them by at a distance, casting discreet glances. But their escort of a squaddie at the head of the line and another behind them kept the pace brisk and ordered the prisoners to keep their eyes front. So they smirked and chattered as they marched and the squaddies gave ineffectual orders for them to 'Shut up.' and 'Stop that bloody row.' The women at the cribs whispered and pointed. The word 'eyetie's' ran along the hopfield and some of the women preened as the men filed past, seeing them in their imaginations as exotic with the mention of the word 'Italian'. But the squaddies glared back, feeling strangely embarrassed because the women's interest was directed at their prisoners and not at them.

"What's they doing here?" Despite the antics of one or two of the women, Rose's question reflected the silent indignation shared by the rest. "They'm supposed to be prisoners of war ain't they?"

Irene was sharing the crib next to Rose and Amy. "They're letting 'em out for a bit to do some work while they waits to be sent back home."

"Quite right too," Amy put in. "They ought to. Instead of sitting around. Make 'em all work that's what I say. Make 'em work for their keep."

"What's they doing here though?" Rose demanded. "We'll none of us be safe. They've only got two soldiers guarding 'em look. And what's to stop 'em escaping?"

"They don't look very dangerous," Irene said.

"Well," said Amy, "as long as they don't put 'em to work in here with us."

Rose looked round suddenly. David was standing at the end of the crib listening to the women's conversation and watching the distant file of men walking past. Aunty Ame's friend was right. They didn't look very dangerous, in fact most of them were smiling and seemed to be very pleased with themselves. All the same he heard Aunty Rose saying, "Now you're not to go far away. D'you hear? Stay playing where we can see you, there's a good boy."

The prisoners passed out of sight and animated chatter rose all around as the picking recommenced.

"He seems to be enjoying himself anyway," Rose said.

"Told you he would." Amy looked down at David playing with the toy lorry he had brought from home. He was making roads in the earth, smoothing it down with a piece of stick then pushing and reversing his lorry backwards and forwards along the road. Then he set about making the road longer. There was no limit to the distance he could make his road go! Another child, about five years old approached and watched David from a discrete distance, waiting for David to catch his eye.

"What's you got?" the child asked.

"It's my lorry," David replied. "My Uncle Bob gave it to me."

The other child fished in his pocket and brought out a small red car. "This is mine," he said. "Can I try it on your road?" And suiting the action to the words he bent and joined David in his game.

Amy watched from the crib and smiled. "Told you he'd be alright." She inclined her head for Rose. "See, he's got a new friend already look."

"Where's your mummy?" Rose called and the child pointed along the row to a crib where a young woman in a turban scarf and wrap around apron gave a smile and a nod of acknowledgement. And for the rest of the morning David and his new friend Andrew alternated between the two cribs.

"Can I go and have my dinner at Andrews crib?" he asked when Amy broke off picking to light the fire for the kettle.

"If his mummy says it's alright. Have you asked her?"

David nodded. "And he's got some pop as well."

The overseer was approaching down the line with the busheller and labourers.

"'Bout time." The crib was bulging and well over half full of hops. Amy turned the hops in the crib and Rose joined her in fishing out any leaves they could see. "He's later than usual."

"Any longer he'd have been too late. We'd had to have stopped picking."

"We thought you was never coming," Amy said as he arrived. "It's nearly too heavy for us to carry."

The overseer cast his eyes up the poles and along the wires above the crib. They were almost bare. It was true; another ten or fifteen minutes and Amy and Rose would have to pick up the crib and carry it further down the line and start a fresh bine. He sighed in exasperation at the labourers lagging behind him. "Come on, keep up will you."

"We'll have a good tally anyway." The overseer glanced with ill humour at Amy and ignored her remark, then with another sigh he began filling the basket while he waited for the labourers to arrive with the sack.

"Hey," Rose whispered, nodding in the direction of the labourer's, "them's eyetie's."

"You sure?" Amy said, eyeing them surreptitiously.

They looked up as the overseer unexpectedly said, "Aye. And they're no bloody good either. At least not for this job."

"Well what you got 'em for then?"

"No choice!" he replied. "They've been billeted. Got 'em to work on the farm."

"You don't have to pay 'em as well do you?" Rose was incredulous.

"Bloody don't," he said. "Good job and all. You can't trust 'em to do the job properly. All they want's to do is lie down and talk. That's all they've done so far. Talk, talk, talk."

"But won't they run away?" Rose asked. "I mean, you couldn't chase after 'em if they did. Don't 'spose you'd want to anyway."

"No," he muttered without conviction. "They've given their parole."

"What's that?" Amy hadn't come across the word before. It sounded rather official.

"Promised not to." He turned to them, still lingering behind. "More's the pity. Come on here!" he snapped at the men, who were falling about and laughing at some joke or other. "Get that sack over here!"

He bushelled out their hops, recorded the tally and moved on. Noncholantly the prisoners of war followed him but not before they had given Rose and Amy a bold look and an unintelligible gallantry accompanied by a smile.

"Well! They're charmers anyway."

"I wouldn't trust 'em." Rose replied. They bent to their picking once more.

But occasionally a woman's wistful eye followed them and then, while his companions watched out for him, the one whose eyes she had met would steal discreetly into the green shadows beneath the untouched bines. In the silence, away from the chatter of the distant pickers and without a word he found her waiting for him and they came together in a breathless embrace, pressing back against the pole with a garland of fragrant green hops falling about them. Quickly, desperately she lay down with him, casting an anxious glance around but only the distant chatter and the hum of insects drowned the sounds of their muffled cries and gasps of ecstasy. "Oh, oh… careful… oh…" Her heart still pounding and flushed with passion she stroked his face and kissed him. "Will I see you again?" And he smiled at her without comprehension and kissed her with a final gallantry. Then she watched him and bit her lip and wondered, 'did it show?' as she smoothed her skirt and hair and tried to remember the expression she ought to wear on returning from an innocent interlude to join the other pickers at her crib.

She avoided looking at them and she reached for a length of bine, only remarking, "Trust me to go and find the only bed of nettles." But they knew and gave each other knowing looks as the woman concentrated on picking with an air of subdued defiance. And she squeezed her thighs together surreptitiously and tried to relive the moment thinking 'Well, it's your lookout. I've had mine. Oh God.' The heat rose around her memory. 'What can you do when you need a man and he's been away so long.' She squeezed her thighs against the stickiness, happy for the moment, glancing about the field but the eyetie's had gone from sight and she was gone from his memory as they chattered and laughed, pushing and jostling one another, uncaring of the misconceived children and the tears they left behind.

But for David and the other children those weeks in the hopfields provided days of freedom to roam and play in safety, spiced with limitless opportunities for adventure. David's band of playmates grew but Andrew remained his special pal above all others. Each morning they sought each other out and the day's new adventure began. It only needed them to step two rows sideways where the hops were still unpicked and they were in a world of their own creation, yet safe within earshot of voices which, because of the intervening curtains of bines, seemed more distant than they actually were. And if they glimpsed an adult moving furtively across the dappled gloom they kept at a discreet distance and giggled.

"She's going to the toilet."

And Andrew, more daring and worldly, being all of one year older than David, said, "She's going for a pee." And they giggled briefly and continued with their game.

They exchanged childish hospitality at each others cribs, shared sandwiches and, because there was safety in numbers and David and Andrew were inseparable, it gave Amy and Rose freedom and peace of mind to concentrate on picking.

A shriek one dinnertime gave them a fright and the women at the surrounding cribs all looked round in alarm to see who it was and what it was. Rose and Amy looked round too. It was David, sitting on the ground beneath Andrew's mother's crib, waving his arms and shuddering. His egg sandwich was scattered on the earth, he was gabbling something and both Andrew and his mother were trying to find out what was the matter. By the time Amy had dashed across the cause of his cry had been established and the panic was nearly over.

"He's alright," Andrew's mother reassured Amy as she bent to pick him up. "I think it was a spider that frightened him."

"Oh that's nothing to be afraid of. A big boy like you." Amy hugged him. "Come on now. You's alright ain't you?" Amy felt him

225

still tense and shaking in her arms.

"It was a big one," David wailed. "And it ran right up me. And it made me drop my sandwich."

"Where is it now?" Amy looked about the ground and on his jumper.

"I brushed it off." David shuddered, remembering the sudden awareness of something crawling, something just below his sight as he sat on the earth with his boiled egg sandwich. Something moving, erratically and quickly. And suddenly catching his breath, afraid to look, afraid to move, lowering his head slowly to see what it was. And the movement on his jumper freezing too, almost as if their eyes met. Then, as soon as David saw and recognised it the spider began to run. But not off him! Not away! It was running up towards his face, a great long legged scuttling thing. And he had screamed, dashing his arm against his chest over and over again, trying not to touch it and flinging his sandwich from him and leaping to his feet and frantically looking about the ground to see where it was and kill it. But it was nowhere in sight. Just strands of hop bine, leaves, crushed hops, earth and stones. And standing there afraid that it would run onto his shoe and begin to climb him again!

"Don't cry," she said, lowering him back down. "Look, Andrew's waiting to play with you." And she saw how timidly he put his feet back down, afraid the spider was just there waiting for him. Andrew was looking at David with an expression of mixed anxiety and amusement. He wasn't afraid of spiders and even if he had been he wouldn't have made such a fuss. But he thought how nice it was that David's aunty had come to give him a cuddle. And then – it was past and with barely a backward glance their game began once more.

Finally hop picking came to an end and it was time to leave for the last time; to say goodbye to friends and hope to see them again next year. They turned from the fields and left them behind, their cribs abandoned in the landscape and standing in a dereliction of stripped foliage beneath the open sky. It was the last wage packet of the year. There was a moment or two of standing in the farm yard to check that their pay was right and giving wistful smiles to each other, then the lorry came and they climbed aboard, waving and cheering at the others from the barracks who, like so many refugees, were beginning to stream out along the country lane, walking back to the station and their homes in the towns and cities of the midlands.

For Amy and Albert there was still enough summer left for them to resume evening strolls along the banks of the canal with David holding hands between them or skipping on ahead, peering into gaps in the hawthorn that lined the path, immersed in the world of his imagination.

226

Beyond the white bridge, up as far as the locks where the grassy hillside rose, they took David's hand firmly in theirs and peered carefully down into the deep lock gates where the sprays of water leaked between the brick and wood into the dark water below, searching for eels stranded on the brickwork above the waterline. It seemed to be as far from the city as you could go. But it was only a short walk along the towpath and from the rising lockside they could see the streets and houses beyond the hawthorn hedges. The pub, just set back from the canalside on the fringes of the streets, was on the way back to their regular haunts. And they sat outside and enjoyed the soft glow of evening before returning to 'The George' to join Rose and Bob.

CHAPTER 27

An end in sight

The kettle began to boil and Rose took the tea caddy down off the shelf, warmed the teapot, swirled a little of the boiling water round inside it then made the tea. It was time for elevenses and Amy was due at any time. Rose put some more coal on the fire and placed the teapot on the hearth to keep it warm while the tea mashed. She gave an involuntary shiver. It was getting colder again; soon it would be too cold to hang the washing out to dry and it'd be back to drying it in the back room upstairs.

'Come on Ame,' Rose grumbled to herself. She could do with a cup of tea but wouldn't dream of pouring herself one before her sister arrived. Elevenses had been part of their routine ever since she and Bob had come to live close to Amy and Albert twenty years before. Three mornings a week they went down town to the shops and on Tuesday and Thursday mornings Amy came to her younger sister's for a chatter and a cup of tea. Monday didn't count; it was washday.

Today Amy was late. Usually she was coming through the door before the signature tune of 'Housewives Choice' had finished. Rose put the tray of tea cups and saucers on the table then she gave the fire a poke to brighten it up a bit. Rotten coal they delivered nowadays. No heat in it at all! She would have to have another word with the coalman. Not that it'd do any good, to judge by the difference her last words had made.

The kitchen door opened at last and David ran in calling, "Hello Aunty Rose, we're here."

"Come on then, where's you been? You'll have this tea stone cold!" She went into the pantry to fetch the bottle of milk. "Come on in and close the door, you'm letting all the heat out. Where's Aunty Ame?"

David ran past her into the living room and tossed his pad of paper onto the table with his pencil calling, "We've had a letter."

"That's nice." Rose poured the milk into the cups and began pouring the tea. "Who's it from then? Grandma?"

"No it's…"

He was interrupted by Amy entering and saying, "He's told you then?"

"What? Yes. Here come on Ame, come and sit by the fire you looks starved to death. Cup of tea'll warm you."

"Ta." Amy took the tea and sat in Bob's armchair by the fire. "Turned really cold ain't it! And there's not a bit of heat in our fire. You got a nice'n going though."

"Will be when it burns up." She gave Amy a critical look. "You alright Ame? You looks like you'm going down with something."

"I'm alright. I'll tell you in a minute." She cast a meaningful glance across at David. Rose placed David's cup of tea near his paper and pencil and poured plenty of milk in so he wouldn't burn himself.

"Here you are, sit down here where you usually sits. What's you going to draw today then?" David sat to the table and took up the pencil. He had shown a precocious talent for drawing and spent much of his time each day with his pencil and paper.

"Going to draw an aeroplane," he said.

"That's nice," Rose said absently and turned her attention to Amy. "What's up? There ain't nothing wrong with our Lilly is there?"

David sat and pretended to draw and listened. He usually listened to what his aunties were talking about until they started talking their Agey Pagey language. At least that's what they called it. Whatever it was, he couldn't understand a word of it. It was some kind of jumbled up words they used and they always spoke it when there was something they didn't want him to listen to. It didn't matter that he assumed an air of total preoccupation in what he was doing; they always knew he was listening and that's when they began it. But today he wanted to join in and tell them. "It's not from grandma..." he began but Amy interrupted him.

"Get on with your drawing, there's a good boy."

He was disappointed. He was excited but Aunty Ame didn't seem very happy and they began to speak it straight away so David ignored them and concentrated all his attention on his new drawing. It was going to be his best drawing ever. It was going to be an aeroplane with a picture of an airman inside it.

Rose looked earnestly at her sister. "What's up Ame?" The concern in Amy's expression was growing.

"It ain't from our Lill. It's from Billy."

"Oh whatever's happened? He's not... He's alright ain't he?" Now Rose was beginning to get alarmed.

"He's getting demobbed."

Rose gave a sigh of relief. "Oh! For an awful minute I thought... When?"

Amy ignored the question; she was beginning to get overwrought. "It's awful. I know it's..." She struggled to get her thoughts in order. She wanted to talk to Rose calmly and tell her but now that she was having to say it she didn't want to. She couldn't get the words to form. And then they came all in a rush. "He's coming to take him back. In a couple of weeks he says. He wants to come and take David off us." Amy paused, turned her face away and began to cry. "I don't want him to go."

Rose looked across at David but he was engrossed in his drawing and hadn't noticed. "Is you sure?"

"It's in his letter," Amy replied. "He's leaving the airforce in a couple of weeks. I forgets the date, he's put it in somewhere, then he's coming to take David back to Sheffield." She wiped her eyes. "Sorry Rose. It's just when I thinks of it. I mean, it's all so sudden. We ain't got time to think of it."

Rose looked aghast at Amy. No wonder Ame was so upset! She tried, just as Amy was trying, to grasp what it meant. Couple of weeks! And then what? What would they do? Their lives would be so… "Well what's we going to do?" She knew the question was futile and Amy's reply was as she expected.

"I don't know! What d'you mean Rose?" Amy grew calmer. "I mean there's nothing we can do is there? We only said we'd have him for Billy while he was in the airforce."

"But he ain't got a mother. He can't go back to her can he?"

"No but Bill's his father. I mean," Amy paused and despite herself she saw the rational argument, "he's every right to him ain't he!"

David jumped down from the table and brought his drawing across for them to admire. "Look," he cried. "It's a bomber." He pointed to the figure sitting in the cockpit in the front of the plane. "And there's my daddy look."

Amy and Rose looked at the drawing and then at David, glowing with the expectation of their praise.

"It's very nice," they said.

"I'm going to see my daddy again soon." David said innocently.

"Has you told him?" Rose asked sharply. It seemed to contradict everything Amy had said so far if she had. "You ain't told him already has you?"

"Not yet. Not properly," Amy replied sadly. "Only that his daddy's not going to be an airman anymore. I ain't said anything about him going…" she paused, her lip quivered then she added. "…leaving Worcester. I ain't got the heart to."

CHAPTER 28

Divided loyalties

All day David had been excited. His daddy was coming for him, just as he always knew he would. Amy and Al prepared to welcome Bill with a nice tea of fish and chips from Benny Pooles, fried to perfection in a batter that was golden and crisp, with bread and butter and plenty of vinegar and salt. Perfect! After tea they planned the regular Friday night game of darts at The Arboretum with Bob and Rose, and because it wasn't a match night, Bill would be able to join them for a game. They didn't want anything to mar the visit.

"How much longer before he gets here?" David cried for the tenth time at least that day.

"It all depends on what train he gets." Amy replied perversely. She was trying to avoid the prospect of David leaving. She felt resentful and she hated herself for it. Looking back at everything that had happened since David had come to stay it all seemed to count for nothing. And yet, she supposed, because David took his home with her for granted that in itself was a testimony to her success in bringing David up these past couple of years and helping him to put the past away. Only – and again she hated herself for thinking it – it was so disloyal of David to be eager to leave her. As though he didn't care for her. Not as much as she loved him anyway! And then she looked down and David was smiling at her. She smiled back and pushed the thought away, chiding herself. He was only a child after all and children of David's age don't think like that. Of course he wanted his daddy! It was only natural. And anyway… They were going to talk to Bill… She went into the front room again to look for Bill coming along the street but there was still no sign of him. She went out for another shovelfull of coal for the living room fire and then tried to busy herself with meaningless activity whilst she waited.

Albert came home early and looked about him with an air of expectation as he entered. "He ain't here yet then?"

"No," Amy replied shortly.

"Time's his train?"

Amy glanced at the clock. "Should be here by now." The clock showed twenty minutes past the hour. "He was due in at five to."

"Perhaps I'd better go and meet him. See what's happened."

"Have a drink you means."

"No!" Albert protested. "Anyway they ain't open yet," he added unnecessarily.

"It never stopped you before," Amy retorted. Albert's drinking was becoming more serious; nowadays it seemed he could hardly wait to get round to the pub.

"He'll want a hand with his luggage anyway," Albert said hopefully.

"He won't have any luggage. He's only going to be here tonight then he goes back tomorrow."

"Well, anyway we ought to know what's happened." Albert persisted.

"Nothings happened." It was enough to try the patience of a saint. "His train's late that's all."

Albert grunted and settled into his armchair. "Well he'll be here soon I expect then we can ask him," he muttered.

"I don't want you saying nothing," Amy cried. "Give him time to get comfortable first."

"Well you don't want to leave it too late. He's going back tomorrow."

"I know that Al. Don't you think I know that! You say's such unnecessary things sometimes." Amy could feel the tension increasing. Oh why doesn't he hurry up and come then they would know where they were!

"Anyway," Albert said, stirring from his chair, "I'll put the kettle on. I could do with a cup of tea."

"It's boiled already. Everything's all ready. We're just waiting for Billy now that's all."

"Oh well. I'll get some more coal for this fire while I'm up."

Amy watched Albert with resignation. The fire was fine! She went back into the front room to look for Bill coming along the street.

Bill was peeved that no one had been at the station to meet him. Not that he had any right to expect them to be there. After all why should they? But all the same he had dropped the window of the carriage door and leaned out to scan the platform as the train, now over half an hour late, emerged languidly from the tunnel at Shrub Hill and glided into the station. He scanned the faces as the carriage rolled to a stop and felt a pang of disappointment. Bloody typical! Five years in the war then you try to pick up the pieces again and nobody cares. There was a deep well of bitterness within him. What had he got? The back bedroom at his mother's, too small for anything but the bed, and a set of drawers. And no more than two feet of floor space between them. Still nowhere to call his own! It was worse than the bloody barracks. Well, they would have to manage somehow that was all!

He picked up his suitcase and folded his Burberry neatly across his arm to walk the short distance to Aunty Ame's. By the time he reached Heenan's he was cold and he wished he had put the raincoat on. But Bill was conscious of his appearance and he fancied that he looked more dashing, the man of the world, striding out with the suitcase and his coat across his arm. He picked up his pace.

The high railway arch was ahead of him and beyond it he could see Aunty Ame's. He began to feel uncomfortable. It was as though the eyes of the street were on him and they knew! As he got nearer he saw a movement in the bay window and braced himself for the gush of welcome he had come to expect. The front door opened and then his aunt was there, stepping into the tiny brick garden to greet him with her arms extended.

"Billy," she cried, then turning briefly to the house. "Al, he's here. Where is you? Our Billy's here!"

Albert appeared and pushed his way past her into the street. "Here come on then Billy." He reached out. "Let's have your case."

Bill gave them a smile and handed it over. Albert reacted with surprise. "There's not much in it."

"Course there ain't you daft thing. He's only here for the night."

Albert ushered him past her and Amy gave Bill a brief hug of welcome. "That's better now the door's shut. Keep the cold out. We've got your bed nice and aired. Come on through and have a warm. Kettle's been on. We'll have a nice cup of tea."

They fussed him into the chair in front of the fire and Amy took his coat.

"You'm in the front bedroom with David. You'll be alright won't you?"

"Course I will. Where is David?" Bill looked about the room in expectation that David would suddenly appear.

"He's been up at Rose's this last hour. I'll take this upstairs." Amy picked up the suitcase. "It is light ain't it. Hardly worth bringing a suitcase for one night."

"I got it to put David's things in."

"Oh yes." Amy hesitated. "I'll take this up then. We got his things all ready anyway. Fish and chips alright for tea? Only they'm lovely and David likes 'em. It won't take long to fetch 'em."

"That'll be fine thanks aunt. Don't go to a lot of trouble."

"It's no trouble. Al, just put the light under the kettle again will you."

"Ah. Then I'll go up to Rose's and bring David down." Albert went off into the kitchen.

Amy turned at the stairs door with the suitcase. "You've got plenty of space in it for him." She paused for an instant. "We ain't half going to miss him. Anyway," she added quickly, "I'll take this upstairs."

Bill sat and listened to the stair rods clanking on the staircase. The same sounds. The same smells. The same warmth. He hoped it would be easy. He sat back in the armchair to wait.

There was a commotion in the backyard. He heard Rose's voice raised in excitement with the voice of his child; the backdoor latch and the clanking stairs again. At his elbow the stairs door opened, Amy was crying, "Is they here?"

Then a rush of feet and Rose in the kitchen calling, "Go and find him then. See if he's there!" and the living room door flying open and the headlong figure pausing in expectation before flinging himself at Bill with a scream of joy.

"Daddy…"

From the door at the foot of the stairs Amy watched and her eyes grew hot with tears. She pushed past Rose and snuffled, "I'll make that tea. You'll have one won't you Rose."

Rose, watching the joyful reunion replied absently, "Ta."

In the kitchen Albert was pouring the water into the teapot. He looked up at Amy just inside the door dabbing her eyes. "Is you alright?"

She sniffed and wiped her nose on the towel. Then she lifted her head and gave a wan smile. "I'm alright. I'll be alright in a second. It's all a bit sudden." In the sitting room the cries of delight continued.

"Do you want a hand?" Rose called.

"Coming," Amy replied. "Shan't be a minute. Here you can fetch these cups if you likes." She began to bustle, fetching the milk and sugar from the pantry for Albert to carry through then, alone again she dabbed her eyes and leaned against the sink to compose herself.

"Now," she said brightly as she went back in. "Do you take sugar Billy? You do don't you."

"Just a little if you please." Best behaviour!

"Is you having one David? Plenty of milk just as you likes it?"

David nodded and pushed his drawing at Bill. "That's you daddy. In your bomber."

"Very nice," Bill replied. "Who told you how to draw like that?"

"He's ever such a good drawer ain't he?" Rose said with encouragement.

Amy passed the cups of tea around. "I'll put yours and David's down here on the hearth shall I Billy? Careful you don't knock it over

234

David. Yours is on the mantelpiece Al."

Rose was sitting at the table and Amy sat to join her. "You and Bob's still going with us up to the Arboretum tonight?"

"Yes," Rose said. She was watching Bill and David together in the chair. Her eyes met Amy's and she gave a tiny grimace of resignation.

"Yes I know," Amy murmured sadly. She sat very still. Then she turned to Bill. "You'll come with us won't you Billy? For a game of darts? Up to the Arboretum later?"

"Yes. That'd be good. What time's you going?"

"After tea. About eight o'clock. Rose and Bob's coming too. Make a nice evening won't it."

"Mmm," he replied. "Yes, that'd be nice. Something to look forward to."

Bill suddenly felt restless. He needed to move from his seat, to be free to move around away from scrutiny.

"Look I'll just pop upstairs and get my case sorted out a bit if you don't mind. Ready for morning. We won't have much time will we."

"What time's you getting your train?" Albert asked.

"Quarter to eight."

"We'll have to be up then."

"To make sure you has a good breakfast before you go," Amy added.

"I'll come up as well to see you off," Rose added quickly. "And if it's that time Bob might be able to get up too."

Amy began to rise from the table "I'll come upstairs with you and get David's things…"

"In a minute aunt," Bill protested. "There's no rush."

"Oh well… You knows where you are. In the front."

Bill departed upstairs and Amy closed the stairs door carefully behind him. She turned to Albert and Rose with a grimace.

"Has you said…?" Rose began carefully but Amy stopped her. She gestured at David playing on the hearth and shook her head.

"It ain't going to be easy," Albert said softly.

"What d'you think?" Rose glanced warily at the stairs door. "After tea before we goes up the pub? Or later on when we've all had a drink?"

But the question begged no reply and they sat in silence. Amy bent and stroked David's head. "Come up here. Come and sit on my knee and show me what you're drawing. Then you can come with me and we'll fetch some fish and chips for our tea. You'll like that won't you? Come on then, come and sit up here with Aunty Ame."

Bill came back downstairs and looked around the empty living

235

room. Again!! They'd abandoned him, waiting for him to go upstairs so they could sneak away! He felt self pitying resentment and he couldn't understand why he felt the way he did. For the past twenty minutes he had sat on the edge of the bed with his empty suitcase open on the bed beside him, staring through the windows and taking in the simple furnishings of the room. David's cot beneath the gas mantle on the wall, the dark oak wardrobe, and chest of drawers beside the unused fireplace. He sensed the tension between him and his aunt. Why? It was supposed to be straightforward and easy! But he couldn't help feeling it was as though he was doing something wrong. But it wasn't wrong for God's sake! They had agreed to look after him for the duration. That was all. The child belonged to him. He was David's father and he had come to take him back! What was wrong with that? There was no point in making a song and dance about it. I mean, it wouldn't have made it any easier if he had come down for two days or two weeks! It was just that, somehow, he felt like a thief. Why? Why did they make him feel that way? He was the boy's father after all! Oh, he could see that they had done a good job. Anybody could see that. Well, he wouldn't have entrusted David to their care if he hadn't felt that they would look after the boy. And his mother had reassured him it would be alright too. Well, now it was time to take him back. It was as simple as that!

Bill snorted in self deprecation and crossed over to the window. There was no reason for him to feel like this; he was making too much of it. He looked with disinterest along the street he had just walked down. It was empty and quiet. Lifeless! He was glad he wasn't staying longer than tonight. He just wanted to gather David's belongings and be on his way back home. Home! What a laugh! Well, back on familiar ground anyway and trying to pick up his life again. Like everybody else. Not quite everybody else! His gaze wandered along the street again and took in the mound over the Anderson shelter in Lewis's garden with the flowers growing on it. They'd had it pretty soft down here! Away from all the raids, all the upset of war. Oh yes! The self-pity mounted. Then logic reasserted itself. That was the reason for sending him down here in the first place wasn't it! Oh God! He just wished it was all over and they were away from here.

"Better go back down I suppose!" he muttered.

Bill stood and looked around the empty living room in irritation and reached for his cigarettes. He heard a noise from the kitchen and Albert appeared with his shirt collar over his arm, carrying a mug of hot water, soap, brush and razor.

"Ah, you'm back down." Albert set the shaving gear down on the mantelpiece beneath the mirror and began to lather up. "They won't be long. They've all gone down the road to fetch tea. We'm going for a drink later." He angled his head and put the razor to the taut skin of his neck. "You plays darts don't you Bill?"

"Yes," Bill lied. "I like a game of darts." He settled back in the armchair. Oh well, it'd get 'em through the evening and he'd show 'em a thing or two about drinking. He'd heard from his mother and father about how they were all big drinkers down here. Well, he could hold his own with them if it came to that.

Albert watched him narrowly through the mirror. "She ain't half going to miss him y'know."

"Yes well she's bound to I suppose." Bill really didn't want to get into this line of talk. He looked around and took the Daily Express from the top of the radio by the window.

Albert scraped carefully at his upper lip. "She thinks the world of him she do."

Bill sensed Albert watching him. He feigned interest in the paper but it was no good, he couldn't relax "Is there anything I can do? Knives and forks or anything?" he asked suddenly.

"She's got some bread cut in the pantry. You can get that out if you wants. And the knives and forks is in the sideboard drawer."

"Right."

Relieved, Bill went into the kitchen and found the plate of bread and butter under a cover. 'Oh God!' he muttered. 'I hope it's not going to be like this all night.'

"There's some hot water in the kettle if you want's to have a wash," Albert called.

"I'll wait 'till after tea," Bill replied.

"Just as you like. Anyway, that's me done." Albert came back into the kitchen with a small square of paper reddening on his chin and replaced his mug and razor on the shelf above the window. "I'd better go and make sure the hen's got some water."

"Right." Bill returned to the newspaper in the sitting room.

The back door opened and David ran in with Amy following. "We'm back," Amy called. "I'll soon get the table done. Oh, you've done it." She put the parcels of fish and chips on the hearth to keep warm and rearranged the place settings round the table. Then she went to fetch the salt and vinegar.

"Come on David. You sit up here where you usually sits. You're over here Billy." The back door opened and Amy called, "Come on Al. Your tea's out. Don't let it get cold."

They settled down to eat. Amy watched David giving Bill sidelong looks of adoration. She made an effort and said, "How's your mum and dad? They keeping alright?"

"Yes," Bill replied. "Me dad's still over at Heeley yard. But he

237

might have to move to another depot."

"He won't have to move from Sheffield will he?"

"No. No, no," Bill reassured them. "It's not settled yet anyway. Just talk. Might have to go to the goods yard in town that's all instead of over the road."

"Is they going to come down for their holidays next year? Has they said anything about it?"

"I don't know. Me mother's just lost her job at Kitchens."

"Oh I'm sorry to hear that," Amy said with genuine sympathy. "We ain't heard from her for a bit. Anyway, I think it's my turn to write."

"Well," Bill said philosophically, "now the war's over there's not the same call for machetes and knives for the army like there used to be. Stands to reason I suppose. There's a lot of 'em got laid off."

"What will she do?" Albert asked.

"Well she's going to stay at home. I mean, David'll be there. Somebody's got to look after him."

Amy saw her opportunity.

"Me and Al's been thinking about things," she said.

Albert, dissecting the last morsel of fish batter from the skin was immediately alert. He looked up, first at Bill, then across to Amy who gave him an uncompromisingly direct look as if saying 'leave it to me'. He turned his attention to Bill again. But Bill was only half listening. He was cutting a small portion of fish and dividing the remaining chips on David's plate into two; those to be eaten and the rest that he could leave.

"We was wondering." Now Amy was committed. "Do you have to take him back?"

Bill stiffened and admonished David to 'eat your tea like a good boy and you can leave the rest.' Then, quietly and without looking up he asked, "How d'you mean?"

"Well," Amy said, "he likes it here. I mean, we loves him. Don't we Al?"

"Thinks the world of him."

"And we could take care of him. I mean, he's got all his things here. His cot. In his own room. The garden to play in…"

For a moment Bill was at a loss. "What are you saying? You mean… come back later or what?"

"No I…" Amy had reached the Rubicon. She flicked a glance at Albert and saw approval in his face. "We'd like to keep him." She paused. "We'd like him to stay here and live with us here in Worcester."

Now it all fell into place! Thoughts began racing through Bill's mind, reaching down and touching the intuitions he had been feeling earlier. He knew it! He knew there was something! But not this! He felt a deep sense of betrayal. With great control he shook his head, very slowly.

"You can't," he said. "He's mine."

"I know it's a bit sudden Billy."

"But she's been thinking about it a long time," Albert added.

"I don't believe it," Bill pushed his plate away.

Amy took David's fork away from him. "Why don't you go up to Aunty Rose's for a bit. You can leave the rest."

David looked up at Bill for approval. Bill nodded.

"Alright then. Shan't be long."

"Close the gate after you," Amy called. "Al. Go and see he gets through the gate alright."

Bill watched them leave the room. Four! He's only just turned four, not yet four and a half. He turned to look at Amy. "Do you realise what you're asking? I'd never see him except at holidays. I've hardly had time to spend with him as it is. No! No you can't."

"Hang on a bit Billy. Just wait 'till Al gets back. He won't be a minute. Here let me get you another cup of tea."

"I don't want any more tea."

"Billy…"

He was mortified. "I don't know how you can even think it!"

"But we was only…"

Silence descended between them. Amy bit her lip and busied herself with the cups and plates.

Bill stood up and prowled restlessly before the fire. He felt confined, trapped. "I'm going out for a bit," he muttered and brushed past Amy, leaving her looking after him, desperately racking her brain to think of a way of bringing it up again. If only they could get Billy to listen to what they wanted to say.

Albert came back in, a worried expression on his face. "I just seen Billy going down the entry. He never said a word. What's happened?"

"Nothing. He's just gone for a walk that's all."

"He's alright ain't he?"

"I don't know."

"What's he said?"

"Nothing. He just said no!"

Albert pondered. "I suppose it is a bit sudden though ain't it!"

"Well he ain't give us much time," Amy protested. "Has he? Just a couple of weeks that's all."

"D'you think we'm right?"

"I wish I knew." Amy sat down, suddenly overcome with weariness. "Has you seen the way he looks at him? The way David looks at our Billy I mean."

"But he thinks the world of you as well. Don't forget that."

239

"Do you really think so?"

"You've worked wonders with him. Has you forgot the state he was in when Bill brought him to us? Covered in sores and rashes. Crying all night."

"I know."

Albert sat on the arm of Amy's chair. He stroked her shoulder. "Perhaps he'll be better when he's had a walk. Time to think about it."

"Perhaps."

They sat preoccupied with their thoughts.

"What did you say to him?" Albert asked at last.

"Well. He was saying 'no' and I just said 'wait 'till Al gets back'. That's all."

"Oh. Well."

"Did you tell Rose?"

"Yes."

"What did she say?"

"Just that it's a big thing for him to think about. That's all."

"Well it is. Ain't it. Perhaps he'll feel a bit different about it when he's had time to think." Amy looked up at the clock on the mantelpiece. "Better get these pots done I suppose."

Albert rose from the chair arm. "I'll go and put kettle on. Rose says her'n Bob'll be down when they'm ready."

Amy was powdering her face at the mirror when Bill came back. He took in David at the table playing with some bobbins and marbles and Albert in his armchair with his jacket on, ready to go out. They turned to look at him. David, on the point of making a dash for Bill, remained where he was. There was something in his daddy's face that warned him to stay at the table.

"I've been up to the station," Bill said and alarm showed in Amy and Albert's faces. "If there'd been a train to Sheffield tonight I'd have caught it and taken David with me!"

"Oh Billy!" Amy cried. "Don't be like that. Let me just…"

Bill raised his hand and turned away.

"But won't you just listen?" Amy pleaded.

"I don't want to talk about it! You all go on up to the pub if you want to. I'm staying here with David."

"There's no need to be like that," Albert said gruffly. "She was only thinking about…"

"I know what she was thinking about," Bill cried. "And it's not on and I won't have it!" Amy looked quickly from David to Bill. He caught her glance. "Well anyway," he continued, "I don't want to talk about it anymore."

He took a seat in the armchair across the hearth from Albert and called David to him. "What's that you've got there? Let's have a look." David clambered from the table and carried his things across. "Come on then." Bill hauled David onto his knee while Amy and Albert watched.

An uneasy silence settled in the room between them.

With relief they heard the backdoor open and Rose calling in her playful way, "Ain't you ready yet Ame?" But her playfulness vanished as she entered. Bob was close behind her.

"God what's the matter?" he said. "You all looks as if you'd lost a quid and found a tanner."

Amy tried to speak. "We've…" She was lost.

"It's Bill," Albert said quickly. "He don't want to come out with us."

But before Rose and Bob could reply with the 'why ever not' that was forming in their open mouths Bill said sharply, "It's not that at all! You know it isn't!" He turned in his seat to face them. "They wants to take him away from me." He pulled David close to him and David began to cry.

"It's not like that! We never said that!" Amy protested.

"Well that's what it sounded like to me!"

Bob saw anger rising in Albert's face and he quickly intervened. "Wait a minute…"

"They didn't mean it like that," Rose put in quickly.

"Well that's what it sounded like to me! Anyway, how would you know? You weren't even here."

"There's no need to speak to your aunt like that." Bob remonstrated.

"Well…!" Bill subsided reluctantly.

Amy sat as if stricken. "He didn't give us time to explain properly." She was close to tears again.

"I'm not talking about it."

"Billy," Rose said. "Come on love. It's no good everybody getting all upset like this."

"Well what d'you expect?" he muttered.

"Come on. Come and get ready. Come and have a drink with us. Don't spoil it."

"It's not me that's spoiling it!"

"I didn't want to spoil anything," Amy wailed. "I only said…"

"I know what you said!!"

"Stop shouting. Will you!" Albert glared across at Bill. "You're upsetting the boy! You reckon you thinks so much about him!"

Rose reached down and lifted David from Bill's knee. Reluctantly Bill let him go. "Come on then. Come to your Aunty Rose. Let's get your eyes dried shall we." She carried him past Bob and into the

241

kitchen.

"I'm sorry Billy," Amy said tremulously. "I didn't think you'd take it like that. If only you'd let us explain…"

"Don't! Just don't start it all over again!"

"I wasn't going to," she protested.

"Come on Bill." Bob reached and touched him on the shoulder. Bill shrugged it off.

"It's her last night." Albert said. "You're spoiling it for her. Don't let it finish like this."

"I'm not spoiling it! It wasn't me that started it."

And the tension in the room began to rise again.

Rose came back in with David. "There that's better ain't it? Look, he's all clean and fresh again."

Bill held his arms out and David ran to him.

"Come on Bill," Rose said. "Come on. Get ready and let's all go out and have that drink. We'll all feel better. I know I will." She paused. They saw Bill's anger start to ebb away. "No more talk. Let's not say anymore. Eh? What d'you say? Eh Billy? Come on love. All of us. All of us together."

Bill started to relent. "But David… What about him?"

"It's alright. David's coming with us. You shan't have him out of your sight."

Bill looked across at Amy. Although she hadn't wept her eyes were red with unshed tears. She made a weak smile but it trembled away. Bill's anger turned to regret. "I'm sorry aunt. But it was just…"

"There was no need to carry on like…!" Albert began.

"Al! AL!" Bob interrupted Albert quickly. "Come on. Let's leave it. Let's go and have that drink."

"Alright," Bill said reluctantly. "Just give me a minute or two." He rose and made his way awkwardly into the kitchen for a wash.

They exchanged glances and Albert sighed and got up. He pulled out his handkerchief and offered it to Amy but she rejected it and looked at herself in the mirror. What a sight!

"Shan't be a minute," she said and disappeared upstairs.

And finally, when they were all ready they went out.

"I'm sorry Billy," Amy conceded in a conciliatory way as they walked up Northfield Street. "Perhaps I shouldn't have said it."

"It's over. Let's leave it at that."

Between them they created a veneer of conviviality. But each harboured their own secret thoughts.

242

CHAPTER 29

Morning departure

Bill woke with an awful taste and a mouth like fur. He sat up suddenly in the gloom and the headache hit him.

Oh God! He felt awful. He lay back on his pillow until the nausea subsided.

Christ! What's the time!?

He twisted around carefully and peered at his watch. Twenty to…? Bloody train! Got to get up quick. Why the bloody hell hadn't they come to wake him? He leaned against the pillows, fighting the sickness rising in him and belched. Better. A bit.

Across by the far wall opposite the foot of the bed the cot was silent. David! He'd got to get David ready! Bill drew the curtains and looked out into a grey wall of fog. He looked in the cot. It was empty. Oh God what's going on? He turned suddenly, staggered and his head began to swim. He sat on the edge of the bed to get his balance and reached for his trousers.

Last night! He should never have done it. Worcester beer, not same as the beer he was used to drinking in Sheffield. No wonder he felt bad. It had been a mess. He might have known they wouldn't leave it alone! Oh they'd started off alright, game of darts, everybody pretending, having a laugh and a drink like nothings happened. David sitting cosy on the bench against the wall with his pop and some crisps. Then when everybody'd had a few and it was really turning into a good night after all she'd started again. And he'd told her he didn't want to talk about it but she went on and on at him. Wants to adopt him!

Adopt for Christs sake! That'd mean he'd have no rights to see the kid at all! And so Bill had said No! and told her to shut up going on about it and Albert had taken nark over Bill's tone of voice. Tone of voice!? For Christ's sake you're trying to take my son off me! Then Rose and Bob had tried to calm things down because it was attracting the attention of the other people in the pub and Bill'd told them to mind their own bleeding business and Albert'd jumped to his feet and Amy'd pleaded with 'em all to sit down and stop showing themselves up and she wouldn't mention it again and that'd been the end of that. But they'd had to have a few more pints because everybody was so wound up, they

243

couldn't go home feeling like that. And anyway it was Amy's last night with David and she didn't want it spoiled. So they let somebody else have the dartboard – well they couldn't concentrate on their game after that – and sat around drinking and trying to pick up the pieces.

Only – when they'd staggered back home under a flag of truce Albert'd made one last attempt and Bill had shouted at him to 'Shut up' at which Albert had risen to his feet and lurched at Bill to hit him for speaking to them both like that after everything they'd done to help him and Amy had come running downstairs leaving David crying at the noise to see 'What's going on? What's up with you two?' And Bill and Albert had stood roaring drunkenly at each other with Amy in tears between them...

Bill pulled his shirt over his head and suddenly realised as his head emerged that there wasn't any sound. And David's cot was empty. "Oh God no!"

He ran downstairs and threw open the door into the living room. David was at the table eating a boiled egg. Amy looked at Bill stonily.

"There's a new laid egg if you'd like one. You can have it with a bit of bacon if you likes."

No mention of last night.

Bill ran his fingers through his hair. "Time," he mumbled. "Got to get ready."

"You've plenty of time," Amy replied. "We thought we'd let you sleep it off. You've got another three quarters of an hour yet."

"Better have a wash first."

"Sink's clear," Amy said. "And there's hot water in the kettle."

"Where's Uncle Al?"

"Gone to see to the boilers. He'll be back in time don't worry."

"I'm sorry about last night Aunt…"

"I don't want to talk about it. What d'you want to eat?"

Bill was humiliated and he didn't want to put her to any trouble. Besides he didn't know whether he could trust his stomach with food. "Is there any tea?"

"I'll make a fresh pot while you has a wash."

They all came up to the station to say goodbye, walking in silence through the early morning fog. Albert insisted on carrying the suitcase with David's belongings in it and Bob had another small box wrapped in brown paper and string with a selection of David's toys. They couldn't take everything. Perhaps they'd be able to send the rest along later, his tricycle and the engine Bob had made him. David walked hand in hand with Amy and Bill. The fog persisted, obliterating everything around them. The chill of the morning matched their mood and it's intensity dampened all sound around them as they walked through the quiet streets.

"You sure you got your ticket's safe Bill?" Amy had asked the question at least four times before locking the door.

"Yes. In my pocket. Here." Bill produced them again to show her.

They were at the station.

Gallantly Bob stepped forward to get platform tickets for them all. "No no it's alright," he insisted. "I got it here." He produced a handful of pennies and busied himself at the ticket machine.

Rose could see the big station clock through the ticket barrier. "Well you'm in plenty of time anyway," she said.

They went through onto the platform.

"Are you coming with us?" David asked.

"No," Rose said, "we've just come to wave you goodbye."

"You got your sandwiches ain't you Billy?" Bill nodded at Amy and patted the packets bulging in his raincoat pockets. She looked down. "Now you be a good boy won't you. And don't forget Aunty Ame. You promise."

Albert returned from the ticket barrier. "She's on time anyway," he reported.

They all turned to the big clock.

"What time's it due?" Bob asked again.

"Twenty five to. Well, eight thirty six to be exact," Bill answered.

"Should be here any time then."

Amy wanted to say so much more but there was nothing more that she could say. How could she stop the time? And make it so that he would never have to go away? The big hand quivered forward, another minute had gone. Wasted time when she should have spent these last few minutes with David instead of dreaming.

"Oh come here." She stooped and threw her arms around him and hugged him to her, whispering and snuffling back a tear. "There's a good boy."

Rose and Bob stood and watched. It was their turn. "Come and say goodbye to Aunty Rose before the train gets here. Come on then."

More hugs. More kisses while Bob stroked his hair.

Eight thirty six came and went. Now they were on borrowed time. How many times can you say goodbye? Once the moment has passed.

"Tell our Lilly we'll write. You won't forget will you Bill."

"We'm sorry about last night," Albert said. "Both of us. Shouldn't have happened."

"Doesn't matter," Bill replied.

Bob, looking along the platform, was suddenly alert. "She's here," he announced and there was immediate bustle.

"Here I've got his case." Albert bent for it and Bob reached for the parcel. "You get a seat. We'll bring his things on."

Now there was an ecstasy of hugging and kissing and queuing around David to make their final farewells. The train glided along the platform with fateful inevitability and squealed and stopped. Impersonal announcements began to echo over them, carriage doors opened and slammed. Steam between the coaches, sudden bustle and rising panic. Bill couldn't see any seats in this coach; he set off along the platform peering in the windows with Amy and Rose pursuing him. A carriage door slammed. "Oh God Billy get on the train you'm going to miss it." The guard was standing with his flag and checking his watch. Bill found a coach and opened the door. They passed David across to him. Now the luggage. "You get your seat Bill, we'll bring these on." Amy followed David on and Albert followed her. Half way down the carriage Bill found a seat and reached back for the case. Amy had David in her arms; Rose and Bob were waving and smiling through the window. "Come on Al. We've got to get off." Reluctantly she put him down and turned to go. "Ta-ra Bill." Albert shook Bill's hand and turned as the guard's whistle echoed out on the platform. Rose and Bob were waving and calling. And walking! The train was moving. Station buildings began to pass the windows. "Hey we're off. Pull the cord! Pull the cord." Albert shouted. Bill struggled but couldn't reach it across the amazed passenger occupying the window seat. "Let me pass!" Albert pushed frantically down the carriage to the door but the window was up. He grabbed the strap but the window wouldn't drop and the train was gathering speed. On the platform Bob was running and shouting, and behind Albert Amy was shouting. Albert took his trilby, wrapped it round his fist and punched the window out. The train shuddered to a stop.

Albert reached through the window and opened the door. Immediately station porters and the guard surrounded the door demanding to know what was going on. Someone was sent to fetch the Station Master. Arguments began, and explanations with the damage being pointed out. The guard left them to examine the window and determined the train was safe to continue. They heard the guards whistle and looked round. The train was moving again, David was at the carriage window waving, and then he was gone.

CHAPTER 30

Flying fields, hopeless dreams

The telegraph wires rose and fell, shredding the wisps of smoke that drifted between them and the carriage wheels chanted the monotone beat of the train; LNER; LNER; LNER. 'Only it's not the LNER.' Bill mused inconsequentially as the train hurried them northwards, 'It's LMS.' But that didn't rhyme. David was sitting opposite, gazing through the window. The man who had been so amazed at Worcester had exchanged his seat with him; now David sat watching the countryside sweep remorselessly by, leaving Aunty Ame further and further behind.

They approached Birmingham through a wilderness of suburbs, then high smoke blackened walls closed in and they descended slowly into a maze of tunnels, until the darkness and smoke gave way to sunlight and they emerged into the crowded station. They had to change. Bill lifted David out onto the bustling platform then turned to reach back into the carriage for their bit of luggage. The station was echoing with indistinct announcements and nervous travellers were besieging the porters for information.

The Sheffield train was full when it arrived and the crowds lining the platform surged forward, scanning the coaches for seats as the train slid to a stop. There was a rush to board it; Bill shouldered his way through and established a place for them in the corridor. He left David with the suitcase in the corridor by the window as the train began to pull away and went off to try and find a seat but there were none to be had. They settled down in the corridor crowded with other weary passengers sitting on their cases who grudgingly made way for others searching for seats to pass by them.

At the far end of the corridor a group of soldiers were engaging a pair of young women in animated chatter. Their banter was loud, fuelled by the bottle passing between them and becoming more boisterous. Bill tried to ignore them. They must have been drinking steadily since before Birmingham. They were already well established at the end of the corridor when Bill and David joined the train. They left the city behind and Bill tried to point out different landmarks to David as they flashed by. But the soldier's innuendos became more pointed and as they drank the women's laughter became louder and more coarse. Bill cast a sidelong glance along the corridor. One of the women was leaning against the carriage bulkhead with a soldier pressed close against her with his hand inside her coat. He was fondling her to the raucous accompaniment of the others. Bill looked sharply around at the other passengers; they were pretending not to notice but David was craning and trying to see what was going on. For Bill it was too much. He repositioned himself so that David couldn't see and hoped he couldn't hear too much of the words that came down to them.

Strange! There was the desire to protect his son from outrage. But a few yards away there was a woman pressed against a wall allowing her body to be explored. A sense of voyeurism arose. What would she feel like? What would it be like to do it with others looking on as they were looking on? In different circumstances he might have been one of them, returning home from his unit with a drink or two and the insatiable desire for the scent and the feel a woman. The trigger a bold glance and the sudden knowledge of what lay beneath her clothes and growing impatience as drink fuelled lust. Her breast in his hand! God! The palm of his hand tingled with the thought. Bill licked his lips and felt the firmness of her nipple against his tongue. The delicate crease above her thigh and her belly where the hair began to spring, thick and dark. And then the inquisitive finger. Heat rising. Her hands fumbling with the buttons of his flies, her groping fingers, seeking, stroking, pulling him free and fondling…

Bill gulped. Christ he was getting an erection! He heard David's repeated cry, "What's they saying daddy?" He looked down and leaned closer to the window. Bloody Hell! The train hurried on and the motion rocked him back and forth, back and forth against the windowsill. Bill tried to keep his mind in focus. He could have wept with frustration.

Along the carriage the rest of the group were crowded around the pair against the bulkhead boisterously egging them on. The noise and language assailed Bill's ears, bringing him back to the present. It was intolerable. Throwing caution to the wind he turned his head and called,

"Why don't you watch your language. I've got a child here."

The squaddie was pushing and moving against the girl. Without stopping he grunted. "Piss off!"

The others cheered.

"I'm telling you to watch your language that's all."

There was a pause and a sudden silence. Two of the soldiers now turned to face Bill with one of the grinning women hanging on their arms. With dismay Bill realised he had bitten off more than he could chew and his residual erection collapsed. The woman gave a soldier a nudge and slurred, "Go on then Gordon. Aren't you going to give him one!"

The soldier's face was shiny with drink. He had a blue chin from close shaving a heavy beard and he looked hard and fit. He was rocking and leaning slightly with the movement of the train but he looked Bill straight in the eye. Bill's heart began to pound.

"I've got a kiddie here. Just don't start anything that's all."

The soldier swayed and turned it over. He was conscious of the drink he'd had and he didn't know what this clean cut young bloke was like. But as he continued to stare at him he saw Bill's gaze begin to falter. He took half a step.

The woman against the bulkhead looked over the shoulder of the squaddie who had her against the wall. "Aw look at him. He's got a little boy." She was overcome with mawkish sentimentality. She tossed her head unsteadily and called, "What's his name then?"

Gordon told her to 'shut up!' and Bill's heart sank but the passion was roused in her and she didn't want her man to lose interest.

"Oh leave him Gordon. We don't want to upset the little boy do we! Come on, leave his daddy alone."

The girl on Gordon's arm tugged at him and he caught sight of the badge that Bill was wearing on his blazer and leered at it momentarily. It was like a challenge. Bloody RAF! He raised a finger and waved it at Bill. "Well just you bloody keep out of it that's all. Bloody pansy boys."

Now his companions were giving Bill the hard stare and Bill's heart started to pound again as he resigned himself to what was coming. But once again the confrontation was broken by the activity of the couple against the bulkhead. His concentration on the woman had scarcely faltered. Now with a growl of, "Come on in here!" he pushed her with her skirt about her thighs towards the toilet door. The others turned and crowded them in with a cheer and Bill was forgotten as they began jostling in the doorway.

He felt sick and humiliated. He had been afraid! He was still afraid and he hoped it didn't show. He wanted to get away while their attention was concentrated elsewhere. And he was ashamed of the prudish revulsion he felt. He wanted to be as free and uninhibited as them. To make love without shame but with their public display these drunken soldiers had made it sordid and dirty. Bill picked up their luggage and took David's hand. "Come on," he said. "Let's go further down the train."

He pushed his way along the corridor to another carriage, avoiding the looks of the other passengers. If he had met their eyes, then he might have seen admiration for the way he had stood up to the soldiers. But all Bill saw was another humiliating episode, being saved from a beating by the intervention of a woman. He stood with his chin upon his arms, leaning on the window rail gazing into space at the wisps of smoke, the flying fields and the hypnotic rise and fall of the telegraph wires as they hurried northwards.

PART THREE
DOROTHY – 1946

CHAPTER 31

Social graces

Along the river valleys the steam still hooted and whistled, an austere unforgiving sound punctuating the life of the city. The steam rose and surged in clouds before dissipating into the drizzle, adding to the damp drabness of the day. Along the roads the tramlines gleamed and the trams lurched across the crackling junctions past the gaunt ruins of the city. The mammoth task of rebuilding had yet to begin and rusting girders rose above the protecting hoardings, adorned with broken masonry like rotten flesh clinging to a corpse. And above it all was the heartbeat of the city, the pounding of the forges in the valley of the Don.

Bill was on twelve hour shifts. Clock on at six in the morning, clock off at six at night. By the time he got home to his mother's he was shattered. He had his tea later than the rest of them. Lilly cooked for the men coming home from work but because Harold got home earlier she served the meal for David, Harold and herself when Harold came home. Bill's was kept warm on the plate under a cover on the Yorkshire range until he arrived to sad potatoes and a crust of gravy burning round the edges. Afterwards, sitting in the armchair with a pot of tea before the fire he was too tired to join in the games that David wanted to play. He listened without interest to their conversations and David's chatter, conscious all the time of the inevitable call to work at five o'clock the next morning.

At work he longed to be home, to be with his son and make up for lost time and join in his play. But home was tiredness and sharing the bed in the small back bedroom with David now that George had got married to Myra. He ought to be grateful for the way things had worked out. If George had still been at home, God knows what would have been the outcome when Aunt Amy said she wanted to adopt David. There'd have been no chance of him bringing David back to his mother's and then what? He ought to be grateful for the way things had worked out. But it wasn't home and he wasn't grateful!

The home he had tried to make was gone and the anger and an underlying sense of shame at what he saw as his failure wouldn't go away. He was in a kind of limbo and sometimes the effort to be civil and cheerful was beyond him. Of course, the unadulterated love of David

253

was worth coming home to! He was five, due to start school in the infants after Christmas. With the lift of the backdoor latch David stopped whatever he was doing and ran into the kitchen to greet him and throw his arms about Bill's neck. But then he would be wanting to show Bill some drawing or to play some game and Oh God! Bill wished he wasn't so tired.

Saturdays were better. The morning shift finished at twelve and he arrived back home almost at the same time as his father and they could all sit down to their dinner together and laugh at Archie Andrews on the wireless with the rest of the weekend to look forward to. And Bill tried to make up for the week's lost hours. After a wash and shave Bill got changed and it became his routine on Saturday afternoon to take David into town and have tea out and then go to the pictures.

"One day," Bill said as they sat with sandwiches and a bun in the British Restaurant, "we're going to have a motorbike."

"What, with me on the back?" David's eyes gleamed with excitement. He saw himself with his arms around Bill's waist riding at breakneck speed with the machine roaring and vibrating beneath them.

Bill smiled back and let his own imagination wander too.

"I'll save up and we can get a sidecar to go with it. Then we'll be able to take grandma and grandad too. Perhaps go to the seaside. Cleethorpes or somewhere like that…"

"Wow, the seaside. Can we daddy? Can we really?"

Ruminating on his sandwich Bill let his dreams follow their course. Around him people were thronging in from the rain, burdened with shopping and jostling together in their macs and cheap plastic raincoats. Their steaminess mingled with the steam rising from the pans in the counter where the thick brown gravy and stodgy vegetables simmered. On the painted walls, green below the waist and cream to the ceiling, the condensation was running in droplets as though the walls themselves were sweating. Bill rubbed at the misted window with his sleeve. In the grey outside the drizzle was becoming more persistent and daylight was fading. Bill's good humour began to evaporate. Bloody day! His mind wandered back to a fine autumn afternoon shortly after bringing David home. They had taken a bus to the village of Holmesfield where the Derbyshire countryside meets the outskirts of the city. They had walked a little way into the pretty Cordwell Valley, massed with rhododendrons above the meandering stream. There had been something idyllic about that afternoon. On the way Bill had pointed to the neat, stone built, comfortable houses from the top of the bus as they passed, secure within well tended gardens behind tidy hedges. Some even had a car on the drive. They had an air of solid confidence here in the suburbs, untouched by Bill's troubled world. "One day we'll have one of them."

Although spoken to David the words had been addressed to himself, as though the dream needed the spoken word to bring it to reality. He had put their name down for a council house as soon as he got out of the RAF. Currently the waiting list was ten years and growing. With any luck they would have a home of their own before he was forty...

"Bill! Now then Bill." The sound of his name being called across the dingy restaurant dragged him from his reverie. Good God! After all this time! Mako was approaching their table with his tray.

"Now then Bill tha' were miles away. Who were she?"

"Mako!" Bill glanced at David who was watching Mako's approach open mouthed. "Here," he called, "come and sit down. David, move your plate. And don't eat with your mouth open."

"Th'art looking well I must say. Still in uniform I see." Bill was wearing his barathea blazer with the RAF eagle on the breast pocket. His new gaberdine was over the back of his chair. "Ow're tha going on then?" Mako took the chair next to David, opposite Bill and set his tray down. "Thou art looking bloody well!" He sat back with confident ease.

David felt the arrogance of the man overpowering them both. He couldn't decide whether his daddy was really pleased to see Mako or not. He heard his daddy reply, "You're looking good yourself." Bill felt careworn by comparison with Mako. Despite the misery and chill of the day outside Mako had an air of wellbeing as though he had just stepped off a sunny beach. It wasn't that he was particularly bronzed, in fact his skin looked no healthier than Bill's. But Mako's manner betrayed a buccaneering approach to the world and life in general. Already Bill found himself regretting they had an empty space at their table. "What are you doing now?"

"Back on't hammer driving at Baileys. Three shifts. Regular work, good wages, bonus. And who's this then? Thy little'un is it? Well tha kept that dark."

Mako ruffled David's hair. David shied away and put his hands up to straighten it again. Mako was untroubled. "He's a fine looking little feller though in't he? What d'you call him?" he turned to David again. "What do they call you?"

"David."

"Ah." He looked up again. "What you doing then? Back wi't springs? Tempered weren't it?"

Bill nodded, about to elaborate on how well they were doing and the responsibilities he had but Mako was already scanning the room beyond Bill's shoulder, only half interested in Bill's reply. David looked from one to the other. He sensed that his daddy was already shrinking in Mako's presence.

"Not taking your missus's place am I?" Mako said with gallant

255

awareness.

"No…"

"Got a passout for the pair of you eh? Hey did you ever get that business sorted out?" Mako asked suddenly. Bill looked at him in dismay but Mako was oblivious. "You know, you managed to wangle a fortyeight hour, she were giving it somebody at home or summat. Didn't she give you…"

How Bill regretted the confidences he had shared so indiscreetly. "I got divorced." He couldn't bring himself to look at David to see what effect this conversation was having on him. "I divorced her. She was no good," he added desperately.

There was no commiseration in Mako. Why should there be? He had skived and survived his way through the war, now peacetime was his for the taking.

"Tha does reight! Love 'em and leave 'em. He's a nice little feller though in't he." He ruffled David's hair for him again and again David carefully tried to restore it to neatness. "So what you doing now then. What brings you down here?"

Bill answered warily. How he regretted Mako's interruption; the last thing he wanted was the man dominating the rest of their afternoon.

"Oh we're just having a quiet afternoon round the shops together. Aren't we."

David nodded dutifully.

"Don't blame thee." Now Mako changed tack; voluble and careless his eyes were constantly flitting beyond Bill's shoulder. "Here, remember that little tart in the village. Tha know's, she fancied thee." Bill shifted uncomfortably, furiously thinking how he could turn the conversation. He sensed David watching him with interest. "You remember?" Mako insisted. "Just after tha got stung wi't barbed wire."

Bill tried to look vague and non-committal. He remembered how coarse he had found Mako at the time and how he had strung along with him because of the sense of danger that Mako carried with him, hoping that he would find opportunities in his wake. Now he wished he'd never met the man!

"Come on David. Eat your bun. We've got to be getting on."

David picked up the bun and took a small nibble. Like his father before him, David found the man's presence fascinating.

"Aye, that's reight. Wrap thissen round that, tha'll come to no harm." Mako turned back to Bill. "She were a trim little thing though. Kept giving thee the eye. I couldn't get near her. Not while you were around. Maureen!" he said with sudden recollection. "That were her name. I had her though before we left. Just before we got posted. She were a right little go'er. Tha slipped up there. You wouldn't believe…"

256

"When did you get out?" Bill demanded desperately.

"Oh I were in one of t'first batches." I'll bet they were glad to see the back of you as well, Bill thought. "Still see a bit of Sammo and one or two of the others, though not much. He's married now. Not me! Make hay while the sun shines. Eh little 'un?" Bill smiled bleakly and David nodded with incomprehension. "Hey remember that stuff they reckoned they used to put in our tea? Eh? I reckon they're putting something else in it now." He was in full flight and scanning the room again. "Some of the women tha see's nowaday's. Eh! Tits out here." He indicated with his hands. "And they're begging for it. You what? After five years with us all in't forces! I should think so. Tha does reight Bill. Get rid on her. There's hundreds on 'em out there. And they're all waiting for a bloke what's going to…"

Desperately Bill caught Mako's attention and gestured toward David who was avidly following the conversation under pretext of eating his bun. Mako reverted to philosophy. "Aye well… Never mind. He'll learn some day. Won't you son? Christ look at 'time." He took a quick gulp of tea. "I gotta go. See you Bill. Don't forget." He made the classic fist and forearm gesture. "Get out there and give it to 'em. Here y'are son." He fished out a shilling from his loose change and was gone.

"Who was that daddy?"

"Oh just somebody I knew in the airforce," Bill replied morosely. He glanced around but Mako had vanished. "Come on, finish up. Let's go. See what's on at the pictures this week eh?"

Was that it then? Was there nothing more to hope for? A home beyond your reach and a motherless son? All bed and work; empty dreams. There was precious little time for dreaming as it was! Turning dreams into reality was a hopeless task. Bill felt oppressed by the claustrophobic steaminess of the place.

"You finished?" He took David's hand. "Come on then."

Bill had enjoyed going dancing before the war. Not that he was an accomplished dancer but he missed the fun and gaiety of the ballroom. And the strange thing was, he didn't realise he missed it for his life had been taken over by so many other things. Everybody said that the war had changed them and maybe it was true. It was certainly true in Bill's case. He was no longer the single carefree man he had been. Five years had made a lot of difference. Nothing was the same any more. He decided to take up dancing again only this time he'd learn how to dance properly instead of the two step shuffle and jive he'd been doing before the war. Ballroom; proper dancing. If you could dance properly it was a social asset. Everybody knew that.

He enrolled at the local dancing school in the dancehall under the

Abbeydale cinema at the top of the gennel. Two evenings a week. Well it made a break. Besides, there was the firm's annual dinner and dance coming up and if you could dance properly there was always the chance you might get to dance with one of the executives wives and get noticed. Social graces were important if you wanted to get on in life. He might move up and become a manager.

The dancing school was home to a gauche collection of aspirants like himself, some completely devoid of any sense of rhythm, who pursued the steps by rote, counting out the timing as they stumbled and jerked their partners round the floor. He had always fancied that he had a good sense of rhythm but somehow he couldn't find fluency of movement with them. He began to feel embarrassed by a sense of his own gaucheness. And Bill didn't even find the assortment of partners especially attractive. After two weeks he left.

But he was still determined to learn. He bought a 'Teach yourself Ballroom Dancing' and because he was embarrassed and self conscious he kept the book in his drawer upstairs and practised the steps on the narrow strip of lino between the chest of drawers and the bed, struggling with the turns and counting out the rhythm in his head so that they wouldn't hear him singing. It became an obsession and most nights, after tea, when he had washed and shaved, Bill would disappear upstairs and they would hear the irregular patter of his feet on the floor above the kitchen.

"Funny way to dance, without any music," Harold observed. It was a strange way for a young man to carry on night after night and it made him feel uncomfortable. "He wants to get out a bit more!"

Bill didn't often use the shops on Heeley Bottom. That was the local shopping area that his mother used at the bottom of the road. It was full of butchers and grocers, a wet fish shop and even a cobbler's shop where Lilly bought squares of leather for Harold to mend their shoes. But there was a Boots the Chemist and that was convenient for haircream and toothpaste when he needed it.

He called in on his way home one Saturday. It was raining again and it would save him coming down later. The shop was full as it usually was and he stood waiting with irritation at the indecisiveness of the shoppers before him with their afterthoughts and fiddling in their purses for change. He turned at the sound of a voice at the small dispensary window calling a customer to collect their prescription. It was a young voice, an attractive female voice and Bill caught sight of a slim hand passing down a paper bag and behind it thick dark curls and vivacious eyes beneath finely arched brows. He smiled, involuntarily and the girl's eyes caught his smile, held it for an instant and disappeared from the window.

He felt...? He didn't dare to look again in case she was there. He bought, not the Brylcreem he had come for but something more expensive and uncommon. He took his change with his back straight and wished he wasn't wearing his overalls and carrying his knapsack. Walking up the road he was oblivious to the rain. Had she smiled? He couldn't say. The moment had been too fleeting. But unaccountably he felt a joyous sense of relief.

CHAPTER 32

Toothpaste and Phul Nana's

He hadn't dared to go back into Boots again that day. She would think..?
Well he didn't know what she would think. But he was sure there had
been a smile, he hoped there had been a smile and he wanted to make
sure. But he was afraid in case he was wrong and then he'd look daft. So
he stayed away and waited for the week to pass.

Saturday came again and he couldn't wait to get away promptly and
catch the early tram. He left his overalls at work. Now he didn't look so
bad; his gaberdine was O.K. and his face was clean. A doubt arose. She
might only have been there for that day, filling in from another branch
or something. He tried to remember the glimpse he had seen but the
memory had gone and he clung to the recollection of the way it had
made him feel. It was stupid but suppose he saw her and didn't
recognise her? Then what!? And so he tormented himself as the tram
jostled its way across the city.

He decided that he would buy toothpaste. It showed he took care of
his grooming even if he was wearing workaday clothes.

She wasn't there!

Bill looked over to the dispensary window but the top of the head
leaning over the bench within wasn't hers. It was a man's, and had a
bald patch. The man in the dispensary looked up and spoke to someone
inside. Perhaps that was her, just out of sight. Now the dilatory shoppers
became his friends. The longer they took the more chance of seeing
whether it was her or not.

"Next!"

Bill turned. He was next in line to be served. There was a small
queue behind him. He stood aside and let the woman behind him go
instead. "I'm not sure what I want yet." he said. "I'm still looking."

He wandered to the back of the shop and peered across the counter
into the dispensary and saw the chemist looking at him. He turned away,
pretending to search the shelves.

"Can I help you?"

She was standing at the dispensary door smiling at him. Bill
searched for words.

"We're quite busy again today," she said, "and we're a bit short staffed. Lunchbreak."

"Ah," Bill said. Her voice was gentle and clear. He wished he could hear her speak again. "I'm… er… do you have Euthymol?"

"Paste or a tin?" She reached over the counter and Bill saw how slim she was beneath the white dispensary coat. Her hair was as he remembered, dark curls that caught the light as she moved. She held up a tin and a tube of toothpaste. Bill found himself looking into her eyes. Again there was an instant that seemed like eternity. She was smiling at his sudden awkwardness. "Or you can take both if you like."

"No." Bill smiled back at her. "Sorry. The tube. Please." He fished in his pocket for the money. "I… er…"

"I'll have to go," she said. "We're short staffed and I've got some prescriptions to get out."

"Yes. Thank you." He doffed the toothpaste at her and she retreated smiling back into the dispensary.

Bill cursed the week. Saturday was the only time the shop was open when he could go back to see her. He cursed himself. Why hadn't he said something when he had the chance instead of stammering like a fool? Another week! She might get asked out by somebody else while he was shut up here surrounded by oil and sweat. Well what the hell! She might be married anyway for all he knew. But there was the memory of the look that had passed between them. She was so pretty! Not in the ordinary, conventional sense of the word. Her nose was rather too long and aquiline for that. But she was so full of vitality. It shone in the brightness of her brown eyes. Bill had never seen eyes so deep. Her gaze engulfed him. And her smiling mouth. And perfect teeth that gleamed when she smiled. It was as if she was the first girl Bill had ever seen and all the rest were merely passing traffic. He wondered what he would buy this week.

He need not have worried.

As the time approached when he had made his last two appearances she glanced repeatedly through the dispensary hatch. Would he come again this week or had the last two Saturdays been mere coincidence? It's no good hoping, she told herself; it only sets you up for a disappointment. And she tried to concentrate on the prescriptions.

She saw him enter before the shop doorbell rang. His eyes rapidly scanned the shelves for inspiration as he made straight toward the dispensary at the back. She went to the dispensary door and stood on the little threshold.

"Hello."

Her voice. It was just as Bill remembered it. He smiled back and all the subterfuge was abandoned.

"I'm sorry. I know you're busy," he blurted. "I was wondering if

261

you'd like to come out one night next week."

"Yes." She glanced fleetingly back into the dispensary. "I can't talk," she said.

"No. Of course. Pictures?"

"Yes."

"I'll meet you. There's a film on at the Abbeydale…"

"Yes, that'd be good."

"Tuesday? Or…?"

"No Tuesday's fine… Seven o'clock…?"

"Seven o'clock…?"

Their voices chimed together and Bill found himself grinning with pleasure.

She smiled back at him. "Did you want to buy anything?"

"No I… I'd better go. You're busy."

"Yes."

"Tuesday then. Seven."

"I'll see you there."

Bill turned reluctantly from her.

"Oh." He turned back suddenly. She was still in the doorway looking at him. Bill glanced quickly round at the other people in the shop but they were busy.

"I don't know your name," he said.

"Dorothy."

"I'm Bill. I'll see you Tuesday then. At the Abbeydale."

"I'll be there."

Her name was Dorothy! Her voice was low with modulations that made Bill's heart beat with pleasure at the sound. He savoured her name; it wasn't a common name he told himself, but a name that was firm when spoken and soft to hear. The repeated pleasure of the memory carried him all the way along the road to home…

"What's up?" Lilly asked, passing Bill his plate of braised meat and yorkshire pudding.

"Nothing. Why?"

"You look different. Nothing's happened has it? At work I mean?"

"No. Why should it?"

"You look different that's all."

"You're seeing things mother!"

Leaving the sweetshop opposite the cinema with his week's ration of chocolate in his pocket Bill saw Dorothy step down from the tram, early, just as he was. He quickly popped one of the Phul-Nana breath fresheners he had just bought into his mouth and went to meet her. She waved at his approach and stepped forward to greet him.

"That was good timing."

"Yes wasn't it," Dorothy replied. "I nearly missed it."

"I'd have waited. Hope you like chocolates." He showed her the small box he had bought. "Biggest I could get."

She smiled. "What time does it start?"

They went into the foyer and checked the programme times.

"Oh we're a bit early."

"It's continuous," Bill said. "We could go in and watch the end then see it through. Might be better than waiting around." He gave a shiver to underline his proposal.

"Yes." Dorothy said. "That would be nice. Let's do that."

She reached into her handbag for some money.

"No, no." Bill said. "You're with me."

"Thank you."

He steered her ahead of him into the darkness and they settled quickly into their seats. Bill sat stiffly, not wishing to appear fidgety and from the corner of his eye saw Dorothy's attention immediately focused on the film. He turned his mind to the screen, acutely conscious of Dorothy sitting by his side. Normally Bill knew he would have reached in the darkness for her hand. He might even have insinuated his arm along the back of Dorothy's seat until it rested around her shoulders and drawn her to lean close against him. Just as other couples in the darkness around them were doing. It wasn't that Dorothy had shown any sign of reluctance. On the contrary.

The end of the film arrived and they stood to let the row empty. For a few minutes they were almost alone in the theatre.

"Looks like it's a good film." Bill reached in his pocket for the chocolates.

"I've been wanting to see it for ages."

Bill opened the box. "Didn't want to get them out earlier. Makes such a noise fiddling with the papers."

Dorothy poised with her hand over the box and Bill admired the slimness of her fingers. They were unadorned by any rings. "Now," she said, "which one?"

"I never asked you where you live. Did you have far to come?"

"No," she replied. "Just up Woodseats. Near Graves Park. D'you know it?"

"Yes. Of course." A fleeting picture; the long meadow and playing field at the top of the hill looking over the woods and the city below. "It's nice up there."

"You look very nice." Dorothy was looking at the badge on Bill's blazer. "Did you used to be in the airforce?"

"Yes. I got demobbed earlier this year. I'm a springmaker now. I was on bombers."

"Gosh."

"I volunteered. I mean, springmaking was a reserved occupation but… well, I wanted to do something. You know." He was going too fast. "Tell me about you."

"Oh there's nothing much really. I always liked science at school and when I left I worked in a laboratory. I had thought of being a metallurgist but, well I left and got a job with Boots. I got my exams and now I work in the dispensary."

"Sounds like it's a good job."

"It is. And I love it."

"Have you always worked down there. Heeley Bottom I mean?" Oh gosh! He could have met her weeks ago!

"No." She laughed a little, as though she could read his thoughts. "I only transferred there last month. I was in the Woodseats branch before that."

She saw the unaccountable relief pass fleetingly across Bill's face and laughed again. "I knew you were going to ask me out."

"How could you know that?"

"Oh, just the way you looked."

"Well," he said, containing his surprise. "Here we are anyway." He proffered the chocolates again and they sat quietly together as the seats around them began to fill.

"What does your dad do?" Dorothy asked after a few moments. "Is he a spring maker?"

"No. He works on the railway."

"Oh!" she cried, "my father's on the railway too!" Her delight was to find something they had in common. "He's an engine driver. He drives express trains to London." She was so proud of him. "On the LMS. Is that what your dad's on?"

"No. I mean yes. He's on the LMS. But not as a driver."

They stood to let another couple pass them on the row.

"My brother used to be on the railway too." She paused. When they were seated again she added softly, "A guard."

"Oh." Bill missed the note of sadness in Dorothy's voice and said, "My brother's on the buses. Conductor."

They paused in their disclosures. Having put each other in a family context each wanted to talk about the other. But Bill knew he would have to prepare the way. He was growing more fond of Dorothy with every minute and the last thing he wanted to do was frighten her off. Thankfully the lights dimmed and the first feature began. They smiled at each other and settled back to watch. Now Bill could take Dorothy's hand in his and he savoured the little squeeze of appreciation she gave him in return. He hardly registered the film at all.

"That was good wasn't it?" Dorothy enthused as they crowded out of the foyer with the others. "I like Humphrey Bogart."

"Yes he's good isn't he." Bill hesitated then said, "We might just manage a quick drink if we're lucky."

Dorothy gave a little grimace of disappointment. "Oh I'm sorry. I really should get back. I don't want to miss the tram…"

"Oh no. No I was forgetting."

"It's not that…"

"No really. I wasn't thinking. We'd be better walking down to Chesterfield Road. You can get a tram straight to Woodseats from there."

"I only came round the other way to save me that walk. I know it's a longer journey," Dorothy explained, "but it saved me having to walk under the railway bridge and cross the river in the dark."

They set off down the gloomy gennel together towards the footbridge at the bottom where it crossed the oily, rusted waters of the Sheaf.

"I'll see you home if you like."

"Do you live at Woodseats too?"

"No," Bill said. "Just around here."

"Oh, it'll take you out of your way."

"No really. I'd like to. If you don't mind."

"Of course I don't mind." Dorothy slipped her arm through Bill's and they walked easily, murmuring their appreciation to each other for their evening together.

Dorothy's home was halfway along the road, a tree lined terrace of small Edwardian villas. They paused at the bottom of a passage between the houses and Bill wasn't certain whether or not he should try to kiss her.

"I'd like to see you again," he said.

"Yes. Alright."

"We could go to the pictures again. Or something else if you like." Was it too soon to think of dancing? He didn't even know if she liked to dance.

"No," Dorothy replied. "I'd like to see that picture they were showing next week. It looked good."

"Next week then." He paused. "Shall I call…"

"No," she said. "It's too far for you to come right up here just to go back again. I'll meet you there same as tonight. Next Tuesday then?"

"Yes. That'd be fine." Again he hesitated. "Well… goodnight…"

Dorothy leaned up to him and kissed his cheek. "It's been lovely. See you next week."

265

Bill stood and waved as she turned and ran into the passage. He heard a door close in the darkness of the yard beyond. Well, next week then! He turned and walked down to the tramstop at the bottom of the road but his footsteps were light.

Another week to wait! Wednesday and Thursday dragged. Friday was an early finish but not early enough. On Saturday he made an excuse to himself and went into Boots. Dorothy was waiting for him.

"I was hoping you'd call in."

"You don't mind? I mean if you're…"

"No," she said. "Only Mr. Baxter's looking so you'd better pretend to be buying something."

"Have you got any razorblades?"

"Over there." She pointed to a display stand in the corner.

"This is daft," Bill said. "I mean, talking to you and you're not supposed to be talking and… Only I couldn't wait 'till Tuesday."

"Neither could I. I'm glad you came."

"Well. I'll see you Tuesday then."

"Yes."

"Unless…?"

"Yes?"

"You doing anything tonight?"

"No."

"I thought… perhaps… Well there's a dance at Nether Edge. If you…?

"That would be lovely."

"I didn't know if you…?"

"Where shall I see you?"

"Meet you at the Abbeydale eh? Seven o'clock?"

"Oh yes. I'll have to go." Dorothy could sense Mr. Baxter wondering why the transaction took so much conversation.

"See you there then."

"Yes." And Dorothy danced back into the dispensary.

Wonderful! And what was more wonderful was the dance would give him the chance to hold Dorothy in his arms. Tonight! He hoped his dancing was up to it. She had seemed so pleased to be asked. She might be a real expert. Then what? He didn't want to look a fool. And there was David. They always went out to tea together on Saturdays. But what could he do? For a moment Bill's footsteps faltered. Oh God! There would have to be explanations to his mother. He wasn't ready for that yet! Not that he needed to explain things to his mother he told himself angrily. Only, they liked to go out for a drink themselves on a Saturday. Oh bloody hell! Why hadn't he thought of that first. Well it was no good now. He'd asked her. And he wasn't going to let her down! He pictured himself with Dorothy in his arms and his pace quickened and his mood lightened and he walked in with a secret smile of pleasure on his face.

"Mother can you do something for me?"

Lilly turned from the sink; Billy was hanging his coat behind the stairs door.

"Not right away," she said, "I'm in the middle of getting dinner ready."

"I don't mean right away. Tonight. Later."

"What is it?"

She studied Bill for a moment. It was so long since she had seen him look anything but worn out. Now all of a sudden, this last week he looked like a young man again. She had begun to think she would never see another smile on his face, now he was positively beaming.

"Mother I'm going out tonight…"

"But you goes out every Saturday." she said.

"No, I mean, on my own. Without David."

"Without…? He'll be ever so…"

"I don't mean on my own!" he cried. "Not just on my own! I've met somebody."

Lilly was suddenly anxious. Oh not another! Not another like Daisy I hope to God…!

Bill saw her face and knew what she was thinking. Why couldn't she be pleased for him. Just for once!

"She's not like that mother. Her name's Dorothy. She's a lovely girl. I've seen her… well I've met her a couple of times and been out with her once. Only I want to take her to a dance. Up at Nether Edge. She's a chemist." As if that made any difference. But it did. Somehow it placed her in a different bracket to Daisy.

"Anyway can you look after David tonight?"

"Just this once then," Lilly said. "You know me and your dad like to go out for a drink together on a Saturday. After the pictures."

"Maybe David could go to the pictures with you. For a change."

"Depends what's on. We'll see. Only you'll have to tell David."

Bill discovered that Dorothy was a good dancer; not expert but better than he was. But with her natural sense of rhythm and sensitivity to his body she allowed Bill to lead her. His enjoyment of the dance increased and he was able to put in the steps he had been practising on the lino in the small back bedroom with mounting confidence.

"How long have you been learning?" Dorothy asked during an interval.

"Not very long. I tried a dancing school but I couldn't get on with them."

"So what did you do?"

"Got one of those teach yourself books," he confessed with a wry grin. "You know, pages of drawings with black footprints for you and white ones for your partner. 'Course what it doesn't give you is the real speed or rhythm."

"Well if that's how you've done it you're very good. Is that really…?"

"Well, you know, apart from NAAFI dances and going out before the war. But this is the first time I've started to take it seriously," he protested. "Really seriously I mean."

"You ought to do it properly," Dorothy said, smiling encouragement. "You could be really good you know."

His bashful grin hid Bill's delight. Such praise, such winning approval! He delighted in her.

"Well…" he began to say but Dorothy cut him off.

"We could go together. I used to have lessons but it's no fun on your own is it. What d'you think. Shall we? I know a good dancing school."

Shall we! Shall I give you the moon?

"Oh yes. It sounds great. Do you really think so?"

"Yes. You could be a really good dancer if you tried Bill. And if we really took it seriously we could go for medals."

Bill started to protest but Dorothy intervened. "I don't mean competition dancing. But we could go for the different standards. You begin with the bronze, then silver and if you're really good, the gold. What d'you think?"

Bill looked at her. This girl was wonderful! There were no obstacles with her.

"We'd be spending an awful lot of time together."

"I know," she said. "You wouldn't mind would you?"

"Mind! I mean, I'm thinking of you. We've hardly met. You don't know me."

"No," Dorothy said, "but I think I'd like to."

The band struck up again. "Oh this sounds like a foxtrot. Shall we try?"

"Yes. Why not." In a haze of happiness Bill led Dorothy back onto the floor.

And so all through the murderous winter of nineteen-fortyseven, with its shortages of fuel and food rationing; its endless cold and freezing snow, Bill and Dorothy went dancing twice a week.

Their pleasure in each other grew and blossomed into courtship. For Bill, smitten as he was, his feelings for Dorothy grew into love. All he had ever wanted was in this girl who looked at him so approvingly and shared the same pleasures. And the future he had dreamed of but which had seemed so unattainable just a few weeks ago – why, he felt that anything was possible with Dorothy! Except; somehow he had to find a way of broaching his secret and confiding it to her in a way that didn't cause her to have misgivings.

The problem was that in the beginning he had carefully avoided talking

268

in any detail about his past, except to make general sweeping references to casual girlfriends, the way any normal young man would. He avoided taking her home in case his mother or father unwittingly betrayed him. But the longer the secret remained, the more difficult it became. It loomed, like a confession, a shameful denouement waiting to be wrung from him. He was fearful of his past spoiling the future. But sooner or later he knew it would have to come out.

By the end of winter when the last of the snow had melted away and the warmth of spring began to fill the air they were ready to compete for the bronze medal of the International Dancing Masters Association. Bill prepared thoroughly. His new dancing pumps that Lilly and Harold condemned as a wanton waste of money – 'You've got that nice pair of black shoes for best. What do you want to go wasting your money on them for? You never wear 'em' – were polished up for the occasion; his suit was carefully brushed and he spent an inordinate length of time at the mirror recombing the parting in his hair until he was finally satisfied. They wouldn't understand how important presentation was to the outcome.

"I'm going mother. I've got me key."

"Good luck Billy."

He accepted their wishes with a cavalier, "Shan't be late." and drew his mac around him.

Dorothy was waiting restless with anticipation. Bill smiled at her with approval. "We'll win it on appearance alone."

Dorothy linked her arm in his. "We both will. How do you feel?" She gave a tiny shrug and bit her bottom lip. "Nervous?"

"A bit. You happy with that turn we practised?"

"I think so. You?"

"Yes. Come on then. We'll go shall we?"

It was strange but the instant they stepped on the floor their nerves vanished and they danced with such fluency and confidence they knew they must have passed.

"Gosh that was great!" Dorothy was flushed with exhileration. "What d'you think?"

"I don't know. Have to wait and see now. It felt good though. Come on, let's get a drink."

They found a table and Bill fetched them both a cup of coffee.

"I'm ready for this. I enjoyed that. It was so…" Dorothy was lost for words in her remembrance of the display they had given.

"You were so light. It was like you were just ahead. At one stage I thought we were going too fast in that quickstep. But it was just perfect."

"And we must have covered every inch of the floor. We must have passed! What do you think Bill? Do you think we have?"

269

"It's the best we've ever danced." He smiled and Dorothy grinned back at him in exultation. He couldn't bear to lose this. The feeling that Dorothy gave him, that life was for living. He had to shed the ghosts hovering about him; he was living a lie. Now was the time, when they were bound together in the competition; when they were, at this moment, so uniquely one.

"There's something else."

"What?" Dorothy looked at him with interest, searching his face.

"Oh it's just…" Bill tried to make the words light and inconsequential. "You know, what I said about, well, girlfriends and that. You know."

Dorothy tried to match Bill's attempt at indifference. She smiled, but only just managed to hold it without faltering and a tiny hand of fear clutched at her heart.

"You're not a bluebeard are you? With a wife hidden away somewhere?"

Up until now Dorothy's career had taken priority. And then Bill had walked into the shop and something fleeting had passed between them. Oh she didn't believe in love at first sight and she had always been very careful and aloof with the boyfriends she had met. But there had been something different about Bill, even before he had spoken to her and she didn't know what it was. Except that she had lived through that first week as Bill had, hoping she might see him again. But what was it? Here she was at the peak of a happy evening and now there was something in Bill's manner and it was all going to be dashed away.

"No, no!" Bill leaned towards her, imploring her with his eyes. "It's nothing like that. Only I'm… I'm divorced."

He waited for Dorothy's reaction.

A million thoughts raced through Dorothy's mind.

"Divorced?"

Bill lowered his eyes. "I'm sorry," he said. "I should…" Was she looking at him? What was she thinking? Was it all over? "I should have told you," he mumbled, like a penitent before a priest. He raised his head.

Dorothy was looking at him with something approaching pity in her eyes.

"I knew there was something."

"Well… I didn't know how to tell you."

"When?"

"Oh ages ago. In the war. I was away and… She was going with other men."

"Oh Bill. You should have told me. What happened?"

What should he say? What could he tell her? That he'd fathered a bastard and married out of duty? Then discovered she was promiscuous! And what about his own behaviour? Seducing her before they were married! Oh God!! He saw everything crumbling before him.

Dorothy saw the conflict in Bill's face. She knew she was falling in love with him. She had never imagined what it could be like to feel for a man the way she felt about Bill. They were so right for each other. Whatever it was she was sure the fault was not with Bill. He was such a good man. She trusted him.

"Come on Bill. You've got to tell me."

He sipped at his coffee. "It was the war," he said. "It makes you do things. I'd volunteered, we didn't know if we'd see each other again. We... got married... And then I was posted away. I came home on leave... she was with another bloke..."

"You mean...?"

"I found 'em together. They were in bed together... Oh Christ..."

"Oh Bill..." She reached out and took his hand in hers. "No wonder you didn't want to tell me."

"I'm sorry..."

"Don't be. You don't have to be sorry."

"I don't know what to say. Perhaps we'd better not..."

"Don't say that!" she cried. "It doesn't make any difference. Do you still see her?"

"No!" he shouted, so vehemently that the couple at the next table looked up at him. "No," he repeated. "I never want to see that... see her again."

"It's alright Bill. It's alright."

He reached for Dorothy's hand. "I love you so much. I'm so afraid I'll lose you."

"It's alright," she coaxed him. "I'm glad you told me. You must never be afraid to tell me things." She lowered her eyes then raised them to him. "I've never felt like anybody the way I feel about you Bill. I love you. I love you. That's all that matters."

"I wish I'd told you before. Would it have made any difference?"

"I don't think so. Who can say?"

"You sure?"

"Come here." She leaned across the table and drew him forward. "I love you," she repeated, "and that's all that matters."

271

CHAPTER 33

A confession

Now Bill's mind was filled with doubt. He told himself he wasn't engaged in subterfuge and that it was merely a question of getting the timing right because he thought too much of Dorothy to spring two surprises on her all at once. That might have been too much for her to take! Besides, the moment when he might have told her had passed. But in his heart, although he wouldn't admit it, he knew he had been wrong. He should have told her about David at the same time. Had it been cowardice? Now he had to face that hurdle as well.

Emotionally, things were moving too fast. He knew he was soon going to ask Dorothy to marry him. Oh they wouldn't get married for ages yet – assuming she said 'yes' – but he wanted to introduce her to Lilly and Harold. He wanted to be able to show her off to George. And he hadn't met Dorothy's family yet. The nearest he'd got was meeting her at the corner of the road.

But would it be too much for her to take on? Oh why hadn't he spoken when the subject was out in the open!

"Are you alright Bill?" They were strolling hand in hand by the side of the boating lake. It was very companionable, walking in the spring sunshine on a Sunday afternoon like this but Bill seemed preoccupied.

"Yes, I'm fine. Warm enough?"

"Yes." Dorothy smiled. "I just thought you were a bit thoughtful that's all."

"No." he said. "It's just so nice being with you." He flashed a smile at her and pressed her hand, quickening his pace. "Do you fancy a cup of coffee?"

Bill took a secret pleasure in Dorothy's preference for coffee. His mother and father only drank tea at home; coffee was for the nobbs and for them as wanted to show off. And even his tea was always taken in a pint pot, never in a cup. 'You never get enough to drink in a cup,' Harold said. But Dorothy took for granted the small civilising things like a preference for coffee over tea.

They strode along the path around the end of the lake and began to walk the gentle slope up the meadow.

"Come on," Dorothy cried suddenly, "I'll race you to that tree."

She set off like a hare, laughing, "Come on."

Bill set off after her as she began zig-zagging across the meadow to avoid him. They reached the tree and leaned against it, gasping and laughing together.

"Slowcoach!" she teased him. "Thought you could run faster than that!"

"You took me by surprise," he said. "Didn't know you could run like that."

"See," she said with a laugh, "you don't know everything do you."

There was a narrow slatted bench nailed around the tree trunk and Dorothy reclined on it.

"Come and sit with me." She patted the seat beside her. "It's really warm. Come and sit down for a bit."

Bill looked at the shadows on the grass and the humour seemed to desert him.

"No," he said, "not here. Let's go up to the café."

"If you like." Strange, she thought, the fleeting changes that came over him.

Beyond the yew hedge the formal rose garden was prepared for its summer show. The pruned roses were sending out leafy red shoots of new growth and the bedding plants around them were already bright with flowers behind the miniature hedges which surrounded the beds. Bill paused and sat on a bench set in an alcove with the high yew hedge behind. Where the flagstone paths crossed in the middle of the garden the centrepiece, an elfin figure of Peter Pan played his pipes to the sunshine with birds and rabbits at his feet.

"I love that statue," Dorothy confided. "It just sums up childhood for me. He looks so happy and bright. He hasn't a care in the world. It's so innocent isn't it Bill."

"I've got a son."

He sat, rigid, waiting for her reaction, her protest and the reasons she would give for her change and sudden coolness towards him. He turned his head to look at her. Dorothy was looking down at the statue's base and the ground around it.

"I've been waiting for you to tell me," she said softly.

"How did you know? I never said…" His voice trailed away.

"Oh," Dorothy spoke with her head bowed. "Little things. I sensed there was something else you wanted to tell me last week. You never lingered very much after dancing. And you haven't let me near your family yet."

"But I've not met…" He began to protest then murmured. "What can I say?"

"We've known each other long enough now haven't we Bill?"

"I know. I... Is that it then?"

There was sadness in her voice. "What were you afraid of?"

"Losing you," he said with quiet simplicity.

"Do you think you would lose me like that?"

"I don't know what to think."

"Oh Bill."

They watched other strollers pass through the garden to the tea room.

"I love you Dorothy," he murmured.

Dorothy reached across for his hand. "You know, you should never be afraid to tell me anything. Anything," she added with emphasis.

"I couldn't bear to lose you. I didn't know what to do for the best."

"You didn't think we could carry on without telling me about him did you?"

"I know. I should have told you about him right at the start. But then you might not have wanted to see me. What could I do? And then when we began seeing each other... It was too late to say anything then. What could I do? I love you. I was going..." He checked himself. Marriage!! What a hope! Now the dream was gone forever. He stood up and stood a little way apart from her.

"How old is he?"

"Five and a... well, he'll be six in June."

"What's his name?"

"David."

"David. That's nice. Has he got a middle name?"

"No."

"Come and sit back down here with me."

Awkwardly, almost reluctantly Bill took his seat next to her. "Anyway," he said with a sigh, "you know about him now. I'm sorry."

"I'd like to meet him."

Bill let the statement hang in the air.

"You know," he said sadly, "it's bad enough you knocking about with a bloke who's divorced. Without kids being involved as well."

"I'm not 'knocking about' as you put it. I'm with a man I care very deeply for. Only he's given me quite a shock and a lot to think about these last few days. It takes a bit of getting used to you know."

Bill was silent.

"And I'd still like to meet him."

"You sure?" he mumbled.

"I wouldn't say it if I wasn't. Now would I? Surely you know me well enough for that?"

"Oh Dorothy!"

274

"What is he like?"

Did he dare to hope?

"Fair hair." She saw a faint smile. "And dirty knees. Just like any other five year old I suppose. He's a good drawer."

"Oh well, he'd better draw me a picture then."

"Are you sure?"

"Oh Bill. You didn't think you could get rid of me that easily did you?" Looking at him Dorothy saw the doubt begin to lift. "You must never be afraid to tell me things you know."

"I've only just got him back," Bill said anxiously. "I mean up until this last year he's been with my aunt at Worcester."

Dorothy watched as the words poured out.

"He was with 'em when I found 'em. His mother I mean. And the bloke she was with. I don't mean he was in the same room, nothing like that but just left in his cot, crying all night long. He was only a baby. And then I found out she was pregnant. Not mine," he protested, "not mine."

Dorothy's heart went out to him and she leaned and kissed him gently. "Come on love."

"You don't mind?"

"Oh Bill. Come on. Let's go and have that coffee shall we. My treat?"

She coaxed him to his feet and slipped her arm in his.

"Come on. No more secrets."

"You're the best thing that's ever happened to me, d'you know that. Are you sure? You still want to see me?"

"Bill, I love you. No matter what's happened in the past you've got to try to leave it in the past. These last few weeks have been so… oh I can't tell you."

"I know. Oh Dorothy! If only… But what about your mum and dad? They won't like the idea much will they?"

"But things are changing Bill." Dorothy was wringing Bill's hand with the strength of her conviction. "Ever since the war, people are beginning to think differently."

He held the café door for her and followed her inside. "I know but some things never change."

"We'll see. Anyway what are you having, tea or coffee? I've told you, it's my treat today."

CHAPTER 34

The dambuster

For Dorothy the next two weeks were fraught with uncertainty about her relationship with Bill. There was no doubt of Bill's love for her and she had been expecting there was something Bill needed to tell her. The revelation of his previous marriage had brought her feelings almost of relief. But Bill's further revelation in the park that a child existed was much more than she had expected despite her brave initial protestations. Dorothy's feelings ebbed and flowed. Why hadn't he told her before?

Lying awake and thinking in the darkness at night, it didn't seem to be a problem at all. She loved Bill; she would care for him and the son she hadn't met. And curling into her pillow she dreamed of the home they would make and the family they would become. But cold dawn brought reality. David was nearly six years old and she didn't know how she would be able to face the prospect of being responsible for a child who wasn't her own. It would be different if he was still a baby. But to be plunged straight into being the mother of a little boy! Besides which she had a job, a good job with prospects and it would mean giving the job up to look after him. Of course Bill had a good job too and no doubt he could look after them all but she had put so much into her career. But it was too soon to be thinking like this! They were just going out together and that was fine. It was better than fine! Going out with Bill was wonderful. And until last week, she had secretly nursed hopes that they would become engaged. When they knew they were ready for each other. But he had kept it such a secret!

And then Dorothy chided herself. Well of course he had kept it a secret. She could understand that. How could he have told her any earlier! But then there was the problem of telling her mother and father. How would they take it! They were expecting her to follow Marge, her older sister, who had married Charlie and started her own family. Her mother and father doted on Joan, their granddaughter but how would they react to David? Oh but here she was running ahead of herself again! Seeing herself already married! Well, and what's wrong with that, she asked herself defiantly! That's where she had hoped it was going to lead.

Only now she wasn't so sure. She still loved Bill dearly. But this last week had suddenly brought so many problems! It was very confusing and she needed time to think.

To all outward appearances everything was the same. Bill and Dorothy continued to meet and go dancing together. But he was aware of a sense of withdrawal as Dorothy wrestled with the conflict inside her.

Now there was nothing to hide and nothing that his parents could betray, Bill invited Dorothy home for tea the following weekend. He still nursed hopes that everything would be alright. All it needed was a little time. And perhaps when she met David...?

When the following Sunday arrived there was a high level of expectation in Lilly and Harold. They didn't need Bill to tell them how important it was, they had seen the difference that meeting her had made in him. But it didn't prevent Bill from telling them anyway what a nice young woman she was and from a good family. Nothing could have been less calculated to put them all at ease.

"What do you think we are, Billy? You'd think we didn't know how to carry on with people the way you go on."

"I didn't mean that mother. It's just that, you know, where she lives and that, she's used to nice things."

"Do you think we don't have nice things? What are you getting at? Anybody'd think you were ashamed of us the way you carry on."

"No of course I'm not! Why do you always have to take things the wrong way? Anyway I've got to go and meet her soon." Bill looked at the clock. "We'll be back for about half past four." He looked round at the table. Lilly had spread the clean tablecloth but hadn't begun to lay it yet.

David had been instructed to be on his best behaviour too. He was beginning to get excited, although why, he couldn't say. It was just that it seemed to be so important to everybody and now he was going to meet 'Aunty Dorothy', the lady his daddy had been seeing so much of.

"Can I come with you daddy and help you to fetch her?"

"No you can't. You can stay here and help grandma to get things ready for when she arrives."

"Oh," David moaned. "It's not fair."

"You'll see her soon enough," Lilly said. "Here, you can come and help me to carry these pots in from the kitchen." She began to lay plates and cutlery. "Not like that." She corrected the layout of the knives and forks. "Go and fetch me the salt and pepper pot. And the vinegar. I've got this lettuce to wash."

Lilly went to the head of the cellar and leaned across the steps to the shelf on the far wall above the darkness. David marvelled as he always did, at grandma's daring, leaning over what was, to him, an

277

abyss. Lilly retrieved a tin of best salmon off the shelf and the lettuce from the food safe on the slab below. "Here," she said. "Pass me the tin opener out of the drawer."

So the careful preparations continued and they tried to beat back their nervous apprehension. David was jumping about on the cushions and for the umpteenth time Lilly told him to stop it and straightened them again. "Why don't you go to the bottom of the terrace and look out for Uncle George and Aunty Myra's bus coming. Put your coat on. It's cold."

Dutifully David went out to the bus stop with his toy gun and began taking pot shots at the imaginary Indians stalking his position from the house fronts across the road.

"Butter's as hard as iron!" Lilly complained, trying to spread delicate slices without the bread disintegrating under the knife.

"I'll have a wash," Harold said.

"I thought you'd already done that! They'll be here any time."

"Won't take me a minute."

"Well hurry up then. I want to use the sink! Put the kettle back on when you've finished."

The back door burst open and David dashed in crying, "They're here!"

'Oh my God!' was Lilly's first thought, 'we ain't ready yet!' And then with relief as George and Myra entered she turned on David. "What d'you mean, bursting in the door like that!"

"Sorry grandma."

David liked his daddy's brother. He took George's hand, dragging him through to the living room. "Come and draw something for me."

"Wait a bit!" George protested. "Let me get me coat off first."

Myra was ahead of him; her coat was hung on the back of the stairs door and she was already bustling about the kitchen. "Now then ma," she said to Lilly, "come on! What wants doing?"

It was in Myra's nature. She was small, as active as a bird with restless energy in contrast to George's placid way. "We're fettlers us. Always have been in my family," she used to say, as if bustle was a virtue in itself. But her sweeping glance took in the absence of fruit in the bowl and she seized the tin opener and began opening the pears. "Where's the cream?" Myra cried. "Have you got a jug for the cream?"

Dorothy approached the visit with judgement reserved. She had always had self-confidence and a sense of her own worth. Meeting Bill's mother and father and the ritual of the Sunday tea was no problem. After all, it was Bill and she who mattered and she knew enough about Bill's feelings for her to know that family approval was not the issue. She just hoped she could like David. And that he would

278

accept her. Without that, she knew they had no future.

They all jumped up with nervous formality when Bill, a proud smile on his face, stood aside in the doorway to bring Dorothy in. For an awful moment he thought his mother was going to curtsey.

"Hello love." Lilly took Dorothy's hand and carefully shook it. "Pleased to meet you." Harold did the same with a beaming smile.

George broke the formality. "Come on love." He patted the seat alongside him on the settee. "Come and sit here."

"Here, I'll take your coat." Myra helped Dorothy with it in the crowded room. "I'll take it upstairs with the others. There's not enough room behind that door. We're all too well off," she laughed, "too many coats!"

Dorothy sat amongst them and saw David peering at her from around Bill's legs in the doorway. He looked away when he saw her looking at him, then peered round again.

"And you must be David," Dorothy said.

David nodded. He liked the sound of her voice and the way she looked straight at him. Not staring, but looking directly and inviting him to make the same contact.

"Are you coming to say hello?"

She was talking to him again. Unaccountably David felt bashful. She was so pretty. He wanted to be loved by her and he became smothered in shyness for fear she should know what he was thinking.

"Come on," Dorothy coaxed, "come and say hello."

David opened his mouth but it stayed open and wouldn't speak. He slid behind Bill's legs to hide his embarrassment.

"Oh well," she spoke partly to David and partly to the room in general, "perhaps later then."

But Bill intervened. "Come on David. Don't be so silly. Come and say hello to Aunty Dorothy." He pushed David forward from behind his legs.

"It's alright Bill. In a minute. Give him time."

"Come on," Bill insisted. "Come and say hello like a good boy."

"Hello," David murmured.

"Hello Aunty Dorothy!" Bill prompted.

"Hello Aunty Dorothy." David felt a strange inner excitement saying her name.

Dorothy extended an arm. "Would you like to shake hands?"

David approached her and she shook his hand properly, not like playing. Then she shuffled on the settee and created a small gap between her and George.

"Come and sit here next to me and tell me what you like doing."

David sat and for the next few minutes he basked in Dorothy's sole attention while everyone looked on with approval.

"Tea's ready when you are!" Myra announced. "It's a bit crowded but we're all family."

Lilly brought the big teapot in from the kitchen.

"Come on. Bill; Dorothy, you're here. Harold you're in your usual place. Can you and our George manage over there Myra? Come on David! Now, help yourselves." Lilly passed the plate of bread and butter round.

"You won't get nothing if you don't." Myra cried gleefully. She turned to Bill. "Why don't you and Dorothy come up to us for tea next Sunday?"

"Oh we can't. Not next Sunday." He turned to smile at Dorothy. "We're going to your mother's aren't we."

"Yes. I wish we'd known. It would be nice."

"They can come the week after can't they?" George said.

"'Course they can." Myra said. "Do that. Come up for tea the week after. Anyway we've got something to show you."

Bill looked up and Dorothy said, "Oh? What's that?"

"Ah well. Tha'll have to wait and see!" George said mysteriously.

"Ooh it sounds very exciting," Dorothy said.

"Can I come too?" David asked.

"Of course you can," Dorothy replied without hesitation. She looked across at David and he immediately dropped his eyes in embarrassment.

"How's your salmon?" Lilly asked.

"Very nice." Dorothy reached for another piece of bread, glancing over at David again as she did so. He was looking at her from under lowered eyes and once again he dropped his glance and giggled. When he raised his eyes once more to look at her Dorothy gave him a smile and David smiled shyly back.

"There's plenty more if you want some. Billy? George?"

"I'll help myself. You don't mind do you?" Myra picked up her plate and went to the kitchen. "Anymore for anymore while I'm up?"

They stayed longer than they had intended to and missed the film they had planned on seeing. But it didn't matter. George and Myra were such good company, especially George who kept surprising them throughout the evening with his innocent jokes. When David's bed time came David wanted Dorothy to take him up and put him to bed but, flattered as she was Dorothy declined and gave him a goodnight kiss instead in front of everybody which covered him in delighted confusion.

They left before George and Myra to have some time alone, walking and talking, unconsciously strolling all the while towards

Woodseats and Dorothy's home. They paused at the railings above the wall at Woodbank to admire the fading view in the afterglow of sunset.

"I'm sorry Bill." Dorothy was looking straight ahead into the evening breeze as though she needed its freshness to clear the contradictions inside her head. "I didn't realise he was like that."

Bill remained silent.

"He's such a loving little boy."

"Yes."

"He put his arms around me and gave me a real hug." Dorothy looked at Bill and he turned to her.

"I nearly lost him," he said quietly.

"Oh Bill." She saw the sadness in his eyes. "It won't make any difference to us."

He gave a half smile of tristesse. "Dorothy… I don't want you to…" He paused and turned his face away. "I don't know what I'm trying to say."

"I love you Bill. It won't make me stop loving you."

The last vestige of daylight had gone and all they could see was the ribbon of street lamps wending along the road below. A sudden chill hit them and Dorothy snuggled against Bill for warmth. "And David too. If he'll have me."

Bill looked down at her. "Do you mean it? Really?"

Dorothy nodded earnestly.

"Are you sure?"

"Oh yes Bill, I'm sure."

The following Sunday Dorothy met Bill at the tramstop.

"They're all dying to meet you," she said. "You look very nice."

Bill was wearing his new dark blue suit with the pattern of lighter coloured flecks in it. What the tailor had called a 'raindrop' pattern.

"Our Marge and Charlie's here as well."

Dorothy had enjoyed meeting George and Myra and, she reasoned, her sister and brother in law would give Bill something in common with them. Charlie had been in the forces too.

They were all waiting up there. Her sister and her family, consumed with curiosity and her parents, dismayed that Dorothy was getting serious about a man who was divorced.

Ernest Bracewell, like most doting fathers, had a keen eye for his daughter's happiness. She was a sensible girl and not likely to be bowled over by some smooth talking fly-by-night. But still, there were two sides to every story and he would be interested to see what this young man had to say. His wife Enid was an angular woman, eaten with bitterness over the death of her eldest son who had joined the railway as a passenger guard and missed his footing as he was about to board the moving train. He had done it a thousand times before; blown his whistle and waved his flag to get the train safely underway and stepped into the open door of the guards van as it slid by. Only this time his foot had missed the step, he had stumbled and fallen and disappeared between the platform and the accelerating train. His body, mangled by the wheels had been difficult to recover and the identification of his remains, restored to the best of the undertaker's ability, had been a horrifying ordeal for the Bracewells. Enid Bracewell had never recovered from the experience. Now she waited in the knowledge that no-one could replace her son.

Dorothy and Marge had been busy, helping their mother to prepare tea and Jean, barely five years old had been delightedly carrying plates and cutlery through to the table for her Aunty Dolly.

"What time is it Marge?" Dorothy had asked, suddenly anxious.

Marge, checking her watch answered, "Quarter to."

"Heavens! He'll be here in a minute," Dorothy had cried. "I said I'd go and meet him off the tram and bring him here."

"What's up?" Charlie called, teasing her from the front room. "He'll find his way won't he? Surely he knows where you live by now."

Dorothy entered and began touching up her hair before the mirror.

"I thought it would be nice to meet him and introduce him properly." She grabbed her cardigan from the back of the settee. "Shan't be long."

"Shall I come too?" Marge grinned at her from the living room door, but Dorothy tossed her the apron and called back, "Mum'll want a hand with the rest of that salad if you like." She went flying down the road to the tram stop as Charlie and Marge exchanged looks and laughed.

Dorothy made it to the stop in time and was there for the few minutes before Bill's tram arrived.

"It's silly," he confessed, "But I feel right nervous."

"Oh you'll be alright. Don't worry." She leaned forward and gave him a light kiss but still Bill found himself overcome by anxiety and a growing feeling of insecurity as they approached the house.

"How are they?"

"They're alright. Really!" Dorothy beamed at him. "Mother's a bit... you know... but she always is when she's having company. She'll be alright once we're all sat down."

"Mothers!" he said. "They're all the same."

"Dad's been up to the allotment this morning and fetched some of the salad stuff back. He's looking forward to meeting you."

Bill was grateful for the information. "And your sister? Did she come?"

"Yes, she's here so you'll be alright. You'll be surrounded by adoring females. Charlie was in the forces during the war. You'll have a lot to talk about."

So Dorothy primed him and tried to put Bill at ease.

Marge was waiting at the open door, smiling to greet them. She appraised Bill appreciatively. "My, she has done well for herself hasn't she. I'm Margery, the older sister. Marge." She offered her cheek for a kiss. What a nice looking man, she thought to herself, what if he is divorced! "Well, come on in." She winked and gave Dorothy a smile of approval as Bill stepped past her.

"Hello. I'm Charlie."

"Bill."

"Here let me take your mac."

Now Mrs. Bracewell came through from the kitchen folding her apron. She was smiling but it was a smile of formality without warmth or conviction.

"Hello Mrs. Bracewell."

"Hello. Here Charlie, I'll take that coat."

Dorothy stepped forward. "Come on Bill. I think dad's through here."

She led the way past them into the living room where tea was set. "Here dad. Bill's arrived."

Mr. Bracewell rose from the fireside chair where he had been relaxing and offered his hand. He was a tall man in his early fifties, a large framed man whose hand took Bill's and held it firmly without the effort of trying to impress by strength. His handsome face carried lines of experience and responsibility and he looked at Bill unflinchingly. Yes, Bill recollected, a top link driver. They all had this air about them. An authority that nothing could erase once it had been earned. A centurion's look. Yes, and this man had a centurion's nose that fitted well on him.

"Mr. Bracewell. Pleased to meet you."

"It's Bill isn't it." Not a question; a fact.

"I'd better go and help mum to finish getting tea ready." Dorothy turned but Marge, just behind motioned her to stay.

"It's alright Dolly. I'll go."

Mr. Bracewell motioned towards a chair. "I don't suppose tea'll be long anyway. Sit down. Dorothy tells me you've been in the airforce."

"Yes." Bill found himself wondering whether to address Mr Bracewell as 'sir' and immediately decided against it. With some relief Dorothy pulled a chair out from the table and sat to give moral support alongside him. "Bomber squadron. Halifax's at first, then we got

283

Lancs."

Charlie entered. "I was in the forces during the war. I expect Dorothy's told you. Did you get very far?"

"Not really. Most of the raids were from home bases. I spent some time at Scampton." Everybody had heard of Scampton. It was probably the most famous of all the bomber airfields. Certainly more famous than little Shobdon tucked away in Herefordshire. Nobody'd heard of that. And Bill suddenly found himself with a desire to impress them. "I knew Guy Gibson."

"Really!"

Bill was gratified with the result his statement created. Dorothy looked on benignly. Things were beginning to go well.

"Then we got a posting to Gib. What about you Charlie? What mob were you in?"

"Oh," Charlie replied, "nothing glamorous. I was in transport. We got shipped out to Burma in '43. I got out before the war ended. Not like some of our blokes. I was lucky."

Bill nodded. He'd heard some of the stories that had emerged from the Far East. His own war experience by comparison was tame and uneventful. Camps in England then a holiday in Gib!

Marge was putting the finishing touches to the table. "Charlie got Malaria. He was ever so poorly." She stood and looked at her husband gently and placed her sympathetic hand on Charlie's shoulder. "You're not right even now are you?"

Charlie dismissed it. "I sometimes get a bout. When the weather's bad. You never really recover."

Mr. Bracewell steered the conversation back to Bill. "So you were one of the Dambusters eh?"

"No!" Bill replied hastily. "No, I wasn't in the same squadron as Guy Gibson. We were in different squadrons. It's just that for a time we were on the same base."

"Oh. I see." The steady centurion gaze never faltered.

Bill felt as if he had been caught out in some great misdemeanour. He knew he shouldn't have done it and he could feel Dorothy's eyes on him.

Mrs. Bracewell came in from the kitchen. "Well if we're all ready…" she said.

"I'm ready for mine." Mr. Bracewell rose and crossed to the table as his wife ushered them all to their places.

It was a very good tea and they ate politely amidst small chatter and compliments to Mr. Bracewell on the produce he had grown.

"Now then," Dorothy said, rising with a knife poised, "who's having a piece of cake. You must all have some because I made it

284

myself. Bill?"

"Just a little." Politeness demanded acceptance with restraint.

"And you Charlie. I know you like it. That's why I made it, just for you."

"I'll bet," Charlie replied. "Go on then, seeing as you made it." He held up his plate and Dorothy cut out a generous wedge for him.

Mrs. Bracewell went off into the kitchen to brew the tea. "Come on Jean, you can bring me those dirty plates." Dutifully Jean picked up the plates which had been gathered into a pile at the end of the table and followed her grandmother into the kitchen. Marge and Dorothy busied themselves with the tea cups-and-saucers and Mrs. Bracewell returned after a few moments with a big china teapot on a tray. When everyone had been served with tea and cake Mrs. Bracewell said, "It came as a bit of a shock to us when Dorothy told us you were divorced."

Her words brought a momentary halt to the proceedings. Ernest Bracewell immediately looked at across at Bill, observing his reaction.

"What can I say?" Bill replied at once. He glanced at Dorothy. She was looking at him too and her mouth held a smile for him. "People do get divorced you know."

Marge and Charlie looked uneasy and Dorothy said, "Mother, please, not here!"

Ernest Bracewell leaned forward. "To be honest," he said, "we never envisaged Dorothy becoming – well – involved," he used the word with heavy emphasis, "with a married man."

"But Bill's not married!" Dorothy cried.

"No! But he has been." Enid Bracewell's voice held something very much like triumph. "And naturally we're curious. Who wouldn't be?"

Now Dorothy was staunch in Bill's defence. "Oh but mother! I've already told you…"

"Well," Mrs. Bracewell continued over Dorothy's protests, "I just thought it would be nice if we heard it from Bill himself."

Dorothy looked helplessly at Bill. She could sense his confidence leaking from him. He pursed his lips in thought.

"Come on Jean," Charlie said, rising from the table. "We'll do these pots shall we. Come and help me to get 'em cleared away. It's alright Marge. We'll see to 'em."

Reluctantly the girl followed her father. Bill watched Charlie leave the room. It was as though an ally was leaving.

"I'm sure you understand." Ernest Bracewell was saying. "We've naturally got Dorothy's best interests in mind. You'd be just the same wouldn't you."

Bill thought of David, he and Jean were almost the same age. Mr.

Bracewell was right. Of course he would have the same concerns. All the same he felt trapped and the pressure of the faces round the table was unyielding. Beneath the tablecloth Dorothy squeezed Bill's hand in reassurance.

"I suppose it was my own fault." he began and Mrs. Bracewell gave her head a little toss as if in triumph. Dorothy shot a look of disapproval at her and Bill continued, "I had a good safe job in civvy street. But I wanted to fight. So I joined up."

"But you were fighting weren't you?" Mrs. Bracewell rejoined. "Surely that was your contribution to the war. I'm sure Mr. Bracewell never felt the need to desert his family and he was doing valuable war work on the railways."

"I didn't desert my family Mrs. Bracewell. I wasn't even married then. My enlistment was deferred. Then later – after I was married – the RAF sent for me."

"I see."

"It wasn't Bill's fault mum."

"Your mother didn't say it was," came the rejoinder from her father.

"Well anyway," Bill continued, "I was called up into the RAF and – well – it all sort of went wrong from there." This was awful. It was like the Spanish Inquisition.

"What happened?" Mr. Bracewell's tone whilst not unsympathetic was uncompromising. Bill turned his attention to him.

"I suppose she became lonely. Or something." It sounded so lame. "Anyway..." Bill paused, searching for an innocuous way to say what they wanted to hear. "She began knocking about with other men..."

"How do you mean? Knocking about!" Mrs. Bracewell again.

Dorothy flared. "Oh really mother! What's the matter with you? Can't you see how difficult it's been? Just because you... and our Marge have never had this kind of trouble..."

"Leave me out of this," Marge said.

"Well anyway," Dorothy cried, "it doesn't mean to say it's Bill's fault or that he's bad or anything."

She turned to Bill and took his hand.

"I'm sorry Bill. I didn't realise it was going to be like this. I wouldn't have asked you."

"It's alright," Bill reassured her. "They have a right to know. I suppose I'd be the same."

He turned to Dorothy's mother. "I'm not saying it's anybody's fault. But if there was a fault it certainly wasn't mine. All I did was what any man would – what thousands did – what Charlie did." He looked across at Marge. "Your Charlie was in the forces wasn't he. And you

286

were married weren't you."

"Yes and they're still married," came Mrs. Bracewell's terse response.

"I can't explain it then. Perhaps I married the wrong woman. Perhaps it would have happened anyway." There was resignation in Bill's voice.

Marge rose from the table. "I'll go and help those two in the kitchen."

Ernest Bracewell turned to Bill. "And what about our Dorothy?"

"I'm very fond of her," Bill replied. He turned to look at her; Dorothy was smiling across at him. "She's a lovely girl and I'm very lucky to have met her. I wouldn't do a thing in the world to hurt her."

"I hope not," Enid Bracewell said.

Ernest Bracewell nodded slowly, reserving his judgement.

After tea, when everything was washed and put away Charlie entertained them on the piano. His repertoire included the popular songs of the day.

"Here, let's see if I can do this one." The sentimental strains of 'Rose, Rose I love you' came from the piano. "It's just come out," Charlie said with a half turn towards them.

Charlie played until it was time for them to go to the 'Big Tree' for the last hour at their accustomed table. Marge and Charlie felt the shadow of the conversation at tea hanging over them and tried to make up for it. Bill found that he enjoyed their company, particularly Charlie's. They got on well together. But with the Bracewells he felt under constant scrutiny.

Tea the Sunday after that with George and Myra was much more relaxed and informal. Myra bustled about them.

"Another cup of tea? Sandwich? Come on Dorothy you've hardly eaten anything. Don't tell me you're slimming; you'll disappear into thin air if you're not carefull." Myra chuckled at her own bon mot. "George, come on that ham wants eating up; it won't keep. Billy!"

George said enigmatically, "She's got something to tell you."

"Not now!" Myra said sharply. "Let 'em finish their tea."

"Is this the great surprise?" Bill asked.

"Sort of," George replied, catching Myra's look.

But Dorothy saw it in Myra's face and she knew, and gave Myra a look of complicity, her eyes smiling in happiness at her.

"Well what's 'sort of' mean?" Bill asked.

"Oh you'll have to wait a bit. Finish your tea."

"Oh well in that case I've finished!"

"You've got to have some trifle yet."

Myra placed the bowl in the centre of the table before them.

"Well what's such a big secret?" Bill asked with a sense of irritability. "Look at them two. They're grinning like Cheshire cats."

"It's no good," George said. "You'll have to tell him."

Bill looked at the three of them. He appeared to be the only one who didn't know what was being shared between them. It was clear that even Dorothy knew, by some telepathy that was beyond him.

"What's going on!" he demanded. He didn't like to be the only one left out.

"Will you tell him then or what?" George said.

"No," Myra replied. "He's your brother. You tell him."

"For goodness' sake!!!"

Dorothy laughed out loud at Bill's exasperation and George said, "She's gone and got herself pregnant."

"I didn't do it!" Myra cried in mock indignation.

"Congratulations." Dorothy rose and gave Myra a hug and kiss. "When is it?"

"Oh not until Christmas. Ages yet."

"Is that it then?" Bill said. "Is that the big surprise? We've waited a fortnight for this?"

"Me mother doesn't know yet," George said.

"We've only had it confirmed this week," Myra added.

"But she thought she was, only we weren't sure. No point in saying anything then. Was there."

"Well." Bill rose and shook George's hand. "I 'spose that makes me an uncle. Fancy that! Christmas eh?"

"Anyway, we've got something to show you. Come on." George took the serving spoon out of Myra's hand. "We'll have the trifle later. Then they can make up their minds."

Intrigued, Bill and Dorothy followed them to the stairs.

"Be careful," Dorothy said and offered her arm.

"Oh there's ages to go yet," Myra replied. "Come on then."

"There's never a minutes rest in this house." George complained.

Obediently they all trooped after Myra to the accompaniment of her voice up the two flights of stairs to the attic. "I don't know what he was thinking of! Coming home with a thing like that. And me! If he thinks I'm riding a thing like that he's got another think coming. Especially now, in my condition."

In the corner of the attic, leaning against an assortment of bric-a-brac stood the tandem. It wasn't new but it was in good condition with a gleaming black frame, drop handlebars and five gears.

"Somebody offered him a bargain and he took it," Myra continued to Dorothy's secret amusement. "I wouldn't be seen dead on that thing. We had a hell of a job to get it up here out of the way! Our Desmond had to come over and help him up here with it."

Bill and George were bent over the bike in close inspection.

"It's thine if you want it. She'll never ride it! I'm sick of hearing her go on about it. Well? What's tha think?"

Bill turned to Dorothy. Her eyes were gleaming and she gave him a broad smile and nodded.

"How much?" Bill asked.

"Tha can have it for what I gave for it."

"I'll be glad to get shot of the thing," Myra said. "It's not bikes we want in this house. It's prams."

CHAPTER 35

Proposal

The tandem opened up a wonderful summer of weekends for Dorothy and Bill. It was a revelation to them how far they could reach in the day and they toured the villages of the Peak District. Hathersage, and the huge grave of Little John in the high churchyard. The annual well dressings at Eyam, commemorating the sacrifice of the villagers who isolated themselves to prevent the spread of plague in 1660. The wonderful view along the dale from Monsal Head and the railway viaduct, which spanned the valley and then ran into a tunnel in the hillside. As the summer progressed they accumulated a vast collection of memories, all faithfully recorded on Dorothy's box Brownie with she or Bill posing, always with the tandem in view, open necked, smiling, happy.

They had picnics on the huge gritstone slabs of rock perched at the edge of the Surprise View with the lush Hope Valley below, spreading endlessly into the distant peaks. They sunbathed by the shores of Ladybower and Derwent, the dams where just a few years before, the roar of the RAF's low flying Lancasters had caused pregnant sheep to miscarry as they practised low level night flying in preparation for their assault on the German dams of the Ruhr. It was a wonderful summer of peace.

Bill felt the burden of work less. Now work assumed a purpose; to pay for their pleasures, clothes, the cinema, dancing and the weekends to look forward to. Bill was deeply in love and the joy of it was that his love for Dorothy was matched step by step by Dorothy's love of him. He began to save for a ring.

And during the week in the evenings they strolled in the park and took David with them. Then all three of them would play together like children; a game on the swings, a kickabout with David's ball. Slowly and carefully they began to become as one...

As the evening light gradually fades the park empties; the picnics are cleared away and games of cricket or rounders come to an end. The few people lingering in the gathering twilight stroll alongside the brook, watching swallows flitting and swooping among the clouds of midges which hover above the water.

In the middle of the field David waits expectantly with the ball at his feet.

"Come on daddy," he calls.

"Got a bone in my leg," Bill laughs in reply. "Oh! Oh!" And Dorothy takes Bill's arm and supports him with mock concern.

"No you haven't!" David protests and kicks the ball across to them but they take no notice. "You always says that!"

But he knows the game is over and he has had a smashing time. Aunty Dorothy has joined in and even though she isn't a very good kicker in her high heels they have beaten his daddy. They have dashed about, laughing and teasing each other. And now the game is over and David stands for a moment waiting.

They have strolled across to one of the park benches and daddy is lighting a cigarette. Ah well!

David kicks the ball again and runs after it. He tries calling them to join in again but to no avail. And anyway the light has almost gone, it is nearly too dark to play.

He approaches the bench and they are oblivious to anything but each other.

Ah well!

David kicks the ball again and runs after it in the dark…

They linger, the two of them alone on the park bench and the child with his football in the gloaming, somewhere on the solitary field. Occasionally David sees the glow of his daddy's cigarette and hears the low murmur of voices, the softness of a kiss.

And the lonely game in the dark begins to pall and on the park bench they become aware of the child's frustrations and their own so hand in hand and arm in arm with Dorothy safe between them they set off for the tram. Bill and David, father and son, each reflecting on the happiness of their evening together…

It delighted David to be able to share in Dorothy's sense of fun. He saw it demonstrated one hot afternoon after a picnic at Rivelin Dams. Beyond the gritstone wall the sun was gleaming on the waters of the dam which spread before them. They were strolling contentedly along the valley to the terminus to catch the bus back home to Sheffield and David was looking forward to a ride in the swing boats at the café while they waited if there was enough time. Aunty Dorothy would climb into the boat with him and daddy usually pushed the boat to get them going.

The late afternoon was still warm and they were tired with the exertions of the games they had played under the crags of Lodge Moor. Dorothy had prepared a picnic of ham sandwiches and jam tarts, and tea from the flask with that peculiar flavour of cork from the stopper. After tea Bill and Dorothy had reclined on the blanket in a little clearing of silver birches amongst the heather and boulders while David went off to play.

This was perfect cowboy and indian country and David scouted around and crept up on them but they were clearly deeply engrossed in each other and he crept away again, embarrassed and hoping they hadn't spotted him.

Now David was tired. The road from the bus to their picnic site hadn't seemed long when they arrived but now his feet were dragging as they walked the rising road.

"Carry me daddy. Can I have a shoulder ride?"

"No, come on, we're nearly there. Just round that bend and we're there."

Ahead of them a policeman on his bike was making his ponderous way along the road. With his tunic fastened his pedalling was becoming slower and slower as he battled with heat on the long slope and the gruelling effort to ride seated as regulations required instead of standing to get more power into the pedals. Finally he wobbled to a standstill and dismounted. He leaned the cycle against the wall with relief and with his back to them he bent down to adjust his cycle clips. Dorothy put her finger to her lips and beckoning David she pointed to the inviting target.

"Shall I go and give him a kick up the bottom?" she whispered.

David was instantly impressed by her daring and he grinned at Dorothy in complicity.

"No you'll get done!" he giggled.

"Go on," she whispered conspiratorially. "Let's see what happens."

"No!" he hissed, "you'll get into trouble!"

But Dorothy seemed determined. The policeman remained bent over and to David's consternation she began to creep forward on exaggerated tip-toes. She got within range and drew back her leg to give an almighty kick then turned to them with a grin of mischief. "Shall I?" she mimed.

Bill was laughing but David was shaking his head and pointing.

"No!"

She turned. The policeman had risen and was looking at her with a quizzical expression. He folded his arms and Dorothy's leg, poised for the kick, returned to the ground. The policeman could see the humour of the situation but, the majesty of the law must be preserved! Keeping his face straight he reached to his breast pocket for his notebook, changed his mind and wagged his finger at Dorothy instead who by now was looking rather crestfallen and preparing her explanation as best she could. The policeman glanced quickly at the other two and without a change of expression he shook his head slowly and wheeled his cycle into the road. But as he mounted and prepared to begin the rest of the climb he turned briefly to Dorothy and winked before proceeding on his majestic way.

"Well that was close," she grinned as David and Bill came up to join her.

"You nearly got done!" David breathed in a voice of admiration.

"Well, come on. Let's go and get that bus."

The episode had revived David's spirits and they set off again, following the policeman who was already puffing and blowing his way along the road ahead. David loved her. Dorothy had the knack of being able to indulge in childish things without losing her dignity or David's respect. He took her hand and they walked together to the bus.

So the summer came to a close and the opportunities for picnics ended. But what a summer it had been! Bill had found new friends in Charlie and Marge and they had spent a lot of time in their company too. Their daughter Jean was almost David's age and they got on and played well together. And most important of all was the way Dorothy had accepted David and he loved her. After that initial setback everything was beautiful. Why? Bill thought to himself, why had he been so foolish and anxious?

It was a grey Sunday evening in October, the coldest for a long time and a presage of winter days ahead. Lilly and Harold were out. They had gone to George and Myra's for tea and taken David with them. Bill and Dorothy had declined to go; they were planning to go to the pictures instead. But anticipating the opportunity for some time alone together they changed their minds as soon as everyone was out and stayed in. Bill drew the fire up and they made themselves comfortable on the settee under the window…

Now only a small flame remained to illuminate the cosy darkness of the room and the heat was beginning to die from the fire just as the heat was draining away from Dorothy and Bill. They lay for another long moment on the settee in the darkness and then Dorothy began to stir.

"Your mother'll be home soon Bill."

Bill raised his arm from beneath her and focused on the luminous dial of his watch.

"Acres of time yet. Come here."

Dorothy allowed herself to be drawn back to him again. But this time there was no passion, only tenderness as he laid his hand on her breast, caressing and gently savouring its contour. Dorothy shivered and Bill knew the moment was past; it was suddenly chilly. He stirred and raised himself, turning to look at the fire.

"Nearly out. Better get some more coal on before they get back."

He lay and watched her as Dorothy stood before the mirror in the fireglow running her fingers through her tousled hair and smoothing down the creases in her skirt. She became conscious of Bill gazing at her in the darkness and inclined her head so that her faint reflection smiled down at him from the mirror.

"I love you."

Bill saw rather than heard the words and Dorothy turned to face him, a shadowy form on the settee with the flickering light of the fire upon his serious face.

"I love you," he replied, softly and earnestly, feeling the inadequacy of the words.

Dorothy stooped and kneeled before him. She took his hand in hers and kissed it, nuzzling her cheek against his, whispering, "I love you, I love you…" over and over again as Bill held her close. Finally she said gently, "Come on, I'll make you a cup of tea."

She made to rise but he held her fast, searching her face intently.

"Dorothy. Oh Dolly I do love you."

"I know you do." She relaxed against him. "I love you too."

"Let's get married."

"Oh Bill. When?"

"I don't know. Next year. Spring!"

Dorothy pulled back and looked at him, searching his face, his eyes.

"Do you mean it Bill?"

"You know I do. Marry me Dolly."

"Where will we live?"

"I don't know. We'll get somewhere. We'll find somewhere. Can't we?"

"Yes. Yes, of course we can. Oh Bill yes! I'll marry you anywhere."

Dorothy leaned against Bill again and took his face in her hands and traced the line of his nose and chin gently with her forefinger and ran it across his mouth and kissed him, lightly, teasingly and laid her fingers on his lips and kissed him through her fingers. And then she rose and said, "Come on."

She went to put the light on but he said, "Leave it. It's nice being in the dark with you."

Lilly and Harold returned to a blazing fire and a freshly made pot of tea. David made a run and was sitting between Dorothy and Bill.

"My that's welcome," Harold said. He turned to warm his back at the fire. "It's turned chilly out."

"Come on, let's get your pyjamas. Bedtime."

"Do as grandma says there's a good boy." With this encouragement from Dorothy, David started to undress.

Dorothy cast a questioning look at Bill then from him to David but

Bill shook his head.

"What're you having for supper. Corn Flakes?"

"Alright grandma."

"How about you Harold. Bit of bread and cheese?"

"Yes ta."

"Nothing for us mother," Bill said. "Dorothy's got to go in a bit. We want to tell you something first."

David looked up. "What's that?" he cried before anybody had a chance to speak.

"Nothing for you. Come on, eat your supper," Bill admonished. "It's time you were in bed. School tomorrow."

"Aw. Nobody tell's me nothing!"

But Lilly and Harold knew, almost before realisation dawned. They knew by the tone of Bill's voice and the light in Dorothy's eyes and the way she looked at him with such a look of happiness. But they had to hear it from Bill and Dorothy's own mouths and they would never get David off to bed in all the excitement that was bound to follow so they chivvied him to hurry up and finish his supper. Then Lilly wiped David's face in the kitchen and brought him back to go round and kiss everybody goodnight. And Dorothy got a big hug and a special kiss because she wasn't often there to say goodnight to at bedtime and then Lilly took David off to bed.

She came back down to a room filled with expectation.

"Well," she said, looking from one to the other.

Bill and Dorothy exchanged glances.

"We're going to get married. In the spring," Bill said.

"Oh I'm so glad." Lilly took Dorothy's hands in her own. "Oh you don't know how glad that makes me." She held Dorothy at arm's length. "Oh look at you." She turned to Bill. "I hope you know what a lucky man you are."

"Oh give over mother. Of course I know."

Harold was standing, beaming at Dorothy. "Here love. Give us a little kiss." Then he shook her hand and said, "Congratulations. To both of you."

There was so much to say and so much to be done and arrangements to be made. Like 'Where's it to be at?' and 'When?' and 'Who's going to be...?'

Finally Bill said, "Give us a chance, we've only just decided! We haven't told Dorothy's mother and father yet."

CHAPTER 36

Smiles and ice

Enid Bracewell, sitting rigidly at the table had listened to what Dorothy had to tell her. It was unbelievable. After the careful upbringing, the love that had been bestowed on Dorothy by Ernest and herself, the fine example set by Marge in her marriage to Charlie, and not least the good job and prospects that she had! That Dorothy should contemplate such an unsuitable marriage was unthinkable!

"And there's the child as well!" she cried and turned to her husband who was listening attentively from his chair by the corner of the hearth. His expression was equally grave.

"Don't take this the wrong way Bill," he said, "but Dorothy's mother and I had expected that when it came to marrying she would find someone more… suitable. You bring a lot of past history with you as well as the boy."

Dorothy, sitting with Bill at the table opposite her mother gave him a look of reassurance and squeezed his hand tighter.

"Well I'm sorry." Bill tried to keep his demeanour as controlled and respectful as possible. "I've tried to explain to you what happened. I can't alter that. I love Dorothy." He turned and smiled at her, adding, "And I think Dorothy will make a wonderful mother for David."

But Bill's smile was interrupted by Enid Bracewell's triumphant, "So that's what this is all about. Finding a mother for your child!"

"No it's…"

"Enid!" Mr. Bracewell warned sternly.

"Oh mother it's not like that at all."

"Well…? But he was careful not to let on about him wasn't he."

"Mother I've known about David for ages."

Ernest Bracewell had always enjoyed the respect and love of his youngest daughter. Now was the time to trade on that relationship. "Why don't you wait before rushing into it," he said. "Give it a bit more time. Make certain before you do something you might regret." He addressed Bill direct. "You of all people should appreciate the sense of that Bill. After all, if you'd waited a bit longer before marrying you might not have had to go through what you did. Would you?"

Bill averted his eyes from Dorothy and looked slowly from her mother, who returned his look with an uncompromising stare, to her father. Both sat waiting for his response. Bill's mind was racing with thoughts and none of them was bringing him any comfort. 'Waited a bit before marrying!' How could he have waited a bit! Daisy was pregnant! She was having his bastard child! He had done the right thing, what any decent bloke would have done in the circumstances. Yes... Except getting her bloody pregnant in the first place!

Bill ran his hand across his brow, searching for words. 'So what do I say?' he thought desperately. 'Your daughter's lucky 'cos I'm free of the pox, I haven't touched her and she's still a virgin!' Good God this was going from bad to worse!'

"I don't know what to say," Bill finally sighed. "I love Dorothy and I want to marry her. It's nothing to do with David. The fact that David loves her as well and that Dorothy is prepared to accept him and help me to bring him up only means that we have a good chance of living a happy life together. I've told you all I can. I can't alter the past but I can plan for the future. I believe I can give Dorothy a secure and happy future. If she wants to wait... six months... a year... then... Yes I'll wait. I don't care. My feelings for Dorothy will never change."

"Dad." The earnestness in Dorothy's voice commanded their attention. "I've told you. I love Bill. We've known each other for almost a year. We're not planning to get married for another six months. In the spring. There's your waiting time! As if we needed it." She turned to Bill and again Ernest Bracewell saw the look that Dorothy had repeatedly given Bill throughout their conversation. "I love him dad, mother. I'm going to marry him."

"Well," her father said and resignation crept into his voice, "you're over twenty-one now Dorothy. I don't suppose you need our permission."

"Oh dad. I want you to be happy for us that's all. Both of you." And Dorothy looked across to her mother but Enid Bracewell gave a slow shake of her head.

"I suppose we've just got to get used to the idea then. I don't know!"

They saw the look of relief that passed between Bill and Dorothy and it brought no comfort to either Dorothy's mother or father.

"Thank you," Bill said.

"Don't thank me," Mrs. Bracewell replied. "If Dorothy had been under twenty-one we wouldn't have allowed it."

"I'll put the kettle on." Dorothy looked round at them, seeking reconciliation. "Come on. You could do with a cup of tea couldn't you."

Now the interview was over Bill wanted to get out of the room. It had become oppressive. He looked at his watch.

Mrs. Bracewell rose to her feet and said, "I'll make it!"

"Dad...?" Dorothy said when her mother had left the room.

"Your mother's right. I suppose we're going to have to get used to it." He looked at Bill and said, "It was a nice speech. I hope you know..." He faltered, resting his eyes on his daughter and sighed. "I wish I could feel happier for you. Anyway..." A look of resignation clouded his face.

Enid Bracewell entered with cups and saucers. "Have you thought about where you'll have it? St. Chad's is where you've always gone. It's a nice little church."

"Oh I expect so," Dorothy said brightly. It was easier now the conversation was concerned with more practical things and she tried to lift the gloom that had settled on them. "We've got plenty of time to think of that."

"Oh I don't know," Bill put in, happier now he was on safer ground. "A Spring wedding! We'd better talk to them soon. I expect there'll be lots of people wanting to get married then."

Enid Bracewell looked at him as if to say, Yes! Well of course you would know wouldn't you! But her uncharitable thoughts were interrupted by her husband.

"On a more practical level," he was saying, "have you thought about where you're going to live?"

Again Dorothy and Bill exchanged glances. But a new air of tension arose. Bill smiled and nodded imperceptibly to her but his smile hid deep misgivings that had been growing as the conversation had progressed. It was beginning to consume him but he couldn't see any alternative. Especially after the brave speech he had made. He was committed.

"We..." Dorothy began hesitantly, then plunged in, "we thought, if it's alright, perhaps we could live here. For a bit. Until we can get something saved. At least until we've enough to think about getting a place of our own."

Mrs. Bracewell froze.

"I've got my name on the council waiting list but you know how long that is..."

As soon as he spoke Bill wished he'd never said it.

Mr. Bracewell shook his head and looked up at his wife in silence.

"I've got some savings put by," Dorothy said.

"I've not got much. I mean, being in the forces and that." Bill added. "But I've begun saving..." It all sounded so lame.

"Well I don't..." Mrs. Bracewell began.

"We're going to have to think about it," Mr. Bracewell said.

Marge and Charlie proved to be staunch allies. They knew how difficult the housing situation was. Charlie was a chauffeur at the town hall with no hope of buying a home of his own on his small wage. They lived in a four roomed house in a yard with three other houses around them. To help out with the rent their front room was sublet as a bedsitting room to a self contained spinster. It was an arrangement that seemed to work well. Miss Buxton wanted nothing to do with them and both Marge and Charlie were content with that. The only time they saw their solitary tenant on the other side of the living room wall was when she came round to pay her rent. Charlie knew that even as a town hall employee their chances of getting a council house were years away.

So Marge was as aware as anybody that setting up a home of your own was anything but straightforward. But it was time for her sister to think of marriage. Time was going by. And Marge could see, anybody could see, how happy Dorothy and Bill were together. And the practical obstacles of finding a home and living together would have to be overcome. "Otherwise," Marge said to her mother, "nobody's ever going to get married ever again. Or at least not until the housing shortage is ended. And who knows when that'll be? Years!"

And besides, there was something else that boded well for Bill and Dorothy's plans. Buckingham Palace had announced that Princess Elizabeth was to marry her dashing sailor too. Nineteen-fortyeight was going to be a good year to get married. Everybody's thoughts were going to be on weddings next year.

Under pressure from both their daughters the Bracewells bowed to the inevitable. David would sleep in the attic; that would have to be cleared out and decorated and God knows where all the stuff would go. Perhaps in the shed at Ernest's allotment! Then Dorothy and Bill would have the front room downstairs to themselves. Dorothy of course would share the kitchen with her mother and she already had her own bedroom so that was no problem. But Enid Bracewell was adamant; she was not prepared to share the same room with Dorothy and Bill. They could have their own sitting room with their own front door. Just as Miss Buxton was doing with Marge and Charlie. The less she had to see of him the better!

And so the arrangements went ahead and in the spring the daffodils in the church garden nodded their heads in approval. The day was bright and sunny. Jean was a bridesmaid for her aunty, escorted by David in a white satin suit. They all stood in a family group on the steps of the little Methodist church and beamed at the camera. Bill was splendid in a dark lounge suit carrying finely woven yellow gloves as befits a groom and Dorothy's white satin dress was set off by her bouquet of spring flowers. It was only looking at the photographs later that anyone was aware of the cool reserve behind Mrs Bracewell's polite smile.

CHAPTER 37

Ask and ye shall receive

As the train drew out of the tunnel beneath Rainbow Hill David ran to the window with grandma close behind him to look out. They were gliding into the station and the platforms were coming into view. Was she among the people waiting…? Was she…?

She was there. He saw her peering at the coaches that were passing by her. David called, waving and calling, "Aunty Ame! Aunty Ame!"

"Be careful," Lilly said and put a restraining hand on David's shoulder. "Don't fall out."

At the sound of David's voice Amy craned, looking along the approaching line of faces leaning from the train to where the shouting was coming from and her face lit in a beaming smile and she waved back. The train was endless, a long express bound for Devon and the carriage carrying David passed her before it stopped and David reached out to her as he rode by. Oh but her face carried such an expression of joy at his arrival.

Lilly had written of course to Amy to tell them Billy was getting married again but when their invitation arrived they regretfully declined. Neither Amy nor Rose could get to the wedding; there was nowhere for them to stay – certainly there was no room at Lilly's – and it was too far, to say nothing of the expense to come up just for the day. Lilly had replied on Bill's behalf and said that of course they understood. But they'd been wondering, while Bill and Dorothy were away on honeymoon, if she could bring David down just for that week. Just so that he wouldn't feel left out of things. What with all the excitement and all that. So Amy had run along to tell Rose that David was coming back to see them and now here she was at the station, and there he was, stepping down from the train and running along the platform to her.

"My what a big boy you'm getting." Amy hugged him again and said, "How old is you now?"

"Six," he replied proudly. "Nearly seven."

"Well you is getting big. Come on then; we'd better help grandma with your luggage."

They went along the platform and Amy said, "What a welcome Lill. Well how are you?"

"I'm fine," Lilly replied matter of factly. "You'm looking well."

Amy looked about the platform but there was just Lilly's large suitcase. "This all you got?"

"It's enough ain't it for one week," Lilly laughed. "Harold sends his regards."

"Albert couldn't get up. This train's a funny time for him."

"Come on then. Let's have you." Lilly reached for David's hand and the suitcase.

"Here you are Lill, let me take it. Oh, it's not too heavy is it."

They crossed the footbridge and left the station, full of gossip with David running ahead because he knew the way, pausing to let them catch up and then scampering and skipping ahead all the way to Aunty Ame's.

It smelled just the same as before. The lingering aroma of bran and peelings from the hen's dinner cooked that morning in the kitchen, the living room smell of well used upholstery and the dusty hearthrug before the fire. His bedroom was unchanged too; there was the big brass bed and motes of dust drifting bright in the sunlight against the dark mahogany wardrobe and the dressing table in the alcove against the unused chimney breast. Here was a feeling of spaciousness, not because the room was large although at was bigger than the room he'd been sharing with daddy at grandma's. But it was a sense of freedom and belonging. There was happiness in this room, in this house with Aunty Ame.

With the luggage disposed of they made themselves comfortable around the table.

"My that's welcome," Lilly said appreciatively. "It's a good cup of tea Ame."

"Rose'll be along in a bit."

Amy turned to David.

"And how do you like your new mummy?"

"She's nice," he said coyly. "I used to call her Aunty Dorothy but I've got to call her mummy now."

"Well she is your mummy." Amy said.

David became unaccountably bashful all of a sudden. "I want to keep calling her aunty," he mumbled.

"Well she's your mummy now," Amy said gently. "She's not your aunty any more."

"I know she isn't. It's just that I've got used to calling her aunty, that's all."

He had been overcome with shyness after the wedding the first time he tried to call her mummy and he didn't know why. So he called her aunty instead and it had made his daddy angry with him but he couldn't

301

help it; it was something to do with how he felt. Aunty Dorothy was so pretty and he loved her. She made him feel all strange inside sometimes when he looked at her and she smiled. And it was so nice when she let him cuddle up close to her and the way she smelled, her scent, it was special and intimate but he knew it wasn't for him. It was for his daddy. And she cuddled up to daddy and David wanted to be able to creep closer too, and when she kissed him… It made him feel a strange sort of longing. There were secrets; he could feel secrets inside that wanted to be revealed and explored. And he dared not tell anyone how he wanted to touch her the way daddy touched her, that only daddy could touch her, more than just holding hands but hand-in-hand, stroking her face and pressing close and kissing, properly. David wanted to do that. But he was not allowed that intimacy, and while she was Aunty Dorothy it was alright, but to call her mummy was to move a step closer to that intimacy. And he was afraid of it because of his feelings, it made his feelings begin to stir inside again just to think of it. The way he had felt standing in front of the mirror when no-one was in the room and pulling down his trousers and trying to see his bum, knowing it was rude. And he was afraid she would find out.

"You know what your daddy says," Lilly was firm. "She's not your Aunty Dorothy any more. He'll be mad at you if you call her aunty when they get back."

David pondered on it. There were so many different things going on. He turned to Amy.

"What does honeymoon mean Aunty Ame?"

"Oh he's been on about that the last couple of days." Lilly said. "I keep telling him."

"I know but what do they do?"

Grandma's explanations had been unsatisfying. If it was a holiday together why couldn't he go along too? It was his daddy. And mummy! But grandma said he couldn't and daddy laughed at him and Aunty Dorothy, when he had asked her, had spoken to him softly and said it was just for a new husband and wife to be alone together. And in her voice there had been more secrets and in her smile there was knowledge of hidden pleasure. David didn't know why or how he knew but there was and they wouldn't tell him.

"What's a honeymoon?" he repeated.

"Well I don't know," Amy said cautiously. "It's been so long since I been on one."

"Does everybody have one?"

"Nearly everybody."

"Do you only get one if you get married?"

"Yes. It's for after you get married. To get to know each other.

Properly."

"What does properly mean?"

"You know what properly means," Lilly said, riding to the rescue.

"Well don't they know each other before they get married? Daddy knew Aunty Dorothy."

"Yes but…"

Amy said, "They haven't had a chance to live all the time together before they gets married. So they has to have a little holiday. Then they can get to know each other properly."

"But I thought…"

"Oh that'll do," Lilly said. "You'll know soon enough. Why don't you go and see Aunty Rose and tell her we're having a cup of tea."

For Amy the week revived bittersweet memories. It took her back to the end of the war when she had nursed hopes of David staying with her and becoming her child. After the drama of the parting at the station she had accepted the inevitable and got on with life. And until now she hadn't realised how much she missed him. She took pleasure in reviving their rituals; a fresh egg for breakfast from the henhouse in the morning. Walking down to the shops with David's hand in hers and hearing his chatter at her side. A bottle of pop and packet of crisps at night before they left the pub to go with Albert to stoke the boilers. She filled the week with memories and relived them all. Until once more it was time to go.

There had been no time for tears before; events had stolen them away. Now on their final night together with David playing outside, safe in the yard of the George and Dragon, Amy turned to Lilly and there was a break in her voice.

"It's been lovely to see him again Lill. You've no idea how much we missed him."

"I know Ame. You know our Billy's ever so grateful for what you done. We'd have had him ourself but, what with me being on war work…"

"D'you think he'll be happy there?"

"Oh I think so. She's ever so good with him. And David thinks the world of Dorothy. Really he does. They're going to be a nice little family together."

"Yes." Amy lapsed into silence and sipped her beer. "Good," she said finally. "I hope so. For your Billy's sake as well."

There was still the memory of the row that had erupted the night before Bill took David away. He needn't have said the things he did and Amy had never shared the details of that night with Lilly. It was all better left unsaid.

303

"Anyway," Amy continued, "it looks like he'll have to be a bit careful living with Dorothy's mother. From what you've said she sounds like a real 'un. It's a pity they can't find somewhere of their own."

"I know. But what can you do? The way things are!"

They mused in silence on the inequalities of the world. Then Amy said,

"Do you think they'll let David come down and see us?"

"I should think so." Lilly could see no reason why not. David had been happy staying with his Aunty Ame. "I mean, if me'n Harold comes down for our two weeks like we used to before the war, we could bring David with us. If you've got room for us all."

"We'll find room, don't you worry. It'd be nice if we could, if Billy and Dorothy don't mind that is."

"Oh I'm sure they won't."

"Come on," Albert said, draining his glass. "Drink up, time for another yet before we does the boilers."

Strange, how long a week had seemed last Sunday when they arrived, with the days stretching ahead. Now tomorrow was Saturday and the pleasure of seeing him again was coming to an end.

This time their departure was far more satisfactory with no lingering ill will or forced conviviality. Amy remembered how she had felt before, trying not to show the mixture of emotions surging inside; anger, disappointment, sadness and then looking up to see the train already on its way with David silently waving through the window and no proper goodbyes said. Now she stood with Rose as the carriage doors slammed all along the train and David was at the open window with Lilly, waiting for the guard's whistle. They had exchanged kisses and promises from David to come and see them again next year when the summer holidays came.

Slowly the carriage began to move away.

"Goodbye," they cried, stepping back from the train, blowing kisses. "Have a safe journey."

Kisses returned. "See you next year."

Dorothy held David before her as they stepped from the train and surveyed him with pleasure. "Did you enjoy yourself? What was it like?"

David's eyes shone with the pleasure of seeing her and the remembrance of the week and what had gone before.

"Oh it was great," he said. "Aunty Ame wants me to go back again next year. Can I? Can I go?"

Dorothy laughed. "You've only just arrived home. We'll have to ask daddy if it's alright won't we."

"Aw say yes. Please say I can go."

"I'm sure you can. Look, there's daddy over there."

David let go of Dorothy's hand and ran along the platform to Bill leaving her and Lilly to follow.

"Aw daddy it's been great. Where were you? I didn't think you were here."

"I was only getting a paper. How was it then? Are you alright?"

They left the station to the accompaniment of David's chatter and caught the bus to Lilly's.

"But we shan't stop mother. We'll just get David's things then we've got to get up home."

How strange it sounded. His mother's house had been his home for so long. Now he was going to live in someone else's house and he was calling that home too.

"You'll stop and have a cup of tea won't you," Lilly said.

Bill sighed with frustration at having to go through these meaningless rituals. People these days drank tea for the sake of it, not to quench a thirst. And his mother was as bad as anybody. Worse! Why wouldn't she see that he wanted them to get on their way immediately. It was alright for her, she'd be home! He still had to complete the final leg and he was anxious to begin his new life.

"I don't think so mother. We only got back ourselves a couple of hours ago. We haven't been home ourselves yet. All our luggage is still at your house. We've got to get back and get settled in."

But Dorothy understood. "We can just have a quick cup of tea can't we. Just while we get David's things sorted out. I expect most of it'll want washing won't it?"

"Not a lot," Lilly said. "He didn't go through a lot. Anyway I can do the few bits and pieces that does want doing on Monday."

Bill paced and fretted about the house at the time it was taking while Lilly took Dorothy upstairs to transfer David's things to Dorothy's suitcase.

David went up to Harold, in his usual chair with a pot of stewed tea by the hearth and tapped his arm.

"Yes David. You enjoyed your holiday then?"

"Yes thank you grandad. Grandad?"

"What is it?"

"Can I have my Saturday pennies please?"

Bill turned sharply. "Come here!" he ordered.

David looked up with a questioning expression. What was wrong? Daddy was looking cross at him.

"I said come here!"

Now Harold was looking nonplussed.

Bill seized David's arm and pulled him roughly to him and delivered a series of sharp slaps to the back of David's upper leg, each slap punctuating his words. "Don't – you – ever – let – me – hear – you – asking – for money – again!"

David shrieked and dangled like a marionette in Bill's grip as each blow landed.

Harold rose out of his chair. "Hey up Bill what d'you think you're doing. Don't hit him like that!"

Hearing the first cry Dorothy ran down the stairs with Lilly close behind and found David in the living room between the two men dancing and sobbing and clutching at his stinging legs.

"Bill, David!" Dorothy cried. "Whatever's going on?"

David's face, contorted with pain, was running with tears.

"I've just given him a bloody good hiding."

Lilly pushed through the door behind Dorothy. "Whatever for?"

"He didn't deserve that," Harold protested. "He weren't doing nothing wrong."

"I won't have it and I'm not having it!" Bill's anger was still boiling over.

"What's he done!!" Dorothy cried, in dismay at David's distress. "Come here. Come on." She crouched in front of David with her arms outstretched. "Come and tell mummy what it's all about."

"Daddy hit me," he sobbed.

"Whatever for? Whatever did you do?"

David looked over his shoulder from the safety of Dorothy's arms. "I don't know." And he burst into fresh tears.

Bill found himself at odds with them all as they turned to him for an explanation. Well, he was justified! He wasn't going to have David showing him up. It was going to be difficult enough as it was without David making things worse by going around begging money as though he hadn't looked after him properly.

"He was begging for money! I won't have him begging money! I won't have it!"

"He wasn't begging," Harold protested indignantly.

"I don't understand," Dorothy said. "How do you mean, begging for money?"

"I went to grandad for my Saturday pennies," David whimpered.

Lilly was dismayed. It had been a lovely week and so far a pleasant journey home. It was a shame for it to finish up like this. "There was no need to hit him like that Billy."

"Oh shut up mother! You weren't there so how do you know. Anyway I didn't hit him that hard. I just gave his legs a slap that's all."

"There was no need for it," Harold said. "I always give him some pennies on a Saturday. For his bank. I do the same for our George's kid as well."

"Well he shouldn't go asking for it anyway."

"Billy I'm surprised at you," Lilly said.

"Well it's his anyway," Harold said. "I might have forgot." He reached into his pocket and produced a half crown piece from amongst his change. "Here," he said, holding it to David but the child turned away and buried his face again in Dorothy's arms.

"Don't want it," David snuffled.

Harold looked across at Bill but he stood aloof from their disapproval.

"Here," Harold insisted, pushing it at David. "Don't be so silly. Take it."

"No!" David cried petulantly. "I can't. Daddy says I've not to."

"Oh for Christ's sake!" Bill fumed.

"Come on," Dorothy coaxed. "Come and take it off your grandad. He wants to give it to you. Look."

With a sidelong look at Bill David allowed himself to be persuaded to take it.

"There, that's better. Come on let's go and dry your eyes shall we."

Dorothy led David into the kitchen and carefully washed and dried his face.

"Better now?"

"Yes thank you mummy."

He had said it and it was done spontaneously! David threw his arms about her and she hugged him again.

"Now it's time for us to go to our new home together," she said.

Watching them, Bill secretly excused himself, saying it was just the frustration of being so long on the journey home and having to break the journey at his mother's and then going to the station for David. All he wanted was to be in surroundings he could call his own.

And David sought their acceptance and approval. His tears turned to smiles as grandma and grandad joined Dorothy in fussing him. It took longer for his daddy to lose the stern look of disapproval but they returned to the Bracewells holding hands and smiling. At Bill's insistence David had not been allowed to see his new home before it was ready. He walked in through their front door and Dorothy said, "Do you like it then?"

The drop leaf dining table was up against the far wall, next to the door leading to the stairs and the rest of the house. Above it Bill had fixed a shelf with Dorothy's record player and small collection of some of her records. Next to the fireplace, in the recess formed by the chimney breast, stood a new cream and green painted kitchen cabinet with a pull down front containing their groceries and cutlery. Other household things like cleaning materials were in the bottom half below the flap. There was another small cabinet in the opposite alcove and, in pride of place before the fireplace a brown mocquette settee with one matching armchair in the bay window.

Bill left the suitcases by the door and marched into the centre of the room, looking round with approval. It was as it should be, as they had left it. The tension visibly fell from him.

David ran to the settee and threw himself on it. It was firmer and bouncier than grandma's.

"This is great!" he cried.

Dorothy and Bill beamed with relief.

"Come on then, let's show you upstairs."

Bill and Dorothy were occupying the front bedroom. The bathroom was over the kitchen at the back and could only be reached through the Bracewell's bedroom.

"That'll be alright," Dorothy had said. "It means nobody'll be disturbing us and it's only when dad's on nights we'll have to be careful about using it."

They went along the small landing to a curtain hiding the attic stairs.

"This is where you're sleeping David. You've got a room all to yourself."

The attic had been cleared and cleaned and distempered in sunny yellow. A frieze ran round the walls, decorated with Donald Duck and other cartoon characters. David's collection of toys and games was piled against the barrier rail above the stairs and next to the hinged window in the roof stood a small wardrobe.

"And a bed to yourself as well."

David's initial misgivings at being alone at the top of the house were offset by the bed of his own to sleep in and all the space to play in this bright and sunny room.

CHAPTER 38

El Dorado!

Enid Bracewell referred to David as 'the boy' and David went in some awe of her. Whenever he was in the Bracewell's rooms he had to be seen and not heard. Outside at the back there was a garden with a dividing path running between it and the garden of the house next door. The small asphalt yard, occupying the space between the two kitchens and common to both houses didn't leave much opportunity for play; the middle aged Duncans who lived next door had no children of their own and resented any intrusion David made onto 'their half'. Tentative games on the Bracewell's tiny lawn were soon abandoned. There wasn't really enough room to play with a ball and anyway it inevitably bounced across the path onto the Duncan's garden, provoking furious knocking from their living room window and muffled cries of, "Keep it on your own side!"

David made friends with the boys from up the road, both of whom were at his new school. They soon learned that play was impossible in the Bracewell's yard for Enid Bracewell only tolerated David's friends provided they played outside and made no noise to disturb the neighbours. But David, Brian Elliott who became his best friend, and John got their own back with a form of mute insolence. Knowing that while ever they were out in the garden, Mrs Duncan would be watching from behind her curtains, they made a show of nearly allowing the ball to cross the hallowed path and then, as though unaware of her watching presence, engaging in loud exchanges.

"Oh! It nearly touched the garden!"

"Be careful. It might have killed the precious grass!"

"Don't let it go across there. The witch might be watching!"

And when their attempts at play palled, which didn't take very long, they retreated back along the garden path like tightrope walkers, swaying and overbalancing as they came with noisy and exaggerated attempts to prevent their feet from straying more than half way across the path. From behind the curtain they would hear, "Yes, I can hear you, you cheeky little monkeys, you needn't think I can't." And having successfully baited Enid Bracewell's neighbour they ran down the passage laughing and went up the road to continue playing in the greater tolerance of Brian's yard.

David usually had his tea alone in the Bracewell's sitting room when he got home from school. It was an arrangement that Dorothy had come to with her mother. Dorothy didn't finish at the chemist's until half past five at the earliest and by the time Bill was home and washed it was seven o'clock, and that was too long for David to wait. So David had his tea alone. It was normally bread and jam although occasionally he would get sandwich spread, one of his favourites.

Enid Bracewell presented his plate of sandwiches without any attempt at hiding her resentment. Not that David cared for as soon as tea was over he was free to go and call for Brian or John.

She pushed his bread and raspberry jam across the table and returned to her preparations in the kitchen. An aroma of cooking drifted through as Enid Bracewell continued with her preparations for Mr. Bracewell's tea.

"I likes fishcakes too," David called hopefully between mouthfuls of bread. On rare occasions Mr. Bracewell's shift allowed him to be home when David was having his tea and then he was allowed to share it. But clearly not on this occasion.

"They're for Mr. Bracewell," came the retort. "Get on with your tea. Jam's expensive."

David got through the sandwiches as quickly as possible and climbed down.

"I'm going out to play," he announced as he made a dash for the kitchen door.

Enid Bracewell turned from the sink. "Where you going to be?"

"Going to Brian's. We're going in the park."

"Well don't get dirty. And don't get your feet wet!" she admonished. "You know what your daddy'll say if you get your shoes wet again." She despaired of the boy. He seemed incapable of going out to play without getting his socks muddy and his feet wet and no amount of spankings from his father cured him of it. She found it very wearing to hear Bill shouting at the boy.

"And don't go over that main road," she called, but the yard was already empty.

The park was a revelation and there were no main roads to cross to reach it. It was just around the corner from the paper shop at the bottom of the road, past the short row of shops, across the bottom of Cobnar, a quiet road safe from traffic and there were the park gates! It was almost completely wooded. From the boating lake a mile away at the top where the formal garden, the meadow and the teahouse were, a stream flowed through the woods down to where the trees gave way to grassy banks with natural gorse thickets and shallow pools. It was a boys' paradise.

There were ravines and the hillsides were steep and tufted with clumps of grass and the spreading tree roots. But they were no obstacle as the boys played and ran through the woods with the confident agility of hares. Their imaginations knew no bounds as they brought their heroes to life; Robin Hood, Indians, big game hunters in the deep jungle. They splashed in the river and found clouds of frogspawn in the pools and collected it in jamjars to watch the tadpoles grow. For David it opened a whole summer of escape from the constrictions of living at the Bracewell's.

As usual he went home with his shoes and socks caked in mud. It wasn't that he paddled in the river but when you are skipping from stone to stone to get across and a stone tips over you are bound to go in! Try as he might he couldn't snatch his foot back out before the water flowed over it although he thought it would be possible if he was quick enough! And then you couldn't get to the frogspawn without stepping down onto the soft mud bank. He tried wiping the worst of it off in the grass but it still left his shoes smeared with mud and his socks were hopelessly wet. Still they had had a smashing time.

"Don't you get into trouble Bri?"

"Sometimes. Why?"

"They're always going off at me."

"Well you can't help it can you," Brian replied with some sympathy. "You can't go in t'river without 'em on. Can you?"

"They ought to get shoes that don't let water in."

David's bravado held until he left Brian and John and then, with retribution imminent he became crestfallen as he opened the door. Bill was waiting for him, glancing at the time as David entered. He hoped, oh! how he hoped that David would come in from playing just for once without being caked in mud. Every night he came in scruffy! It would be a good job when the dark nights were here and he couldn't go out to play. Well, September was nearly over and already the evenings were drawing in. Thank God!

David stood sheepishly by the door pulling his shoes off.

"Just look at you!" Bill said. "Come here!"

David looked down at his legs and feet. He'd tried to keep clean and they didn't look as bad as last time.

Dorothy came in from the kitchen with hers and Bill's dinner on hot plates. She put them hastily on the table.

"Come on Bill." Her glance took in the state of David's socks. It wasn't really as big an issue as Bill was making it but he seemed determined to have his way with David. "Leave that," she said, "come and have your dinner while it's hot."

"Get 'em cleaned!" Bill ordered. "Get some newspaper and get 'em cleaned up! Look at you!" He couldn't understand why was David so insistent on showing him up like this!

"Come and get your tea Bill. David'll get his shoes cleaned up won't you?" Dorothy looked down at him and her face was stern in support of Bill but there was humour in her eyes. "And then it's bedtime."

"I don't know what to do." Bill said. "I just wish he'd take notice."

"Don't smack him again Bill. He'll grow out of it."

"He's ruining his shoes." Bill turned from his seat at the table and addressed David, busy with the newspaper on the hearth. "Well you're not getting any new ones. D'you hear? Not yet anyway."

He turned back to Dorothy.

"Had a bit of news today."

He waited for her interest.

"Go on then," she said. "What is it?"

He made her wait while he patiently finished his mouthful and swallowed it.

Dorothy knew what he was up to. "Oh you are exasperating Bill!" she cried and gave him a playful dig in the arm. "Come on, what d'you want to tell me?"

"Well it's not really settled. I mean, they're just talking about it." He took another careful forkful of vegetable.

Dorothy put her knife and fork down and looked at him quizzically. "Well tell me then if you're going to."

Bill was enjoying the build up. He waited, sensing when Dorothy was on the verge of exasperation and then said, "How do you fancy living in America?"

It was Dorothy's turn to pause.

"You what?" she said finally.

"America. We might get the chance to go there."

"But what…? When?"

"Don't know yet."

Dorothy pushed her plate away, her interest in eating gone. She looked across at Bill to speak but couldn't find words.

"How do you mean?" Dorothy said at last.

"Come on," he said, enjoying the sensation and pushing his plate from him too. "Let's get David ready for bed."

It wasn't something Bill wanted to share with childish chatter. If it was going to happen then he and Dorothy would have to consider it very carefully and they couldn't begin to do that with David around. Just for once the wet shoes were forgotten as David was undressed and Dorothy brought his pyjamas out.

"Come on then. Say night night to daddy."

David gave Bill a kiss and received a hug then she took his hand and led him upstairs.

"What was daddy saying?" David asked as they crossed the landing.

"Oh it's just something that's happening at work. I expect he'll tell us all about it when he finds out."

"Are we going away?"

"I don't think so. Well, not for a long time yet anyway. We'll have to see what he says won't we?"

She tucked David in and sat with him while he said his prayer then returned to their sitting room. Now curiosity was burning in her.

She closed the door carefully. "Well? What is it?"

"Is he tucked in alright?"

"Yes. Come on!"

"Well it's all very secret at the moment. Not everybody knows about it."

"Well who am I going to tell?" Dorothy said.

"Well they're trying to do a deal with a firm in California. They don't have the knowledge that we've got and so they want us to show 'em how to make high performance springs. The sort of thing our department specialises in."

"How long have you known?"

"Just today. They called me in. Well, me and a couple of the others. Told us it was very hush hush because it's not all settled yet. But if it goes through they would need to send specialists over to show 'em how to carry on."

"Is it permanent? I mean, would we all have to go? And live there?"

"Well it depends how you get on once you're there I suppose."

There wasn't very much more that Bill could tell Dorothy. Management were taking soundings from a few key personnel under conditions of absolute confidentiality. But if the negotiations for a joint venture were to succeed it would mean having the commitment of key people to enable the transfer of skills to take place.

"When? I mean, when will you know?"

"Well there's still a lot to be decided yet."

"I mean, are you sure it's definitely going to be you? If they decide to do it I mean?"

"Well that's why they've sworn us to secrecy. Not everybody'll have the chance to go."

California! Dorothy was almost speechless. What an opportunity! The images she had seen flickering in the darkness of the cinema came

313

to her. Palm trees and swimming pools. Endless warm sunshine.

"Where abouts? I mean I know you said California but… I thought that was just, well, Hollywood and that. I didn't know they had steel factories…"

"I don't know exactly. They haven't said yet. But I think it's somewhere up near San Francisco. Somewhere like that."

"And we could come with you? You wouldn't be going on your own?"

"That's what they've said. That's why I had to come and talk to you about it tonight. See what you think about it."

"Oh Bill."

"Just think of it Dolly. They earn three times what we do over there. And they say the cost of living's cheaper! And we could bring David up in the sunshine. And there's no problem with housing."

Dorothy threw her arms about him and tried to imagine this sudden dream as reality.

"Oh, if only…"

"Go and put that record on. The one I like."

"Oh!" she cried. "I'll have to go and tell our Marge. And my mother."

"Not yet. Wait 'till we know a bit more. 'Till we've got something to really tell 'em. Anyway," he added earnestly, "we're not to start spreading it around just yet."

"Just my mother. She's got a right to know and she won't tell anybody."

No, Bill thought, she won't. She's as tight as a clam. He relented.

"Alright," he said. "Just your mother. But she's got to keep it a secret. But not just yet. Put us that record on. Then come and sit here with me for a bit. Go on, let's just have it to ourselves. Just for a while."

"Faust?"

"Yes. That's it."

Dorothy checked the needle and wound the gramophone up and placed the arm carefully on the record. Bill sat back with Dorothy smiling close beside him and listened with moist eyes to the final rout of Mephistopheles as the wonderful chorus of angels intervened to save the soul of Margeurite.

"Oh Bill," Dorothy whispered. "I love you."

Enid Bracewell was sitting with her crotcheting as she listened to the radio. She looked up with a smile of motherly concern as Dorothy came in and put her wool and needle down. Her smile remained fixed when she saw Bill following her in.

"Here," she said, straightening the cushion in Ernest Bracewell's

314

chair. "Come and sit over here."

"We've got something to tell you mum."

Enid Bracewell looked with interest from Dorothy to Bill and then back to Dorothy. "Come on," she repeated, "come and sit here nice and comfortable."

Dorothy giggled; she suddenly knew what her mother was thinking and it was fun to tease her.

"Shall I tell her Bill or do you want to?"

"Oh well. I don't mind. You can if you like."

"No," Dorothy replied with her face as straight as she could keep it. "You do it."

"Oh alright then."

Enid Bracewell sat patiently waiting for their playing to finish.

"Well ma," Bill began. She cringed. How she hated that form of address. Wherever had he got 'ma' from? It was so like him. Why he couldn't address her properly! "We might be getting a chance to go to America."

Enid Bracewell's smile remained frozen. She looked quickly into the hearth and back up again to her daughter. "D'you mean… to live?"

Dorothy knew that her mother's relations with Bill were unsatisfactory and she felt the underlying strain for them both, especially sharing her mother's house; maybe this would be the piece of news that would bring them together. Perhaps now her mother would see that Bill was respected and highly thought of. After all they wouldn't ask just anybody to go overseas on the company's business would they? "Yes mum," Dorothy said. "Isn't it wonderful."

"Well I don't know," she replied. "What about the boy?"

"Well…"

"Well he'll come with us of course," Bill said.

"When?"

"Well, not straight away," Dorothy said.

"It's not going to be for ages yet," Bill added. "Nothing's really been fixed yet."

"I should hope not!"

"It's just that, well, the firm's thinking of opening up out there," Bill ploughed on. "And they've asked me if I'd be interested. It'll be with an American company," he added.

"And are you? Interested?"

"Well," Bill was a little nonplussed at Mrs. Bracewell's attitude, "Of course."

"There's no 'of course' about it is there!" Enid Bracewell riposted. "I mean, all your family – and Dorothy's – to say nothing of her friends, are all over here."

315

"Oh Mum." Dorothy shared Bill's disappointment at her mother's reaction. "It would mean we'd have a brand new start. We wouldn't be living here with you for years to come."

"And what's wrong with living here? This has always been your home!"

"Yes but… It's not the same. I mean, living here like this. Sharing."

"Nothing's fixed yet ma." Bill tried to take the problem away. "They only wanted to know if I'd be interested."

Ma! There it was again!

"Yes well. It's all very well to use people isn't it. You come here when it suits you! We put ourselves out, give you a home, you and the boy. And now it's suddenly not good enough. And you want to take our daughter away from us into the bargain! It's nice isn't it! The sort of gratitude you get from some people! To get it thrown back in your face. Some people don't deserve kindness!"

"It's not like that mum!" Dorothy said staunchly. "It's a big opportunity for Bill. We'd have a wonderful life out there. A car. Swimming pool…"

"Hmmph!"

"…and you and dad'll be able to come out and visit us."

"And what about the boy?"

"We've told you already, he's coming with us!" Bill's patience was wearing thin.

"I mean have you told him?"

"No. Not yet."

"There's no point yet ma. What's the point in getting him all excited about it until it's fixed! It all wants going into properly first."

"Well I don't know what your father's going to say I'm sure. Still I only hope you know what you're doing. But you want to make sure you go carefully into it all before you do anything rash." Enid Bracewell looked with meaning from Dorothy to Bill. "There's some of them GI brides gone over there and their family's never heard of them again."

"Oh mother!" Dorothy exclaimed in exasperation. "I'm not going off like that!"

"Well I should hope you're not," came the tight lipped response. She rose from her chair. "Well I think I could do with a cup of tea." She glanced at Dorothy. "I expect you could do with one too."

"Not for me thanks ma," Bill put in, "I think I'll just pop down for a pint." But she ignored him and Bill left Dorothy and her mother together. There was just no pleasing some people…

Bill wasn't late back. Dorothy was in her pink candlewick dressing gown waiting by the fire when he returned.

"Getting colder." He shuddered and stood before the fire.

"I'm sorry about mum," Dorothy said.

"Well," Bill was philosophical, "she's never liked me. I don't know why. I've never done nothing to upset her."

"I know. She just… never approved for some reason."

"We've got to get out of here Dorothy. We can't carry on living like this."

"I wish we could…"

Dorothy roused herself from the settee.

"Where are you going?"

"To make a cup of tea. Would you like one?"

"Come here." He reached out for her but Dorothy evaded him with a smile.

"I'll make us a cup of tea first. Then we'll go up to bed." She pulled her dressing gown back around her and went through to the kitchen. Bill sat waiting, listening to faint sounds from upstairs.

"Won't be long," Dorothy said when she returned. "My dad's back. He's just brought an express up from London. He's having a bath."

"Oh. I don't suppose you…?"

"No. Didn't want to start going through all that again. My mother's told him. I think I heard 'em talking about it."

"Oh…" Bill relapsed into non-committal silence. "He's not said anything about it?"

"No. Anyway let's not talk about it anymore. It only gets everybody upset. We're still going up to Marge's for tea on Sunday aren't we."

"Yes. It'll make a nice change."

There came a sharp knock on the door and Enid Bracewell's voice.

"Kettles boiling Dorothy. I'm going up."

"Thanks mum. Shan't be long."

They sat together on the settee, secure in their room, waiting for the activity upstairs to subside. Bill smelled Dorothy's scent rising to him as she lay with her head against his shoulder.

"If it could only stay like this." He reached into the folds of her dressing gown and gently fondled her. She shifted against him and closed her eyes.

"Love you," she murmured.

"Love you."

There was definitely something in the air. It wasn't just because bonfire night was coming and Grandad Bracewell had some garden rubbish to burn and he said they could have a small fire at the top of the garden and Aunty Marge and Uncle Charlie were bringing Jean with her

317

fireworks. But Grandma Bracewell didn't seem so cross and David could sense a difference in the house.

Of course, they didn't know that he knew! They didn't talk about it a lot, in fact they didn't talk about it now as much as they had done at the beginning. Mummy and daddy had kept referring to it when they thought he wasn't listening but David had heard their conversations and he knew about their secret. He was just waiting for them to tell him so that he could be excited too. And it looked like it could be soon!

Daddy had bought him a box of fireworks at the weekend and David had inspected them, especially the rockets and he couldn't wait until bonfire night. Two more days! Now they had all started getting all excited too. And today mummy had been looking at him in a strange sort of way ever since she got home from work, as though the secret she and daddy had was on her lips and just waiting to be shared with him. Perhaps it was going to be tonight.

Bill arrived home and David watched as Dorothy greeted him with suppressed expectation and nodded, beaming.

"Have you told…?" he inclined his head towards their adjoining door.

Dorothy shook her head. "Waiting for you."

"Come on then, let's go and tell her now. Before we have our tea." Bill turned to David and said, "You wait here. We're just going through to tell grandma something. We shan't be a minute."

"Aw. Can't I come with you?"

"No. Wait here a minute. I've told you, we shan't be long."

David grimaced and returned to the book he'd been reading. It wasn't fair; they never told him nothing.

From next door he heard the sudden sounds of raised voices, but they were not angry voices. Why couldn't he be in there with them? He could have shared it and known what was going on. Well he knew what was going on! So they didn't need to tell him!!

Dorothy and Bill returned and Dorothy sat on the settee and patted the cushion next to her. Bill looked on benignly.

"David come and sit here next to me."

David looked at her reluctantly.

"Come on," Dorothy coaxed, "we've got something to tell you."

"Why couldn't I go with you next door to tell grandma?"

"We wanted to tell her on our own that's all. So that we could come and tell you specially without sharing it with anybody."

"Go on David. Do as your mummy tells you."

Obediently David put his book down and went to sit next to Dorothy.

"Now," Dorothy began, "we've got something really special to tell you."

David, looking down between his knees at the hearthrug murmured, "I know what it is."

"Don't be so silly, let mummy..." Bill began but Dorothy interrupted him.

"Oh! Well what do you think it can be then?" she said with a smile.

"We're going to America."

There was an instant's silence and David continued, "I've known about it for ages," as though he was saying 'everybody knows that!'

But he wanted it to be exciting, the way it was for them, the way it had been for Grandma Bracewell but now it didn't seem exciting anymore.

Dorothy looked up at Bill and Bill turned his face away. Why was he always such a disappointment? Where did he get America from? They'd never mentioned it in front of him, he was sure they hadn't! He'd been listening, that's what it was. Well what else could it be? Sneaking about and listening to things that didn't concern him. Well, that's something else that would have to be straightened out.

Bill wished he had never mentioned America now. They'd all been excited at the time but, he remembered, he hadn't been under any pressure to say anything. Not from work anyway. It was a deal the company had been working on that's all and because he was a 'key figure' as they put it, in the Heavy Spring Department the management had shared their aspirations with him, and a select group of others, under the strictest confidence. And at the time Bill had thought it would make him look good. It would show the Bracewells who he really was, if he came home with news like that. But even that hadn't worked. If anything it had made old ma Bracewell even more rat faced!

Oh it would have been good if it had come off. They could have taken off and left her behind, left it all behind and got off to a really good start. But the deal hadn't gone through, at least not in the way the company had painted it. Now it looked as though they were going to sell the yanks the technology or something and leave 'em to get on with it. Bloody typical! Give it you with one hand; take it away with the other. He gave a sigh of exasperation, and turned back to David. "Will you listen to what your mummy's telling you."

It came out almost as a bark and Dorothy's look turned to surprise and disappointment.

"Bill! He's alright. Don't shout at him."

"Sorry," Bill mumbled. "I didn't mean it to come out like that. Go on, you tell him."

Dorothy took David's hand. "How would you like to have a little brother? Or sister?"

319

Now they were both beaming at him in self conscious expectation and David found himself trying to suddenly understand and match their mood.

"Alright," he replied shortly. They seemed to want something more but David didn't know what to say, or what sort of questions to ask.

"Well," Bill said, "mummy's going to have a baby. A little brother or sister for you. Next summer." And they exchanged smiles replete with secret pleasure. Their coyness was making David feel embarrassed.

"How do you feel about it?" Dorothy asked.

"Alright." David ransacked his mind for a question to ask. "What's it going to be called?" he said at last.

"We haven't made our minds up yet," Bill said. "It's a bit early for names 'till we know what it's going to be."

"When will you find out?"

Dorothy stepped in and deflected the question. "If it's a little girl we might call it Susan. Would you like that?"

David considered then said, "I've never had a brother. What's it like?"

Dorothy took his hand. "Oh you'll have great fun. You'll be his big brother. You'll be able to take care of him and show him how to do things and take him to your secret places in the woods when he's old enough.

Oh, David thought with interest, it might be fun after all. He might be in charge of it.

"And if it is a little boy we're going to call him Robert," Bill added, smiling that smile at Dorothy again.

David wriggled his hand out of Dorothy's and said, "Can I read my book now?"

So there it was. Bill had expected the news to have more impact and to arouse greater curiosity. He was a continual disappointment.

Dorothy sat in the sitting room on bonfire night, watching the goings on through the window. Both Marge and her mother had insisted that 'in her condition' she should not be exposed to too much excitement, so despite her protests Dorothy stayed indoors to watch the fireworks.

Charlie and Bill displayed great bravado with the bangers. Bill lit them and held them until they started to fizz before tossing them to the ground and sending Marge laughing and screaming with fright. He tried to show David how safe it was to hold them until they fizzed but David insisted on tossing them away the instant Bill put a match to them. Charlie put a banger under the dustbin lid to see what would happen. The explosion made a satisfying reverberation and lifted the lid from the ground. So then Charlie fetched a chair from the house and sat on it with the dustbin lid and a banger underneath, miming comic unconcern while he waited for the bang.

"Perhaps it's gone out," Marge said hopefully.

Bill took a step forward to the concern of Dorothy watching from the window and David cried, "No daddy don't!" and then it exploded with a resounding bang which made Charlie jump from the chair. Everybody laughed except Marge who ran to see if he was alright.

The chestnuts thrown into the embers round the edge of the fire proved almost impossible to retrieve but Dorothy had put some in the oven so that saved the day. And Marge's bonfire toffee, strongly flavoured and treacly sticky was declared a great success. David and Jean ran around the garden from the glow of the fire into the darkness and for once there were no admonitions to 'mind the plants'. Later they all came back inside to share the jugs of beer that Enid Bracewell and Charlie fetched up from 'The Big Tree' at the bottom of the road. Bill sat with his arm protectively around Dorothy. It was the best night David had enjoyed for a long time and although he protested when it was over and time for everybody to go he was comfortably tired. Dorothy took him into the bathroom for a wash and then it was time for bed.

Bill arrived home from work the following day and found Dorothy waiting for him with a look of bitter disappointment on her face. His mood of blithe euphoria evaporated when he saw her.

"What's the matter?"

"Oh Bill. I'm so sorry."

"What is it? What's wrong?"

"I've started."

He didn't grasp at first what Dorothy's words meant. "What…? I mean…?"

Dorothy gave him a wry look. "My monthly… You know, my period."

"What? You mean… you've lost…?"

Bill's mind was working on a range of scenario's to cope with what Dorothy was telling him.

"Bill. I wasn't pregnant. It was a false alarm."

He sat down heavily at the table. "But you'd missed. You were more than three weeks over. You said…"

"I know. I'm as disappointed as you are. I thought I was. I'm normally as regular as clockwork. I never miss."

"Then why?"

"I don't know," Dorothy replied. She pulled a chair out and sat

321

opposite him. "It sometimes happens. You can't explain it."

"What about you." Suddenly here was another concern! "Are you alright? I mean…?"

"Yes!" Dorothy replied earnestly. She looked into Bill's eyes. "Yes, don't worry about me. Of course I'm alright. It's perfectly normal."

"Well I don't know about that. First time I've ever heard about it."

"That's because you're a man. There's nothing wrong. I promise you." She reached out and took his hand. "I'm just a bit disappointed that's all. I'm just as disappointed as you are."

"Are you sure?"

"Honest."

Bill squeezed her hand in return. "As long as you're OK."

"Just my pride's dented a bit that's all. Telling everybody like that. But apart from that everything's alright."

Dorothy smiled at him and Bill's anxiety lifted. He smiled back and a roguish glint came into his eyes. "Well," he said, "we'll have to try again then won't we."

CHAPTER 39

Angel voices in the stars

Christmas approached and they planned parties and trimmed their houses. The Christmas trees were brought out and their branches unfolded. The boxes of baubles were dusted off and cotton wool snow was carefully laid upon the branches of the trees. Paper chains festooned the walls and ceilings and they basked in mutual admiration of each other's efforts. The strategic mistletoe trapped the unwary; Bill stole a kiss from Marge and even Enid Bracewell received a conciliatory peck. The holiday beckoned with the anticipation of merriment and joy.

Christmas Eve was clear and cold. The stars twinkled in the darkness with brilliant intensity and the pavements glistened with diamond points of frost. The Bracewells were in The Big Tree, David was carol singing with Brian and John. The doors were locked and the curtains securely drawn. Safe from intrusion, Dorothy and Bill lay naked in the darkness before the fire. In the softness of the fire's glow Dorothy looked like an alabaster nude reclining on the eiderdown they had brought from their bed upstairs. The recesses of her body were hidden in shadow but the contours of her breast and thigh were highlighted in the flickering from the fire. Bill reached down again to touch her and Dorothy shivered and closed her eyes in expectation. He drew her to him and pressed close with renewed passion. Dorothy kissed him eagerly, greedily and reached down to guide him into her. "I love you… love you…" she sighed. And Bill responded breathlessly, grunting, "…love you …love you."

Oh God! There was someone knocking at the bloody door!

Bill froze upon her and listened.

Silence. Then the knocking started again. Christ! How long had it been going on?

"Who is…?"

"Quiet," he whispered. Passion melted and Bill rolled limply away from her. Dorothy began to move but he held her still.

Silence.

They relaxed and Bill reached for his watch and checked the time in its luminous dial. "Have your mum and dad got their keys?"

"Yes," Dorothy whispered, "but they wouldn't come straight in here."

That was true. The one saving grace was that the Bracewells practically needed an invitation before they entered Bill and Dorothy's rooms.

"Perhaps it's David," Dorothy said.

"I thought he was going back to Brian's after they'd finished carolling."

They lay, tense with discovery and waited. With the silence came relaxation and Bill reached for Dorothy again.

"What time is it?" she murmured.

"About ten past nine."

"Oh good heavens," Dorothy cried.

"What's the matter?"

"I told David to be in for nine."

They heard knocking again, this time faintly, coming from the back door. They lay in the tension of discovery, poised for flight, ready to grab the eiderdown and their clothes and make a dash for the stairs. But the knocking ceased and they began to relax.

"Come on Dorothy. Just a few more minutes."

"But what about…?" Dorothy began but Bill soothed her and she allowed him to lay her down once more.

"He'll be alright. He's OK. Just a few more minutes…"

Dorothy felt him lay astride her and her mind was listening and waiting for the knocking to begin again. But none came and passion began to rise and she felt the tingling begin as he moved in her. She pulled Bill to her and closed her eyes and closed her mind to everything else and focussed only on the movement between her thighs and the unbearable pleasure shivering through her.

David couldn't understand it. There ought to be someone at home. It was Christmas Eve and it was getting late and he was cold. But the house was dark and silent. He knocked again, not as loudly as before but the sound of his knocking was loud in the darkness all around him. He looked about fearfully and wished he hadn't come up the passage into the silence of this dark yard. He was afraid of the darkness but he didn't want to admit it to himself because that made it worse. Silent as the grave! Unbidden, the words people used to describe this silence came to him and they settled in his mind. He tried to suppress the images they brought but the more he tried to suppress them, the stronger the images became. And there was no answer to his knocking, no sound from inside the house. He was alone and trapped, here in the corner of the yard with the cold starlight on him. And he had to go back into the dark passage, down the tunnel where he couldn't see and things were waiting to reach for him in the darkness. He longed for the safety of the street and the lamplight beneath the trees, and the glow from the windows of the pub across the main road, the shops and the tram stop. The pleasures of carol singing were gone!

Dare he try another knock? He raised his fist and looked about him. He felt the vulnerability of his back and a tingle as though finger tips were about to touch him. But he didn't dare turn around for fear of what was there. He hesitated and was lost. Panic took over and he dashed in terror from the yard and flew down the passage with phantoms at his back, and didn't stop until he reached the safety of the lights at the bottom of the road. He paused for breath at the sweet shop window. It was alright; he was alone, there was nothing there.

From across the road he could hear the sounds of laughter and singing in The Big Tree. There was light and warmth and people behind the steamy windows. But he couldn't go across and join them. It wasn't like at Aunty Ame's; Grandma Bracewell would send him out. He wanted his mummy and daddy. Where were they? Why weren't they at home?

The cold was becoming more intense, as though it was falling directly onto him from the dispassionate stars in the darkness above and David retreated into the shop doorway for warmth. Why won't mummy and daddy come? He wished he could have stayed longer with Brian but Brian's mummy was getting him ready for bed and he'd had to come home. His feet were cold but stamping them only made them hurt. His hands in his trouser pockets were cold too and he could feel their coldness against his legs. He was getting cold all over. He looked out from the sweetshop doorway but the road was empty. He began to sing a carol; not with joy as he had earlier with his friends, his voice lifting clear and true but quietly and tremulously, a small thin voice seeking comfort in itself from the fear and self pity crowding in on him. Cold and alone on Christmas Eve! Across the road a man appeared hurrying home with a parcel under his arm, a scooter, a Christmas present for his child. Watching the man hurry by David's sense of righteous self pity grew. How could they leave him? Enjoying themselves somewhere and with no thought for him? It wasn't fair. To be locked out and nobody cared. He stopped singing.

He didn't want to feel small and insignifican't! How could they!? They must be home by now. They must be! Perhaps he had missed them somehow.

He went back to the corner of the street and looked up it. But it was darker up there and the street lamps were overshadowed by the trees that lined the pavement. David's angry courage began to falter and he returned to his vigil in the sweetshop doorway.

But he couldn't stay there long for it was too cold, he was too tired and he was hungry. They must be home. They must! He had to face the darkness again.

He looked up at the sky and walked a little way into the dark street. This time it was better; the stars were just as clear and bright but somewhere beyond them there was God. David stood in awe. The heavens were still but a trace of angel voices lingered in the silence of the stars. Silent night. Holy night. And children are beloved of God. And suddenly David's demons vanished and he walked along the dark road and there was welcoming light in the window.

"You're a bit late aren't you?" they said.

"I've been waiting for you to come home," David replied.

"We've not been out," they answered.

"But the door was locked."

"Well it shouldn't have been. Should it?" And they looked at each other as if saying 'well I didn't do it, did you?'

David was sure he hadn't been wrong. But... but... here was mummy with some mince pies for his supper. Then they hung his pillowcase at the foot of his bed in expectation and mummy tucked him in and kissed him, leaving the soft scent of herself in the room. David opened the bedroom curtains; the sky was still clear and sharp and he fell asleep hearing the sound of distant sleighbells approaching across the rooftops.

David awoke early. It was cold but the daylight coming through the skylight window was filled with sunshine. He looked along the bed but the pillowcase was nowhere to be seen. He suffered a pang of disappointment, then crawled along the bed and looked over the foot. There it was, with the most intriguing shapes and lumps. Joyfully David grabbed the neck of the pillowcase and hauled it back up onto the bed then he snuggled under the bedclothes to start the unpacking. Great! The first book was a cowboy annual filled with cartoon strip stories and articles about indian villages, and outlaws and... He put the book down and began to ransack the rest. Oh yes! A bird whistle; he'd been wanting a bird whistle for ages. It was a hollow round disc, the diameter of a shilling with a hole through the centre. You placed it between your lips and teeth then blew through it. He tried it. It worked! And a piercing tuneless high pitched note announced to the house below that David was awake. He kept the whistle in, alternatively sucking and blowing, emitting the whistles shriek while he carried on. More books. Rupert. Great! A proper reading book with no pictures and the same size as the ones on grandma's shelf, a grown up sort of book. Hello! A box. He unwrapped it and gave a cry of delight. Wow!! A colt 45 just like the one he'd looked at in the toyshop and they had said he couldn't have it. With a pearl handle! And a break open action to load the caps in. Oh, he couldn't wait to go out to play with this. He rummaged deeper. A softer parcel, bendy, with a funny shape. Yes!! A cowboy belt with a holster! He tried it on over his pyjamas and put the gun in it. Now he could be a real cowboy. The whistles continued coming thick and fast.

Dorothy appeared at the stair rail above the landing with Bill close behind.

"What have you got then?" she asked.

"A real cowboy gun," David cried, "with real pearl handles." He pulled it from the holster and took pot shots at imaginary bandits. "Look at this." He thrust it back in the holster and did a quick draw, except the holster rose with the gun and failed to clear as slickly as he'd seen the cowboys do it in the films. Bill and Dorothy were smiling with pleasure.

"You like it then?"

"Yes. It's great." Bang! Bang! Two more outlaws dead. "And my bird whistle."

He held up the small sixpenny plastic object and put it back in his mouth.

"Save it for outside," Bill said with his hands to his ears. "Grandma and grandad's still asleep."

"Come on." Dorothy held her hands out to him. "Let's get you washed and dressed. Then you can show me your books."

Last night was forgotten. They went downstairs and after he was washed and dressed they brought David his sack of presents down while Dorothy went to help her mother to start preparing Christmas dinner. Ernest Bracewell had the day off and he went to his allotment to cut sprouts for their meal. And they all sat together for Christmas. Later, when Ernest Bracewell had snoozed the afternoon away they walked to Marge and Charlie's in the failing afternoon light and had a party in their cramped living room. But it was fun. They played charades and teased young Jean over a crush she had on one of the teachers at school. So much so that Jean had a tantrum and burst into tears and David laughed at her and she screamed at him to 'shut up!' and then the family realised they had taken the teasing too far. Reluctantly Jean allowed herself to be cajoled into joining in with them again and then it happened all in a rush; she burst into shrieks of laughter and everything was alright.

On Boxing Day David went with Dorothy and Bill to George and Myra's. Lilly and Harold were there, fussing over Myra who was heavily pregnant with her second child. But it hadn't stopped her producing trifle and apple pie to follow the roast pork tea. Everyone commented on Myra's apple pies. She had a way with pastry, Lilly said.

It was light and, if anything it was even lighter now she was pregnant.

Myra basked in Lilly's compliments and Dorothy thought her secret thoughts and smiled across the table at Bill.

After tea, more games, drinks. "Anything tha wants," George said expansively. "I've got whisky, sherry, port, gin. Or a beer?" Harold forsook his usual and drank whisky instead of beer as it was the season and regarded his son's wives through an increasing haze of happiness.

And later, Myra took herself off into the kitchen and cut pork sandwiches with pickles to round the evening off. As if they hadn't already had enough!

They protested gallantly.

"Never mind," Myra said, "it all wants eating. It won't keep you know."

And so they sailed into nineteen fortynine.

CHAPTER 40

Pearls and wisdom

It was Saturday morning, there was unexpected February sunshine illuminating the room and Dorothy thought that all things considered it couldn't have happened better. She had felt a slight tingling in her breasts and an unexpected nausea in the morning that got worse, especially at the thought of breakfast. Only this time she needed to be sure. No more false alarms.

But the doctor confirmed it with a smile and cautioned her to, "...be sensible; take things easy. You want to enjoy all the fuss and attention you're going to have."

He leaned back in his chair and watched as Dorothy prepared to leave. He'd known the family for close on twenty years. Not that they'd been regular visitors, always in and out of the surgery like some of his patients. The usual childhood ailments with Dorothy and Margery. Ernest Bracewell he hardly ever saw, but Enid, his wife had come to him four years ago after the tragic accident to their son. She had taken it badly and he had been glad to do what he could to help. It amounted to talking her through it more than medication; he recalled that she had been reluctant to take the prescription for pills that he'd offered. But Dorothy had coped with it admirably.

She was such a sensible girl, a lovely girl. And now she was married and expecting her first child. He was very happy to confirm the news and see the look of fulfilled happiness that lit her face when he told her. Just as long as she was sensible. There had been an uncle – a brother of her father's if memory served – had some problems to do with...? Was it his kidneys? Not that he, the doctor had anything to do with it; the uncle wasn't his patient. And he didn't want to alarm anybody but he would make sure she kept an eye on her blood pressure. And Dorothy was sensible. A nice girl. A gentle word of caution, given with a smile.

Dorothy shook his hand. "Thank you doctor." She grinned with delight. "I can't wait to tell Bill. And David. And everybody."

He rose and went to the door of his room with her. "Remember what I said. You just sit back and let them all make a fuss of you." Then he returned to his chair, made a brief note on Dorothy's medical record card and waited for his next patient.

Dorothy stepped into the sunshine. It was unexpectedly mild for February and that alone was enough to give your spirits a lift half way through the cold gloom of English winter. She called at the bakers for the regular weekend bread order and the way the assistant looked at her, Dorothy was sure the girl knew. But of course she couldn't! Perhaps it was the smile that Dorothy carried into the shop with her and the warmth that remained after she had left. Bill wouldn't be home for at least an hour and as she walked back along the road she passed the park gates. On an impulse she retraced her steps and turned in. There weren't any people about, not even kids splashing and building dams in the shallow stream. Probably all still at the Saturday morning cinema where David was, watching the Superman serial. To Dorothy's left the long grassy bank climbed behind the spread of gorse towards the distant woods. The trees were bare but in summer it was lush and dense. As girls she and Marge had played endlessly in the park and she understood David's love of it. She paused, gazing up along the bank. If snow had fallen it would have been teeming with children. She saw herself as a girl, racing down the slope on her sledge with her feet extended high in front and the spray of snow like ocean foam splashing into her face, laughing. And Marge screaming and laughing at her and stamping her feet as she waited at the bottom for her turn.

In the flowerbeds beside the path the green tips of daffodils were showing amongst the crocuses. And inside her something was growing too. Instinctively Dorothy placed her hand protectively across her belly. Even though it was the same, now it felt different. She strolled further, up the slight rise in the path, past the ponds on her right where the frogs lay their spawn in spring. This year David and his friends would be down there again, just as she had when she was a tomboy girl. The surface of the pool was still in the sunshine but somewhere under the dead reeds that trailed lifelessly on the water the frogs would be getting pregnant too. Dorothy's stroll took her into the wood. Even in winter there was discreet activity in the branches; a solitary bird call echoing above. She felt at one with the nature all about her. The world wasn't dead, only sleeping but stirring as it slept. And inside her something was awakening, something precious. A sudden movement caught her eye. It was a squirrel, poised and alert, clinging to the trunk of a tree and then with a sudden darting movement it vanished round the tree.

It was suddenly colder under the trees and the stream carried dead brown leaves and dammed them against tree roots in the bank. The damp earth looked black and she felt a chill. She wasn't going to go any further into the woods anyway. It was time to get back and have a cup of coffee and wait for Bill.

She was sitting in the armchair where she had been trying to read when Bill walked in. David had returned from the matinee filled with excitement as usual. She had listened to his chatter, said nothing and given him a sandwich and he'd gone out to play again. Dinner was ready for when Bill got home; all she'd had to do now was wait.

She planned for him to have his wash and shave and get changed before she said anything. She would have liked him to have his dinner first and then they could sit comfortably together afterwards and then she would tell him. She had even mused as she sat there with making him wait until Valentines' day and making a romantic announcement. It was only a couple of days away but even Dorothy conceded to herself that she couldn't keep the news back that long.

In the end it didn't matter. Dorothy turned to look at him with her usual smile as he walked through the door and he knew. Just by looking at her Bill knew. There was a look, no different to the way she had looked at him a thousand times before, but this time that look told him. And she knew by the expression that grew on his face like the blossoming of a flower, and unaccountably she burst into laughter.

"I wasn't going to tell you straight away," she cried before Bill had time to open his mouth. "I was going to make you wait a bit before I told you." Her laughter carried sobs of joy.

"Are you sure?" Bill tried to resist the feeling suddenly growing inside him.

"Yes."

And the simple affirmation told Bill it was really true this time. He ran across to her and Dorothy rose to greet him. He threw his arms around her. "Really?"

"Yes." She nodded in delight. "Yes. Yes, yes. I've been to the doctor. It's true."

"Oh Dolly." He swept his arm across his forehead, stammering with joy. "I don't know what to say."

The way David took the news left Bill wondering if he would ever take anything seriously. They waited until dinner was coming to a close. David was on the point of leaving the table to dash back out to play when Bill sat back and said,

"We've got something to tell you."

David looked up at them with a quizzical smile. Bill and Dorothy exchanged glances and David continued to look expectantly from one to the other. The sooner they told him the sooner he could go out to play again.

"Well don't you want to know what it is?" Bill prompted.

"Yes," David replied.

"Well," Dorothy said, "you remember last year when mummy thought she was going to have a baby? Well, this time it's true. You're going to have a little brother. Or perhaps a sister," she added. "Won't that be nice?"

For David, who had no concept of what having a brother of his own would be like, it was difficult to know what to say. Brian Elliot had a little brother but he was always in the way and sometimes when they had wanted to go and play in the park, Brian's mother made him stay in instead to look after the toddler and amuse him. That was boring because Brian's little brother was too young to play. And this new brother that mummy and daddy were telling him about would be even younger. Anyway, what did he know about babies! And there was something about the way mummy and daddy looked at each other when they talked about babies that made him feel funny and squirmy.

"Well what do you say? Aren't you pleased?"

David looked at his daddy; he didn't understand what daddy was expecting. He just seemed to be demanding something of him and he didn't know what to say. So David just said,

"Oh."

Bill sighed and felt he would never understand the boy.

"Well don't you want to know when?" Bill said testily.

"Well I didn't know…" David couldn't put it into words. He looked up to the ceiling for inspiration. It was such a grown up thing and he didn't really know what was supposed to happen next, or what to ask.

"It's after the school holidays," Bill continued. "The end of summer."

"Oh."

Mummy was smiling at him. "What do you think we should call it?"

David's mind instantly went back to Aunty Ame's when he was little and the little rag dog 'Ruff' he had played with and the doll. He knew boys didn't have dolls; he couldn't remember where she had come from or where she went but something must have happened to her and she was a nice doll and her name was…

"Isabel."

David's unexpected reply took Dorothy aback. Both she and Bill had been assuming they were talking about a 'little brother'. "Oh," she said, "That's a nice name." David was beaming at her in satisfaction. "And what about if it's a little boy?" Dorothy added.

"I don't know." And hoping it would close the conversation he said, "Bill."

"Oh what a good idea." Dorothy looked at Bill and said, "We

332

hadn't thought of that had we?"

"Can I go out now?"

"Well don't you want to know any more about it?" Bill said.

David bit his lower lip and screwed his teeth over his lip and furrowed his brow and tried to think of something else to say but there was nothing he could think of. He looked up at them both with expectation and poised himself on the edge of his seat in anticipation of release.

"Oh go on," Bill said in exasperation. "But don't be long. We're going down to grandma's for tea. You've got to come in and get changed."

David scrambled down from the table and ran for the door, leaving Bill and Dorothy looking at each other with a profound sense of anti-climax.

But when David reached Brian's house he couldn't wait to tell him.

"Hey, Bri. Guess what. My mummy's going to have a baby!"

Brian looked at David with interest and Brian's mum said, "How is your mummy? Is she alright?"

Why did she want to ask if she was alright? She was only having a baby. David replied, "Yes." He couldn't think of anything. "Course she's alright."

"Come on Dave." Brian called to his mum as they ran out of the door, "We're going in the garden."

Brian's garden was much more fun than David's. It wasn't as neat and tidy and there weren't as many flowers to get in the way as there were at home. But here in Brian's they could build their den with the old bits of wood at the top end against the wall and keep Brian's little brother out.

"Is John coming?" David asked.

"He's had to go out."

"I've got to go out in a bit. Going to me grandma's for tea."

"Come on then. Help us with these."

Brian pulled out the pair of pram wheels he was hoarding. When they could find another pair of wheels on an axle they were going to get Brian's dad to help them to make a trolley. Then they could take it in the park and ride it down the hill.

Brian looked at David in a knowledgeable way. Brian was older than David, already eight and in a different class at school. And he knew about things. He leaned close and said, "Is your mum really having a baby?"

"Yes," David said. "They've just told me."

Brian looked sly and said, "They've been fucking." Then he smirked and giggled.

David jumped back shocked and embarrassed.

"They haven't," he said urgently in a whisper and looked round in case Brian's mummy was near.

When they talked about it in the schoolyard and tried out the words the older boys used to see what it felt like, it gave them a thrill and sometimes it made them feel funny. And although they didn't really know what it was they knew it was something secret and it had to be done quietly with girls. But not mummy and daddy. At home. Round the fire. Making tea.

"'Course they have," Brian insisted with a swagger.

David was silent, trying to understand the feelings the words aroused in him and to picture his mummy 'doing things' with his daddy but he couldn't reconcile the images. That wasn't it. For some reason he didn't want that to be it.

"They haven't."

"They have." Brian aired his superiority to the limit of his knowledge. "Where do you think babies come from? He's put his willy in your mummy's bottom."

"He hasn't! Don't say it. I'm going home!"

"What's a matter?" Brian mocked. "Didn't you know then? Fancy not knowing."

"I'm going home!" David cried. "And don't you say anything."

"Else what?" Brian taunted.

"Don't you dare that's all."

"Well I will. I'll tell 'em all at school."

"I'll bash you if you do. I'm going home."

David flushed with anger. He was angry with Brian. He didn't want anybody to talk about his mummy like that. He clenched his fists at his side and said, "You just say anything that's all." Then he turned and strode off leaving Brian to his pram wheels.

But David also felt angry and embarrassed about what Brian had said in case it was true. Is that really what daddy did to mummy? He didn't know if he would be able to look at mummy again without her knowing. He loitered about the street in confusion, half way between Brian's house and home. Then he crossed to the other side of the road and ran past the Bracewell's as quickly as possible in case mummy or daddy saw him and fetched him in and went to the park.

He ran about on the hillside, recklessly leaping across tree roots and slithering on the bank. He was an Indian, a Seminole tracking the white men who were coming to take over his forest. He knew the secret tracks which only an Indian would know. And he waited in ambush to pick them off one by one and then moved again to catch them unaware, a solitary hero. He saw the hare that lived on the edge of the meadow and gave chase and although David was swift and fleet of foot the hare outstripped him. Then he bethought himself of the time. Reluctantly he realised it was time to leave and get ready to go to grandma's for their Saturday tea.

"Where've you been?" Bill demanded when David walked in.

"Been up to Brian's."

"No you haven't. I've been up there looking for you."

"I didn't stay. Then I went in the park."

"I thought I told you not to be long! We've got to go out. You know we always go to grandma's for tea on a Saturday."

"I'm sorry daddy." David looked round with apprehension and asked, "Where's mummy?"

"Never mind about mummy. She's upstairs getting ready." Upstairs! In the bedroom! Getting ready! And there was uneasiness in the unformed thoughts that came to him. He heard daddy saying, "Go and get yourself washed. And you'll have to get changed too. Look at you!"

Obediently David went into the Bracewell's kitchen and ran some hot water into the bowl. He felt someone at his back; it was Dorothy, come down to inspect his hands and face. She took the flannel and turned his face to hers but David averted his eyes.

"Come on," Dorothy said, "there's no need to be so upset. You should just come home at the proper time that's all."

Lilly had been boiling mussels for their tea. She was very partial to live mussels and she prepared them herself, removing the 'poisonous whisker' from inside after boiling them in the bucket on the gas ring to get their shells open. The back door was wide open when they arrived!

"They won't be long before they'm ready. I've put 'em to cool." Lilly said. "I'll put 'kettle on for a cup of tea."

"Come on mother." Bill started to close the door behind them. "We've got something to tell you." He spoke in the brusque manner he always used to his mother.

"Leave the door open a minute. Let's smell out."

"Well come on," he said, and went through to the living room, closing that door after him.

"Shan't be a minute." she called from the kitchen.

Bill took a seat at the table and Dorothy went to the settee beneath the window, patting the seat for David to sit next to her.

Harold had a big fire blazing. "Won't be long," he said rubbing his hands. "Get the back door closed in a bit."

David began to say, "Mummy and daddy have..." but Bill interrupted him.

"Wait! Do as you're told. I'll tell her."

"I'm here now." Lilly came in, wiping her hands on the towel. "That's a nice bit of fire Harold."

"Need it with that back door open," he replied. "Is 'kettle on?"

"Won't be long. Now then Billy, what is it? You've got something to tell us?"

Again the looks from one to the other. Coyness and satisfaction. Dorothy's eyes were on Bill. David looked at the hearth and waited for his daddy to say it.

A pause, to get their attention, for effect.

"We're going to have a baby."

"Oh!" Lilly's exclamation accompanied her look across to Dorothy. "Oh!" she repeated, "Oh I am glad." Then she said, "Are you…?"

Dorothy anticipated the question and nodded, smiling, "I've been to the doctors. September."

"Oh that's such good news. Ain't that good news Harold?"

"I'm very pleased love." His understatement hid the enormous pleasure that Harold felt. He liked Dorothy; he'd liked her from the minute he first met her and this was perfect. He sat and smiled at her as though the smile was fixed on his face forever.

"Oh a September baby," Lilly gushed and found merit in every aspect of the news. "Oh that's a lovely time. And a little brother or sister for you David. And you won't have to share birthdays, three months apart like that. Oh you couldn't have managed it better."

In the kitchen the kettle began to boil and Lilly rose to make the tea.

"I'll come and help you," Dorothy said.

"No you won't." Lilly was completely old fashioned where pregnancy was concerned. "You just sit there. You're not to do anything now until that baby's born."

Lilly wouldn't even allow Dorothy to help with laying the table.

"It can't go on like this," Dorothy said. "I can't spend nine months in a chair. Come on, pass me the tablecloth."

But Lilly insisted and Dorothy looked at Bill with a smile and resigned herself to being denied any activity by Lilly over the coming months.

Tea was soon ready once the mussels were cool enough to serve. With bread and butter and pepper and vinegar they were a treat they all looked forward to.

Half way through the meal Harold cried out and began to work something out of his mouth. With his thumb and forefinger he delicately removed it.

"Look at that!" he exclaimed. "A pearl."

They looked. David craned forward from the other side of the table to see it.

There was a minute shiny object between Harold's fingers.

"Nearly broke my teeth on it," he said.

"Can't see nothing," Bill mocked.

"It's there, look!" Dorothy said. She held her palm open and Harold dropped it in.

"What a poor thing," Lilly said. "I thought it was going to make us rich the way you carried on. D'you reckon it's worth anything?"

"Shouldn't think so," Bill said dismissively.

"Even so it might be worth something," Lilly said hopefully.

"You could have it put in a ring," Dorothy said laughing.

"Oh no!" Lilly replied. "They're supposed to be bad luck ain't they."

"That's old wives tales mother. Look at all the pearls the queen and them wears. Anyway it's too small. Look at it."

"I've found a pearl as well!" David shouted, pointing to his plate.

"You ain't," Lilly said admonishingly.

"Made you look though," David said.

CHAPTER 41

Banner in the park

The whit sings were held in May. From churches and chapels all across Sheffield the Sunday Schools marched behind their banners. Each Whit Monday they marched to parks in different areas of the city; Endcliffe Park and Concord Park; Meersbrook and Firth Park. And in the southern suburbs they began to congregate in the high meadows of Graves Park.

The Holmhurst Road banner was as big and colourful as the rest, bigger than the biggest blanket you could imagine and embroidered with the Sunday School motto and scenes from the bible. It was held upright between two poles and it was the honour of two senior captains from the chapel to carry it. To help them to keep it upright, especially in the wind there were two bracing lines on each pole, one forward and one behind and the juniors vied for the privilege of being in charge of a line. To David's joy he was assigned to the rear line on the right.

Mr. Betham, the Sunday School superintendent, a veteran of Whit Sings since before the war, instilled the need for punctuality on the whole school. It had to run to a strict timetable, he said, taking into account the distance each school had to march, in order to have them all assembled in time for the service to begin.

"I've got to be there early to help with the banner," David told them when he got home from Sunday School the week before Whitsun. "There's going to be hundreds there. We've got to be there at our special time or we'll miss our place and then everything'll go wrong."

Bill and Dorothy listened to David's earnest instructions with humour and a mask of serious attentiveness.

"And you've got to be there early too," he insisted, "or you won't get a place. You are coming to see me marching aren't you?"

"Of course we are," Dorothy assured him. "Do you think we wouldn't be?"

"Great! I'm just going up to tell Elliot."

"Don't get dirty," Bill called.

"I won't." The door slammed after him.

"I wish he'd learn not to slam doors." Bill was conscious that it wasn't his house and the sound of door slamming had provoked Enid Bracewell to speak sharply to David on a number of occasions. The telling off produced careful passage for a few days until boisterousness reasserted itself once more.

Bill looked at Dorothy. Now the baby was beginning to show Dorothy had begun to wear her maternity clothes. "You'll be alright won't you? I mean going up Meadowhead, walking up into the park?"

"Course I will." Dorothy laughed at him and his tender solicitude for her.

"Good. Come here then and give us a kiss while no-one's here."

On Whit Sunday morning as tradition demanded, they had dressed David in his new suit and new socks, new shoes, in fact new everything. After showing Dorothy's mother and father how fine David looked they had taken the tram to Lilly and Harold's and they too had given him a sixpenny piece for his pocket. Then he had been taken round the neighbours in the yard and they gave him a penny or two for his pocket as well and David had strutted around proudly and considered himself well off.

Whit Monday morning was sharp and bright with scudding clouds and a breeze that threatened to test the resolve of the seniors responsible for the banners.

Now, dressed in his Whitsun clothes again, David was ready for the parade. They stood on the front doorstep and waved him off down the street.

"He's ever so pleased with himself," Dorothy said, "Just look at him."

Bill smiled with pleasure. "Gosh, it feels a bit cool in that wind though. Better make sure you put a scarf on. You sure you're going to be alright?"

"Course I am silly. Come on, let's get ready. They won't wait once it's time for them to leave. We don't want to miss him."

They went inside and Dorothy put on her new blue coat. It was the latest fashion, belted across the front but the belt went underneath the coat at her hips leaving the back loose and swinging.

"How do I look?" She pirouetted. "Will I do?"

Bill, reaching for his new gaberdine turned to look at her. "You look wonderful! Now are you sure you'll be warm enough?"

Dorothy nodded. "Come on, let's see if mum's ready."

Mrs Bracewell, right on cue, was knocking on their door before they had time to move.

"Come in mum," Dorothy called.

"That's nice," her mother said as she entered, taking in Dorothy who was just about to fix her scarf about her throat. "Yes, I think you'll need that. It looks a bit chilly out."

"Just what we were saying," Bill said cheerily.

"Well let's hope the rain holds off," she replied.

"Right," Dorothy said brightly. "Shall we go then?"

They walked along the main road, passed the park entrance and went on towards the upper entrance and the meadows at the top.

"Are you sure you're alright?"

"Course I am," Dorothy said. "Don't fuss."

The pavement was busy, lined with a scattering of onlookers waiting for the parade but most of the people were steadily making their way to the park. From the distance the wind carried the faint notes of bugles as the band of the Boys' Brigade leading the procession struck up. At the top of the hill they paused at the park gates and waited. A murmur started to run through the people lining the road as the band approached. Dorothy looked from Bill to her mother and her eyes were shining with excitement.

"I can't wait to see him." she said. "I love bands."

Now the call of the bugles was stronger and beneath them they could hear the sharp rattle of drums and the reverberation of the bass drum striking the beat. Then the first of the banners breasted the hill and ahead of it, resplendent in their black uniforms with white piping, the band of the Boys Brigade with flanking officers marching proudly alongside and a drum major flinging the staff and swinging it with white gauntlets. Behind, the Sunday School banner of Holmhurst Road with the seniors doggedly grasping the uprights and David hauling on the line like a ship at sea as the banner streamed and billowed before them.

Dorothy smiled and waved and tried to catch David's attention as he marched, and she bit her lip as her eyes moistened with the emotion of the sound and the sight of the children marching.

David glanced, turned his head and saw them, almost let go of the line to wave, thought better of it and marched on with his head higher and a grin of delight upon his face.

More banners, more children and as one the crowds on the road turned and followed the procession into the park.

On the meadow the crowds were building round the assembly area for the bands and more Sunday Schools were marching in along converging paths. Despite the freshness of the morning there was an atmosphere of anticipation in the crowd as the music of the bands mingled and grew and the banners cracked and billowed in the breeze. The minister officiating made a short address and introduced the first hymn. Then the bands started to play and the people began to sing. It was soft and self conscious at first, relying on the children and the minister's voice ringing out through his microphone. And then it swelled as the congregation began to sing out and their voices carried across the meadow.

Bill mouthed the words; he knew them from his own Sunday School days, 'Fight the good fight with all thy might...' but he hadn't sung openly since he was a boy and like many others he was embarrassed at the sound of his own voice. He gazed around him as he quietly sang. Across the meadow where the trees began the ground dipped away to the boating lake. It used to be a millpond powering a waterwheel and forge in the days of the industrial revolution but the wheel and forge were gone long ago and now it was landscaped. The path around it opened onto to the long sloping meadow on the far side of the lake, leading to the teahouse beyond the oak tree at the top. Bill lost himself in memory. The sun was bright but not as warm as on that day so long ago when he had paused in frustration along the path and looked down on his city and dreamed of being a pilot. Despite the horrors of the war the world, his world, had been innocent then. There had been an innocent girl at his side saying no, you mustn't. How had she become what she had become? She had cried and wept for him at the end but in between something dark, something terrible had surfaced.

The trees were in leaf and the sound of people singing rose all around him and those days were past. He put the memories away, never to be revisited again. He heard the sound of Dorothy's voice at his side and turned to look at her. She half turned and smiled at him as she sang and Bill put his arm round her waist and drew her to him.

"Warm enough?" he whispered.

She nodded and smiled at him again.

When the service was over and the last hymn had been sung David ran across to them.

"That was lovely." Dorothy stooped and hugged him.

"I've got to go back in a minute," David said with excitement. "We're marching back with the banner. Did you see me holding it?"

"Yes," she said. "We thought you were ever so clever didn't we?" Dorothy turned to Bill and her mother and they nodded their approval.

"Are you warm enough?" Bill looked at David just in his jacket and trousers.

"Yes," David said, anxious to return. "I'm boiling."

The school captains were trying to reassemble their contingents, at least those that were not returning home with their parents.

"Got to go now."

"We're going to go straight back home then." Bill said. "Mummy's getting cold."

"I'm alright," Dorothy said. "We can stay and watch them set off back if you want."

But Mrs. Bracewell shivered and said, "I want to get back for your

341

dad's dinner. He'll be back at two."

"I'm going then." And David dashed off.

They watched him in the distance. There was another boy on David's bracing line and he wouldn't let it go. They began pushing and shoving each other with increasing forcefulness until a compromise was reached and David agreed to let the other boy hold the line as well. But it wasn't the same and David was glad now that they weren't staying to watch him.

Dorothy folded her hymn sheet and put it in her pocket.

"I always keep them. I've got them going right back to about nineteen thirty. I don't know what I'm going to do with them all."

They set off back home through the park and down into the woods, following the rest of the people streaming away. It had been a lovely morning, one of the year's highlights. Bill was happy to have participated again in something he thought he had left behind in his own childhood. It was wholesome and good and they had been able to share it equally as a family. Dorothy looked radiant. There was a healthy glow about her and the morning spent in the open air made her look more vibrant than ever. Bill took her hand as they strolled and chatted and followed the stream down through the wood. Even Mrs. Bracewell seemed relaxed and friendly towards him.

Dorothy returned from her monthly visit to the ante-natal clinic and announced that housework was over! Marge, who had been to Nether Edge with her said, "It's alright for some."

Marge had come over and they had spent the morning browsing round the fashion shops together before Dorothy's appointment but Marge hadn't found anything she wanted to buy. Or at least nothing that she could afford.

"So what have they said to you this time?" her mother asked.

"Nothing much. Blood pressure's up a bit so I've got to take it easy. No hoovering or strenuous work," Dorothy said casually. She flung herself into her dad's chair by the fire and put her feet on the fender. "So," and she flung them a coquettish smile, "I'll have my lunch now if you please. And a cushion for my feet!"

"And then there's the garden wants digging," Marge said. But she passed Dorothy a cushion all the same.

"I didn't mean it," Dorothy laughed. "Still…" she arched herself and wriggled it behind her back. "…that's better. I'll come and give you a hand with some sandwiches in a minute mum. I'll have a cup of coffee first."

Mrs. Bracewell was hovering by the kitchen door. "You having one as well Margery? Kettles just boiled."

"Here mum." Marge rose and headed her off. "You get the cups, I'll make the coffee."

Dorothy made to get up but her mother stopped her. "What else did they say?"

"Nothing much. Asked me about my diet. Exercise. Usual things. Everything's fine. Anyway what's for lunch? Is my dad in today?" If he was on a London train she knew it would be difficult for her mother to predict exactly what time he would arrive home.

"No he won't be back 'till about three o'clock. At the earliest," Mrs. Bracewell said. "We'll have some soup to be going on with then I'm cooking for our tea. What're you having?"

"I've got us some liver for later. Bill likes liver and onions."

"Oh well," her mother said, "the soup's oxtail so that won't hurt you."

Marge came in with the coffee.

Dorothy, rising from her chair, said, "I think I'll have a biscuit to go with it."

"Stay there, I'll get it." Margery put the coffee down and turned for the door.

"Oh don't be silly," Dorothy reached for Marge's arm and stopped her. "I'll go. Anybody else want one?"

They organised a party at the City Transport Department Sports Club for David's eighth birthday. There was an enclosed playground adjacent to the pavilion, well away from the cricket pitch, with enough space for David and his pals to run about, play cricket and spread a picnic for their tea. And they could get a variety of drinks from the bar inside.

They chose the nearest Saturday to the actual date and it was a perfect midsummer day. Brian was invited, and John, together with two or three other friends from school. They wanted Dorothy to join in the games with them but she declined and said she would get the sandwiches and pop ready while they played cricket. Bill played a token innings but when it became clear they weren't going to get him out and he kept hitting the ball all over the field for them to run after he sensed they were going to lose interest so he declared and left them to their game.

After tea they went into the playground and had a competition on the swing boats to see who could make their boat go highest. Brian was reckless in swinging the boat until the seat felt as if it was almost vertical but David, in the other boat wouldn't go that high and Brian mocked him unmercifully for being scared, which David denied heatedly.

Bill said, "Come on, I'll take you up."

"Not too high then daddy."

David climbed back in and held the rope nervously and clutched the boat's support with the other hand, trying to look brave and conscious that his friends were watching.

Bill pulled on the rope and the boat began to swing. Bill made it go higher than David had taken it before, and then higher even than Brian's boat. David froze with fear. He was certain the boat was going to eject him like a catapult and when it went backwards to the height of its swing he was looking vertically down past his daddy to the ground below. There was nothing to stop him falling out! Desperately he let go of the rope and clung with both hands to the metal supports, imploring Bill to slow it down and let him off.

"Don't be such a baby, it's alright," Bill said. "Look, I'm not holding on to anything." And he gave the rope another heave. The boat swung through another arc.

"I want to get out. I want to get out!" David cried.

"Alright. Don't start crying." He looked down at David's friends watching from the ground. "What a baby. I don't know." He looked down again and called, "Come on Brian. You coming up? Or you John? Anybody else?"

Brian stepped forward and raised the brake bar beneath the boat to stop it. "I'll come up."

"Come on then," Bill said with bravado. "Let's see how high we can go."

David stepped down with relief as Brian boarded. He felt humiliated. He wanted to go and sit by Dorothy but it wouldn't be right to go to his mummy for comfort with the rest of his friends looking on. They'd only call him names later. Bill was sending the boat whizzing higher and higher. He'd show 'em. Brian was pulling on the rope too. He was thinking, 'Wouldn't it be great to send the boat as high as the top bar of the frame.' And suddenly he looked up and saw that as the boat momentarily hung at the top of its swing before rushing back down, the top beam of the swing boat ride was level with his eyes and Brian's nerve suddenly failed as well. He steeled himself to grip the rope and stop pulling but he wasn't going to let the others see how scared he was. But he was white and shaking when he stepped off.

Dorothy, sitting on the bench at the edge of the playground, had been watching them. She hadn't wanted to intervene, not with David's friends around. But when Bill came to join her she said, "That was a bit high wasn't it? I don't think they liked going as high as that."

"Rubbish," Bill said with a smirk. "Brian loved it anyway. Didn't you see the way he was pulling on that rope?" He grimaced and shook his head. "It's David. He's such a sissy. Crying to be let off like that." It disappointed him to think that it was his son who was lacking in nerve. Not like that Brian. He'd got a bit of something about him.

"He's not a sissy Bill. And don't let his friends hear you talking about him like that!"

"Well!" Bill growled.

"Look at him. He's alright now."

David was running and laughing in some game with the rest of them, the incident forgotten.

"He won't come to any harm," Dorothy continued, "if he can have good friends like that around him."

"I just thought it'd give him a bit of excitement that's all. I didn't mean to show him up. I just wish he was a bit less – oh! – I don't know, less timid about things."

"But he's still a little boy Bill. And when you think about what's happened, what he's been through. Both of you. Look how you felt, how you were when we first met. I know it wasn't the same for you as it was for David but you were very…" she chose carefully, "…cautious about the things you said and did at first."

Bill turned and looked at her.

"Yes," Dorothy said with emphasis, "even you. With you it was the other way Bill. The things that were important for me to know, you kept hidden. It was ages before you even admitted to the existence of David. But the stories you put about, you know, about knowing Guy Gibson and that…"

"I did know him! What…? What are you trying to say? That I made them up or what?"

"No Bill I'm not saying that at all. But you were anxious to make a good impression and…"

"Well of course I was!" Bill said sharply. Then, "I thought a lot about you and I didn't want your parents thinking I was just anybody!" he protested.

"But don't you see Bill, that sort of thing doesn't matter. Who you know and name dropping and… It's you! You're the one that's important."

"Well I don't know how we got onto this. What am I? A liar or… A snob or something?"

"No Bill. I'm not saying that at all."

"Well what are you saying then?"

David looked across from his play and saw Bill and Dorothy in earnest discussion about something. Their faces had changed and they looked serious; the playfulness had gone. He turned to his friends and ran back amongst them with a shout and hoped they wouldn't notice.

"I'm not saying anything Bill. I've told you!" Dorothy turned and sat looking ahead but her eyes were on the middle distance. "I wish I'd never said anything."

"So do I," Bill snarled. "Just because I wanted to give the lad a good time. You make me out to be an ogre or something."

"Oh Bill you're being silly!"

"Oh am I!"

"And don't shout. The kids'll notice."

"Aw so what!"

Now Bill and Dorothy were almost back to back on the bench and an unreasonable silence descended between them.

"All this!" Bill said at last. "Just because the kid got scared on a swing! And with me! As though I'd do anything to hurt him!"

"Oh let it drop Bill."

Dorothy stood and stretched then wandered away from the bench, across the grass towards the children. She felt so pent up and she sighed. It was so unnecessary.

The children saw her watching and ran across to her.

"Come and play."

"Come on," they cried.

And they tugged at Dorothy's sleeves and tried to drag her into their game but she smiled at them and shook her head.

"Oh no," she said brightly, "I can't run about like you. I've got a little baby to think of."

There were cries of, "Aaw." from the boys, a spontaneous expression of disappointment. But David understood why she had come to stand amongst them. Dorothy looked at him, with the lingering smile barely hovering on her lips.

"Come on," David said. "Last one to the top of the slide's a..." The rest was lost in the dash.

Dorothy could not return to the bench. Instead she walked with slow, measured steps around the perimeter of the playground, listening to their play with her head lowered like someone making a detailed examination of the ground. It was such a shame to let small misunderstandings spoil a beautiful afternoon.

The following week Dorothy attended for her regular monthly ante-natal at the hospital.

"Well Dorothy, step down," the nurse said as she slid the weights back along the beam of the scales. "You haven't been listening to us have you."

"What do you mean?" Dorothy replied. She reached for her dress and began to put it on and button it. "I'm not overweight surely. My

346

diet's alright isn't it?"

The nurse finished entering the figures on Dorothy's weight chart and said, "Oh your weight's fine. It's your blood pressure." She pursed her lips. "It's still higher than it should be."

"Well I don't understand it. I'm not doing anything I shouldn't. I'm sure of it."

"What about vacuum cleaning? Making the beds?"

"No."

The nurse looked at Dorothy with a quizzical expression and a smile as if to say, 'come on, you can't fool me!'

"No!" Dorothy insisted. "We live in rooms at my mother's. She does all that kind of thing. In fact she's sometimes too protective."

"Oh! And then what happens?"

"Nothing. You don't know my mother. She insists that I've not to do anything too strenuous, and that's it. Honest."

"Well Dorothy it's got to come down."

Dorothy was dressed and the examination was coming to a close. "I don't know what else I can do," she said. "I take my rest, eat plenty of greens. Perhaps it's the warm weather."

The nurse filed Dorothy's record away and ignored her attempt at levity.

"We'll have to see what it looks like next month. If it's not improved well…"

"Well what can I do?"

"We'll see. You might have to come in for complete bed rest." The nurse consulted her appointments list. "You're down for the twenty seventh of July aren't you. Let's see… Why don't you come back on the nineteenth." She looked up. "Can you make that?"

Dorothy pulled her little diary from her handbag. "Yes, I think so." There was a hint of… sadness…? apprehension…? in her voice and she withdrew the pencil from the spine of the diary and made a note of the date.

The nurse, watching Dorothy closely, became brightly professional. "It's alright," she said reassuringly. "There's nothing to worry about. All mums-to-be get blood pressure and we just want to make sure we're keeping an eye on it." She went to the door and opened it for Dorothy. "So, we'll see you on the nineteenth of next month."

"Yes. Bye."

Dorothy walked down through the hospital grounds with a feeling of calm determination. She would just have to make sure she followed the regime to the letter. But it didn't help when they had arguments like the one on David's birthday. Oh it didn't amount to much and before the day was ended it had blown over. But at the time it filled her with

347

tension and anxiety and she was sure that it didn't help. It would be a good job when it was over. Not that she wished to rush things. 'All things in good time' she had been taught and that was true for this baby as well. She hadn't had any problems so far and everything was going fine. It was just a question of taking things easy and letting nature take its course.

At the hospital gates she saw the bus already at the stop. The examination must have taken longer than usual. Unless she had been late going in. Well, be that as it may, Dorothy decided, she certainly wasn't going to run for it! If the bus went she would just sit on the wall and enjoy the sunshine while she waited for the next one.

CHAPTER 42

Precautionary measures

The following Saturday they went as usual to Lilly's for tea. It was another hot day and Lilly had the back door wide open to try and get what little breeze there was into the house. Despite the promise of the warm day to come Lilly had made a fire that morning because she needed the oven hot for the braised steak and Yorkshire pudding she was making for Harold's dinner when he got home from work. As soon as it was cooked she let the fire go out but even so the oven retained its heat and by mid afternoon when Bill and Dorothy arrived with David, the house was stifling.

Bill shed his jacket and took Dorothy's cardigan and laid them over the chair in the corner against the front door.

"You want to get this door open," Bill complained. "Get some air in here."

"We never open it, you know that. It ain't been opened for years."

It was true, Bill could never remember having seen that door open, not even when he and George were lads. And with the armchair in front of the door blocking access to it, they couldn't open it even if they wanted to. The armchair would have had to be moved and there was nowhere else for it to go in that cramped room.

"Well what do you want to go lighting fires for on a day like this?" The heat was making him surly.

"Can't cook without a fire," Lilly said and that was the end of the matter. "Kettle's on. We'll have a nice cup of tea then you'll feel better."

"That'll be nice." Dorothy leaned back against the cushions and closed her eyes.

"Anyway love how are you this week?" Harold asked solicitously. He was busy dissecting Woodbine stubs and tipping the residual tobacco into his dish where he stored it on the shelf in the kitchen with a slice of raw potato on it to keep the tobacco moist.

Dorothy answered with her eyes still closed. "It's the heat. It's getting more uncomfortable." She stirred a little. "Apart from that I'm alright."

"Here," Lilly said, "let's get that window open a bit more."

She leaned over them and tugged at the vertical glazing bar in the centre of the window above Dorothy's head. The window reluctantly moved another inch; it wasn't opened very often either and it stuck with only about six inches open at the top.

"There, that's a bit better."

"Thank you," Dorothy said.

Bill laid his hand on Dorothy's where it rested on the arm of the settee. "It's not good for her this heat." Dorothy's progress from the tram stop, over the wooden bridge across the oily river had been slow; they had paused to gaze down into the water with its rainbow streaks and Dorothy had unnecessarily apologised to him for her slow pace. "It's her blood pressure."

"What's they said to you?" Lilly knew that Dorothy had been to the hospital the previous Thursday.

"Usual thing. Got to take it easy." She closed her eyes again and lay still against the cushions. "It gets so boring," she murmured. "You've no idea."

"Never mind love," Lilly reassured her. "It won't be for much longer will it. And you have to do what they tell you."

Dorothy heard the well-meaning platitudes but they offered no consolation for the way she was feeling. Her eyes remained closed against the world and she replied shortly, "It's another eight weeks yet."

"Never mind," Lilly said again, "we'll have a nice cup of tea. That'll make you feel better."

Harold began to roll himself a cigarette from the tobacco in the bowl. David was at his elbow, watching the operation, hoping his grandad would let him lick the paper and complete the turn of the machine to eject the finished cigarette.

"Go on then," Harold said. "Not too much, don't want it soaking wet or it won't light."

It was strange, what a sense of achievement it brought to the child to deliver the finished article to his grandad. David watched with interest as Harold trimmed the excess tobacco from the ends of the cigarette and deposited it back into the bowl before lighting it. The cigarette flared and burned straight back for about a quarter of an inch. Harold sat and smoked it with satisfaction.

"Can I make you another one grandad?"

"Not yet. Here, go and put this dish back in the kitchen where it goes."

Lilly turned from making the tea as David entered the kitchen. "I got a surprise for you."

David's eyes lit. "What is it?" he cried.

"Tell you in a minute. Wait 'till we get back inside. Here, you can

350

carry the sugar and milk. Don't spill it."

Lilly poured the teas and handed them round.

"No sugar for me," Dorothy said.

"Very wise," Lilly replied, though why she should think it wise, if she had been asked, she could not have said. But it was an encouraging thing to say.

"What's my surprise grandma?"

"How would you like to go to Worcester in your six weeks holidays?"

"Really?" David jumped up and looked from Lilly to Bill and Dorothy. "Can I? Can I go? Daddy," he pleaded. "Can I go? Please." He turned his attention to Dorothy. "Oh say I can. Make daddy say yes." He grabbed Dorothy's hand, shaking her arm up and down in excitement.

"Hey!" Bill ordered. "Calm down! Settle down or you'll not be going anywhere."

David subsided onto the settee next to Dorothy and fidgeted restlessly, waiting for their answer.

Lilly continued, "I've written to our Ame. Me and your dad's going down for our fortnight. She wants to know if we can take him with us. It's her idea."

Dorothy looked up at Bill. "Why not?"

"Yes!" David cried triumphantly. "Great. Oh thank you mummy. Thank you grandma."

"It all depends if you're a good boy whether I take you or not."

"I'll be good, I'll be good," David yelled, dancing about in the room.

"Not if you carry on like that you won't."

"Alright then grandma. Sorry."

"When were you thinking of going?" Bill asked.

"Sixth of August. About five weeks time. That's when Harold gets his holiday."

"Oh that's alright," Dorothy assented. "I'll be back by then."

"That's if you have to go," Bill added quickly.

"Go where?" Lilly asked.

"Oh it's nothing mother. They're just talking about having Dorothy in for a few days bed rest that's all."

"That's if I have to go," Dorothy echoed Bill.

"Well they know best don't they," Lilly said reassuringly.

"Yes but Myra never had to go in did she." Bill took Dorothy's hand again and held it reassuringly. "I mean, look how tiny she is and she had Raymond and then our Peter without any bother."

"She certainly has bonny babies," Harold put in.

Lilly smiled encouragingly at Dorothy. She took in Dorothy's

351

swollen ankles. If you looked closely you could see she even looked puffy round her face but that wasn't surprising in this heat. "Never mind love. They're just being careful that's all."

"Anyway," Bill grumbled, "I don't see what bed rest in Nether Edge is going to do that she can't get resting at home."

"It's alright Bill," Dorothy said. "don't get worked up. I can do without it. And anyway they haven't said I've got to yet."

On the nineteenth Dorothy went to the hospital for her check up with a mixture of feelings. It was cooler than it had been at the weekend; there was a covering of cloud and a breeze that felt like it might bring summer rain. She felt much more comfortable for the drop in temperature and better than she had for days.

During the preceding days Dorothy had been resting until she could rest no more. Sometimes she felt that if she didn't do some sort of exercise she wouldn't be able to sleep at night. Especially as the enforced idleness induced her to sleep and catnap at intervals during the day. But Enid Bracewell was adamant; Dorothy had to do nothing strenuous. So Dorothy put up with the stultifying boredom of sitting around all day being waited on by her mother. The stupid thing was, that in herself she felt perfectly alright. Oh of course the baby was starting to grow much bigger now and that brought some discomfort from time to time. But she certainly didn't see herself as an invalid and that's how she was being made to feel. She longed to rebel against it.

The nurse greeted Dorothy brightly. "How do you feel today? How have things been these last couple of weeks?"

"Fine," Dorothy said. She smiled and shrugged. "I'm perfectly OK."

"Good. Well let's have a look at you then."

Dorothy started to undress and in response to her questioning she told the nurse about her regime, her meals, the hours she spent with her feet up.

The nurse went through the examination. When it was over she looked at Dorothy ruefully and shook her head.

"It's no better."

"What isn't? What d'you mean?"

"Your blood pressure. If anything it's worse than it was before."

Dorothy felt a wave of resignation come over her. She sensed what the nurse's judgement would be.

"Would you like to get dressed now." The nurse picked up Dorothy's notes and headed for the door. "I shan't keep you a minute." She closed the door carefully behind her.

Dorothy stood and placed her hand beneath her belly and moved her other hand gently over and round it. It felt smooth and firm but not uncomfortably so and a smile arose as she felt a flutter of movement from inside, a pulse of pressure against her palm. And then it came again.

"Oh you are certainly letting mummy know you're here aren't you," she murmured. She sat and nursed her belly again, waiting for the involuntary kicks. They were so strong against the gentle pressure of her hand. It's as though he knows I'm here, she told herself, and trying to touch me back. But that's irrational, she thought, and she laughed at her logic. Of course I'm here; he couldn't be if I wasn't. She sat, waiting and smiling, oblivious of time passing, savouring each contact with her child.

The nurse came back in and said brightly, "Not dressed yet?"

Dorothy was completely self composed. "We've been having a conversation." The nurse smiled at her.

"He's been kicking me. When I moved my hand around like this." Dorothy demonstrated what she had been doing. "See! There's another one."

"He's probably just woken up after that examination. Unless he's hungry. Well, he's a very healthy baby anyway."

The nurse became official again. "I've just had a word with the obstetrician and it's as I thought. We'd like you to come in for a few days complete rest."

"But I have been resting. I haven't been cheating."

"I know you haven't Dorothy. But your blood pressure needs to be kept under observation until we can get it down to somewhere near normal. And Mr. Wilkinson thinks it would be better if we kept you under observation here in the hospital. Don't worry, you'll be in a room to yourself and your family will be able to come and see you. It's not like being in an open ward. You've got a little boy as well haven't you?"

Dorothy sat to put her shoes on. "He's not really mine. I'm his stepmother. It sounds awful doesn't it? I mean, everybody thinks about the wicked stepmother don't they after 'Snow White'. It's not like that."

"I'm sure it's not. This is your first isn't it."

"Yes."

"How old is he?"

"David? He's just eight. A couple of weeks ago. Well," Dorothy corrected herself, "three weeks."

"Well he'll be able to come and see you as well. If you want him to."

"How long do you want me for?"

"A week. To see how you get on."

"When do you want me? I mean, I haven't anything… You don't

353

want me to stay now. Do you?"

"No, no," the nurse protested. "Go home and get your things ready. Enough for a few days. Come in on Monday." She consulted the clipboard with Dorothy's notes. "Say, about half past ten? Is that alright?"

Dorothy was beginning to feel helpless; her life was being taken over.

"Is there anything special you want me to bring?" she asked.

"No," the nurse replied. "Nightie, underclothes, brush and comb. Your prettiest bed jacket for receiving your visitors. You'll want to be seen at your best, won't you."

Dorothy left feeling a little bemused. How much more rest could she have? Why would she be better and more rested in hospital than she would at home? It was taking her away from the convenience and familiarity of home. Away from Bill. Away from David.

It was the inconvenience it would cause that she resented as much as anything. Despite what the nurse had said, Dorothy knew she would only have her family with her for limited periods. It wouldn't be the same; she wouldn't have her mother popping in to see her at frequent intervals during the day, or sitting and chatting. Ah well, it was only for a week and it couldn't be helped, so why did she feel like this? 'Still it's for the best I suppose,' she thought with resignation, walking gently past the flower beds and round the hospital lawn to the hospital entrance. It would be a good job when it was over. And as she walked Dorothy pictured herself with the baby she could feel kicking inside her, wrapped in his shawl and sleeping in her arms.

Anxiety does strange things, not the least of which is it feeds off itself. Bill had no reason to feel anxious. After all Dorothy was only going to be in for the week and she might as well have the benefit of care if it was offered, with people around her night and day if that was what it took to deal with this blood pressure thing. But it was the fact that they deemed it necessary that made him feel uneasy. He wanted everything to be just right; not that everything wasn't just right. It was just…? He couldn't put his finger on it. And there was no doubt that the inconvenience while Dorothy was away looked like being considerable.

Take mealtimes! Dorothy had made all the arrangements and Bill would be given his tea by Dorothy's mother. Huh! That was really something to look forward to, 'I don't think!!'

Then there was his packing up. He would have to do it! Making sandwiches last thing at night, ready to take with him first thing in the morning.

Washing and ironing. Well Ma Bracewell already did that but it was Dorothy who handed the dirty washing to her. Bill kept well away from that area. Now, unless he hung onto the dirty linen for a week, he would have to take it in to the old lady and face her grumbling at him.

None of it was a great inconvenience in itself. He told himself that he was being unreasonable even thinking like this when it was Dorothy who was going to be away. But it wasn't as if it was anything serious. Just bed rest. Only it was going to bring him into more regular contact with her mother and Bill knew what it would be like. He would have to face her resentment; her stony faced silence and her icy politeness.

Bill would never have admitted it, not even to himself, not even at this time when for some indefinable reason he was feeling so insecure, but the fact was, he was frightened of the old lady. He was not looking forward to the week without Dorothy and he knew it was selfish but that's the way it was.

So the pleasant, relaxing weekend they should have spent together as they prepared for Dorothy's visit to Nether Edge was spent in moodiness. And Bill knew he was wasting precious opportunity but his perverse spirit wouldn't allow him to relax and let the mood slip from him. Silent and aloof, Bill watched Dorothy with disapproval as she busied herself with her suitcase, packing her clothes for the coming week.

He would not be coaxed out of it, not even when Dorothy played their favourite records. He listened to 'Tit-Willow' with an expression of distaste and when she put 'Faust' on Bill got up and went upstairs on the pretext of going to the bathroom.

And then, late on Sunday evening Bill's mood suddenly changed. He became contrite and apologised for spoiling the weekend. Dorothy immediately forgave him.

"It's alright Bill. I know you've been worried but really there's nothing to worry about."

"I just don't want you to go."

"I know."

"Here, come and sit next to me. Bring your cushion."

Dorothy heaved herself from the chair where she had been comfortably reading and crossed to the settee to join him.

Belatedly Bill said, "Are you sure you've got everything you need to go with?"

"I think so."

"What time do you have to be there. Was it half past or ten o'clock?"

"Stop worrying Bill. Everything's taken care of."

"I'll come and see you. I mean, I'll come straight from work. Oh, you know what I mean."

Dorothy patted Bill's hand and placed it on her belly. They sat in silence for a while.

"He must be asleep," Dorothy said.

The following morning Marge arrived straight from dropping Jean off at school.

"Are you ready?" she cried, entering through the kitchen door.

Dorothy rose from the breakfast table and started to put her coat on. "I think so."

"You look nice anyway," Marge said admiringly. "Have you had you hair done?"

"Yes. I got a 'Toni'. Did it yesterday." Dorothy's dark auburn hair was gleaming in a perm of close curled waves falling round the side of her face into the nape of her neck. "I wasn't sure what I'll look like after a week in bed. And I want to keep looking nice for when Bill comes to visit."

"It looks lovely."

"Have you time for a cup of coffee before you go?" Mrs. Bracewell asked.

Marge looked enquiringly at Dorothy but Dorothy shook her head. "I don't think so. We've got to get two buses remember and we don't want to miss the circular. It goes at ten past and if we miss that I'll be late."

"Are you sure?" Mrs. Bracewell asked Marge. "It's only half past nine."

"No really mum. I had breakfast before I came out. We don't want Dorothy having to rush about."

"Well you take care then. And me and your dad'll come to see you later. When he gets back. And you'll be nicely settled in as well."

Marge picked up the suitcase and its weight surprised her.

"Blimey Dolly what've you got in here? How long're you going for?"

"There's nothing much," Dorothy said. "A few changes that's all."

A last look round. Nothing left on the mantelpiece.

Her mother said, "Got your keys?"

"What do I want my keys for?" But Dorothy patted her pocket and gave her mother a smile. "They're here." She looked round again. "Ready Marge?"

Margery nodded.

"Come on then." Dorothy kissed her mother and said, "Well, I'll see you later. You'll look after David won't you. Make sure he eats his tea."

"I will. Now go on. We don't want you missing that bus."

Marge stood by the open door. "Come on Dolly, you go first. See you later mum. I'll pop back before I go home."

The ante-natal ward in the maternity wing of the hospital was along a corridor opposite the examination rooms. The nurse marched briskly along with Dorothy and Marge trailing behind. The smell of Lysol hung in the air and they were reflected in the gleaming lino floorcovering as they walked. A nurse sitting at a table covered in notes looked up and smiled from the open door of a tiny office as they passed.

"They all seem very nice here," Marge said.

The nurse ahead of them paused before reaching the ward. She was standing by an open door, the sunshine from outside was spilling from the room into the corridor and she was waiting to beckon them in.

"Here we are," the nurse said. "Just pop your things over there." She gestured towards a table in the corner of the room, left of the window. "I'll be back in a minute or two when you're settled. And then Mr. Wilkinson will want to see you." She smiled at Marge and left them alone in the room.

"Oh it's quite nice," Marge said, looking around her.

The window was high and light, directly opposite the door, allowing daylight to flood the room. The bed was situated with its headboard against the left hand wall and across the room opposite the foot of the bed, a chair with a grey tubular metal frame and a varnished seat stood adjacent to the sink. An upholstered visitors' armchair was next to the bed and Dorothy draped her coat across it while Marge opened Dorothy's suitcase.

Dorothy wandered across to the window. She was on the ground floor in the left wing of the building, well away from the main entrance but from where she was standing Dorothy had a view of grass and flowerbeds. The room smelled fresh and clean, albeit the smell came from the hospital disinfectant. Despite herself Dorothy found it was actually quite pleasant.

Behind her Marge was in the middle of the room holding Dorothy's coat and looking round with a lost expression.

"There's nowhere to hang things," she complained.

"You'll have to use the hook behind the door," Dorothy said in a rather disinterested way. "I've put a couple of wire coathangers in the bottom of the case somewhere. Not that I've brought very much that needs hanging."

She tested the bed; it was hard and the bedclothes were pulled tight across the mattress and folded underneath. "Well, now what?"

"Just have to wait I suppose until they tell you what to do. I wonder if there's somewhere you can get a drink?" Marge opened the door and peered along the corridor but it was empty with no signs anywhere giving any indication of refreshments. "We'll have to ask the nurse I suppose. Here Dolly," Marge indicated the armchair by the bed, "come and sit down for a bit."

"No I'm alright. You sit there if you want to."

Dorothy was restless; she didn't want to sit, she'd be doing enough sitting and waiting over the next few days. She began to wonder how she was going to pass the time. She realised, too late, that she hadn't brought any magazines or books to read. She turned to Marge.

"You don't have to stay if you don't want to."

"It's alright love. I haven't got to get back for ages."

Marge crossed to the window and leaned on the sill. "It's quite pleasant really," she said optimistically. "A bit of lawn, roses. There's a bench just over there. You might be able to go out and sit in the sun. Do a bit of sunbathing."

Dorothy smiled ruefully. "Shouldn't think so." She indicated the bed. "Once they get me in there they'll make me stay there."

She joined Marge at the window and they stood together listening to the birdsong coming faintly to them from outside.

The door opened and the nurse came in.

"Right," she said. "We'll just give you an examination. Did you bring a dressing gown?"

"Yes," Dorothy said. "Where did you put it Marge?"

Marge crossed to the door. "It's here. Underneath your coat." She lifted it off the hook and replaced Dorothy's coat behind the door.

Dorothy looked a little uncertain. Did they want her to get undressed here or down the corridor, in the examination room?

The nurse anticipated Dorothy's thoughts. "If you just leave your things here then we'll go into the other room and examine you. You can wait if you like," she said to Marge.

Dorothy began to undress and Marge assisted, trying to look useful. She felt strangely self conscious with the nurse watching and Marge taking her clothes and folding them onto the table next to her case.

"Right," Dorothy said, pulling her dressing gown around her. She flashed them a smile. "I'm ready. What are you doing Marge?"

The nurse opened the door and said to Marge, "You can wait here. You won't be disturbed and there should be a tea trolley along shortly. They'll give you a cup of tea."

Marge nodded reassuringly at Dorothy. "I'll wait then. See you in a few minutes love."

Bill dashed home from work to get changed, announced to Mrs. Bracewell that he'd have his tea when he got back from Nether Edge and arrived with a bunch of flowers. He laid them on the bed and leaned over to kiss Dorothy.

"Well how are you love?"

Dorothy smiled at him. Flowers! Well, how nice.

"I'm fine," she said. "Had my examination this morning and I've been laid here ever since." She reached for the flowers and smelled at them. "They're lovely Bill. Thank you."

He took them from her and looked around the room. "Where shall I put them?"

Amongst the array of lotions and creams assembled on the table adjacent to the bed there wasn't anything resembling a vase.

"Just put them in the sink for now. I'll get them to bring something to put them in later."

Bill carried them across the room and ran some water into the sink. He took in the functional furnishings, the curtains at the window overlooking the flower beds, the gloss painted walls in pastel shades of pink and green. But there were no screens around the bed, it wasn't a public ward after all, and Dorothy had enough of her own belongings in evidence to give the room a personal air.

"It's not bad is it?" he said.

"It'll do."

He came back and disdaining the visitors chair, sat on the bed next to her and placed his hand gently on Dorothy's tummy.

"And how's his nibs?"

Dorothy placed her hand on Bill's, pushed the bedcovers down and pulled her nightgown up, guiding his hand over her.

"You might be able to feel him. He was very active earlier."

They played the game together, hoping the baby would play it with them but he was still.

"They gave me another examination this morning. They're very thorough. Our Marge stayed with me until dinner time."

"What's the meals like?"

Dorothy made a face. "A bit like school dinners."

"So what's next?" Bill asked.

"Just got to lie here." Dorothy smiled at him with resignation. "I wish I was back home. I could snuggle up to you in bed together."

Bill leaned forward and kissed her gently. "Won't be long. A few days."

"How's David?"

"Oh he's fine. Sends his love to mummy. He was out playing when I left home."

"Oh good. Give him a big kiss from me won't you."

"Course I will."

"Mum and dad came earlier."

"Yes. She said. Didn't have much to say though."

"Well there's nothing much to report is there. Just lie here and be good."

Bill reflected that if they had been at home in their normal surroundings they would have been talking normally to each other about mundane, normal things. But just the mere fact of Dorothy being laid in a hospital while he was cast in the role of 'visitor' made everything change. Dorothy was still the same as she was yesterday. She wasn't suddenly invalid. But now their conversation bordered on the formal. Question. Response. The commonality between them was distorted, as though the surroundings imposed an unseen barrier.

"So what have they got lined up for you tomorrow?"

"Much the same as today I suppose. They come in and take my blood pressure and see that everything's alright. Bring me meals. A book trolley came round this morning thank goodness."

Bill suddenly realised an overwhelming need to do something more for Dorothy, something personal that the staff, however well meaning could not.

"Is there anything I can bring you? Anything you need?"

But Dorothy's needs were disappointing in their ordinariness.

"A shower cap if you can get one. They've got a very nice shower cubicle next to the bathroom. Oh and something to read. Most of the magazines were out of date."

"Right." He said it as though he had been given an order for stores vital to the survival of the garrison. "Shower cap. We've got one at home haven't we?"

"Yes but that's an old one. The elastic's getting loose. See if you can get me a new one will you."

"Right," he said again.

He stayed an hour and then decided it was time to leave. He had his list of messages to deliver and items to bring. The evening was still warm and light. Normally they might have taken a stroll, called for a drink.

"Shall I leave the curtains?" he asked.

"Yes. I'll draw them later."

He bent over her. "I hate leaving you like this."

"I know," Dorothy replied. "And this is only the first day."

"Never mind love. It'll soon pass. Get you home again and then just take things easy until this little one's born."

They exchanged a smile.

"Right love. I'll see you tomorrow. About the same time."

"I can't wait." She pulled him down to her and kissed him.

Bill turned at the door, suddenly reluctant to leave. "You won't forget my things will you?" she said. She looked so vulnerable all of a sudden, alone in the bed with evening sunlight glowing in the room. He crossed back to her quickly and kissed her again.

"I love you." he whispered.

"Love you too…"

When Bill visited Dorothy on Friday he found her in some distress. She was sitting in bed propped up against pillows, a discarded magazine thrown across the covers and a handkerchief crumpled in her fist. Her expression was forlorn and her eyes looked red and puffy as though she had been crying. At the side of the bed her flowers were wilting in the vase. He knew he should have brought her some more; he could kick himself for forgetting. Bill closed the door softly and put a brave smile on his face as he turned to her.

"Hello Dolly, how are you today then?"

The effort at cheerfulness was completely lost on her. Dorothy turned to him with a wan smile and murmured, "Hello Bill." But her greeting was lost in a snuffle, a sound like the stifling of a sob and she put her handkerchief to her mouth quickly to hide the trembling of her lip.

Bill sat and faced her on the bed.

"Dolly? Love? What is it?"

She shook her head and half turned from him.

"Dorothy?" His voice carried gentleness and concern. "What is it, what's the matter?"

"They won't let me come home."

The words she spoke were so muffled in her effort to fight back tears that it was a few seconds before Bill understood what she had said.

Slightly bemused he said at last, "I'm sorry Dorothy, I'm sorry but I don't understand."

Dorothy gave a final snuffle and regained some of her composure. "I've got to stay in. At least another week." And she gave a gasp of exasperation. "I can't come home. They won't let me."

"Oh Dorothy." Bill shifted his position and put his arms around her and drew her close. Her forehead felt hot and clammy. He kissed her and nuzzled his face against her forehead as if he could draw the heat from her. "What's wrong? What have they told you? You were only supposed to be in here for a week's rest."

"They've said it'll take longer than a week and I've still got to stay in bed here until the blood pressure comes down."

"Oh God!"

"I was afraid of this. I don't know why. I just had this fear that once

361

they'd got me in here they'd never let me out."

"Oh Dorothy." Bill was at a loss. "Perhaps if I have a word with them. There's nothing wrong is there?"

"Not as far as I know. They just say that I need to be kept rested."

"I'm sorry love. I know it's frustrating for you. But, if they think it's best…" He sighed in exasperation and smiled ruefully at her.

"Can you get me a clean hanky. They're in the drawer."

Glad of the opportunity to do something, Bill took the used handkerchief, damp with Dorothy's tears and fetched her a clean one.

"I'll take this and wash it," he said. "Is there anything else that needs to go?"

"No. My mum took the other stuff this afternoon."

"Have you told your mother?"

"No. They didn't come and tell me until just before you came." She was on the verge of weeping again. "I'm sorry Bill. To be like this I mean. It's just that I was looking forward so much to coming back home again."

"Oh Dorothy. It's alright. It'll be alright. I'll go and have a word with the sister in a minute and see what she says."

He went round the bed and carried the vase of flowers over to the sink.

"Better throw these out, they're past their best. I'll fetch you some fresh ones tomorrow." A trail of petals drifted to the floor as he moved.

"Don't let the water drip," she said. "It'll smell. In fact you'd better throw them away outside. There's a bin out there."

"Right." He hesitated. "I'd better not put this water in your sink either. It's all brown and smelly. I'll pour it down the toilet I think." And it would give him a pretext for being in the corridor to go and see the sister. Why did he need a pretext? Nobody had said anything, just 'she needs to rest'. He didn't want to show concern, just an opportune moment to talk to someone about Dorothy's condition. "Shan't be a minute."

He disposed of the flowers but there was no one in the little office on the corridor when he passed. He stood and looked about him, momentarily undecided. A nurse appeared briefly passing the windows in the door of the ward at the end of the corridor. Bill strode quickly down and peered inside. A few heads turned to look at him with disinterest, women in advanced stages of pregnancy, all lying in bed except one who was moving heavily along the ward in her night gown.

Embarrassed, Bill mumbled something like, "Sorry, excuse me." He saw the nurse at a bed on his left looking at him. "I was looking for the Sister," he said and prepared to withdraw.

"Yes. Can I help you?" Her voice was unconcerned, matter of fact.

"Em… It's about my wife. Dorothy…"

"Oh yes. Would you mind waiting outside a moment."

"Yes. Right."

Bill withdrew into the corridor and closed the door after him.

After a few minutes the Sister appeared. She lifted her head with authority and repeated, "Can I help you?"

"It's about Dorothy," Bill said, indicating the door to Dorothy's room along the corridor. "I thought… we thought she was coming home tomorrow but she says you've told her she's got to stay in a bit longer."

"That's right."

There was no further information forthcoming to judge from the Sister's demeanour of abrupt efficiency.

"Well," Bill continued carefully, "I just wondered why that was all."

"Because she needs the bed rest."

"Well yes, I know that. I mean Dorothy understands it too. But she could get her rest just as well at home. Couldn't she?"

The Sister looked at Bill carefully and he began to feel intimidated under her gaze but he ploughed on, unsure of what he wanted to say in response to the monosyllabic replies. "We live with her mother. I mean, we haven't got a place of our own yet. What I mean is, there'd be someone there all the time to keep an eye on her. To make sure she didn't do anything she ought not to. Housework. You know…"

The Sister's eyes flicked quickly along the corridor. Satisfied that the door to Dorothy's room was shut she said, "Dorothy has very high blood pressure. You know that."

"Yes, yes of course."

"It's not uncommon. And normally with rest, the proper diet… well it can be brought back down. In Dorothy's case it isn't doing. So we need to keep her in so that we can keep an eye on her and make sure that it doesn't go any higher." Her voice carried the message, 'this is perfectly normal and we are following the tried and tested procedure'.

"But it's another fiveweeks. I mean…" Bill's voice, raised in protest trailed away under the Sister's professionally quizzical stare. But there was an implication here that Dorothy wasn't aware of. From what Dorothy had said to him a few moments ago she was only anticipating a further week. He adopted a more conciliatory tone of voice. "You don't think she'll have to stay in for…?"

"There are side effects that we have to guard against."

"How do you mean?"

"You must be very careful what you say to her. But if her condition were to get out of hand it could be prejudicial to the baby's well being."

Bill tried to grasp the meaning behind the sister's words without reading too much, without reading anything, into them. He looked at her for further explanation and his furrowed brow betrayed the working of his mind.

He struggled to find a question to help him to understand. "How do you mean? The baby?"

"Now I must stress," the Sister said earnestly, "There is nothing to worry about and we certainly don't want Dorothy getting anxious."

She paused and looked directly at Bill. He gathered himself and said, "Of course not."

"If her blood pressure were to rise unchecked it could mark the release of toxins into her system. And we certainly don't want that to happen while the baby is still waiting to be born do we."

"No." Bill bit his lip, gave a snuffle and reached in his pocket for his handkerchief. "No. Excuse me." He wiped his mouth and blew his nose.

"Now we haven't spoken to Dorothy about any of this because it's very unlikely and we don't want her to start getting anxious."

"No of course not," Bill agreed and snuffled, reaching into his pocket again.

"So we are keeping her in, so that in addition to the rest she needs, we can monitor her progress as well."

"Thank you Sister."

"Does that answer your concerns?"

"Yes." Bill was relieved to have been taken into the Sister's confidence. It was so much better to know what was going on. "Thank you Sister. I'm sorry to trouble you, but, you know, Dorothy was disappointed and, well I didn't know…"

"Of course not. Now you go and spend some time with Dorothy. We'll look after her. And not a word about things that needn't worry her. Alright?"

She waited for Bill's reply.

"Yes Sister. Thank you."

"Good." The Sister turned briskly and returned to the ward.

Bill returned to Dorothy's room with the empty vase in his hand.

"Sorry if I've been a long time." He replaced the vase on the table.

"I thought you'd gone." The playfulness with which Dorothy might once have said it was no longer there.

"I saw the Sister," he said and sat beside her on the bed.

"Did you find anything out?"

"She just told me that here was the best place for you. Just so that they can keep an eye on you. You know," he continued light heartedly, "until your blood pressure's low enough for you to come home and wait for the baby to be born."

"So she told you nothing." Dorothy sounded terribly downcast and Bill tried to rally her.

"There's nothing to tell."

"Well I don't know. None of my friends have had this problem. Our Marge! Myra!"

"It's just one of those things love. Tell you what! I'll bring David to visit you tomorrow. How would that be?"

"I'd like that."

"Good. Well he won't be able to come next Saturday 'cos he's going to Worcester with my mother and dad."

"Next Saturday!" Dorothy cried. "How long do you think I'm going to be in for?"

"No I didn't mean that Dolly!" Too late, Bill was suddenly aware that he had nearly broken the Sister's confidence. His face was burning; he hoped to God he wasn't blushing. Desperately he tried to cover himself. "I mean, if you're in here until next weekend, you'll want to see him before he goes won't you. And there's not much chance in the week. Is there?"

"I hope I'm going to be out next week! You don't know what it's like just lying here."

"Of course you will," he said bravely. "But not if you keep getting yourself excited like that. Come on." He coaxed her, "Just relax and take things easy and stop worrying about things."

Dorothy allowed herself to be fussed and Bill straightened her bed jacket around her shoulders and smoothed the covers.

"Would you like a chocolate? My mother brought them for me but I'm not sure I should eat them." She reached into the cupboard and Bill took a chocolate from the box she offered him. He stayed on for as long as he could and they sat in desultory conversation.

After almost an hour a nurse looked in to check that Dorothy was alright, gave Bill a reassuring smile and left, glancing pointedly at her watch as she did so.

"It's quiet here," Bill observed as a distant sound of steel dishes being wheeled on a metal trolley came from somewhere within the building, transient, as though the trolley had bumped over a threshold then continued on its silent way.

"It's always quiet," Dorothy said.

Drowsiness crept over her and she suddenly pulled herself up and shook her head. "I'm sorry," she said, "I shouldn't do that."

"It's alright love." Bill pulled the coverlet up around her. "You doze if you want to. It's the best thing for you."

"I don't want to sleep when you're here. You won't want to come and see me if I'm asleep," she replied softly.

365

"Of course I will. I don't mind. It's nice sitting with you quietly like this."

Dorothy reached out and squeezed his hand but lethargy was steadily overtaking her. The soft glow of evening filled the room, reflecting off the walls in a comforting pink light.

"You'd better go Bill. You'll be late."

"I'm alright. Really."

Dorothy leaned against him and her eyes closed again. "Hmmm." She sighed.

"I love you," he whispered. "See you tomorrow."

Dorothy nodded and slid deeper into the bed. Bill turned and smiled back at her and closed the door softly as he left.

CHAPTER 43

Secret City; welcome home!

High in the wood, beyond the footpath that overlooked the stream below, lay the Secret City. It was concealed from view by a series of banks and shallow canyons covered with trees and dense undergrowth. David and Brian had discovered it quite by accident when they strayed off the top path into unfamiliar territory. It was a sunken area of evergreen, mostly mature rhododendron with some laurel, clearly established there in the past when that area of the park constituted a landscaped 'quarry'. But for years it had been allowed to develop in the wild.

At first glance it looked like an impenetrable area of dense greenery, but when the two boys approached it and descended into it to investigate they discovered neglected paths weaving amongst the luxuriant foliage. It became everything they wanted it to be. From the Amazon jungle alive with wild creatures and cannibal indians, to a Wild West town where the bushes represented buildings lining the earth streets that meandered through, it became their favourite haunt. They adopted it as their own, telling no-one else, not even parents, about it apart from John. It was their playground, their den of dens, their Secret City.

Every day after school they called for each other and ran joyfully into the park. And at weekends too, other plans permitting, this was where they played. Scrambling up the banks, building hideouts under the foliage, withstanding sieges from imaginary hordes.

This particular Saturday morning he was alone in the Secret City. Brian and John had gone to the Saturday Club and normally David would have gone to the pictures to watch the serial with them but it finished too late for him to be ready in time for when daddy got home from work. David had to be home early to get changed into his best things. He was going to see mummy in hospital.

He had no idea what the time was. He'd been out playing since nine o'clock but he sensed by the feeling of the sun on his skin and the way the light changed, the way it felt in the woods, that time must be getting on. Something told him that it was time to leave and go back home. He hesitated in his game, on the verge of abandoning it. But he had been

367

stalking Jap snipers in the jungles of a Pacific Island and there were still three out there. He paused, squatted, and made his way stealthily into the bush once more. He got one of them up a tree. The sniper didn't see David coming and David carefully drew back the bolt on his rifle and pushed home a bullet, then he got him with a perfect single shot. The man fell from the tree without uttering a dying scream and that gave David a chance to go for the other two who had no way of knowing that their compatriot was dead. Suddenly he turned! There was no-one there. It must have been a wild beast.

It was no good, he would have to go.

The rifle, helmet, camouflage clothes and ammunition vanished as he switched his imagination off and he set off through the rhododendron at a run, his game abandoned. He ran as though he was on the meadow, but full tilt vertically down through the wood. It was exhilerating to challenge the wood like that, choosing your footfall at that speed almost at the instant your feet landed upon the ground, avoiding roots and protruding rocks, loose shale, branches. Within a minute he was on the footpath beside the stream below and he set off to run back home.

Bill had arranged that, for a change because mummy wasn't there to cook their Saturday dinner as usual, he would collect David when he got home from work and they would go to grandma's for dinner. From there it was easy just to step outside and catch the bus direct to the hospital gates. Now, running back as fast as he could David was beset by fear that he might have stayed out playing too long. His daddy would be mad with him if he was late back and not ready in time. Worse still, he might have gone to the hospital without him and David would not see mummy before he went to Worcester!

"Where've you been?" Grandma Bracewell said sternly when he burst through the door into the kitchen. "Come on. You'll never be ready in time!"

She ushered him upstairs and disappeared through her bedroom into the bathroom. "Go and get your clean things out while I run some water for you to get washed."

David continued up into the attic to change his underclothes then went down to the bathroom for a wash. With relief he realised he was home in time to be ready for his daddy after all.

He was reading alone in their sitting room when Bill got home from work.

"Daddy," he cried and threw the book down, running to him with his unfailing greeting.

Bill gave David a cursory hug. "Be careful," he said, "I've still got my working clothes on. You'll get messed up." Then he went straight upstairs to get washed and shaved.

David returned to his book. It seemed to be ages but at last his daddy came down and said, "Are you ready then? Come on, let's get going."

Bill turned back to the door by the record player leading through into the Bracewell's. As he closed it he called, "We're going then ma."

He paused and listened but there was no response.

"We're off," Bill called and waited again.

Silence.

David knew! He had seen it before in the way Grandma Bracewell cast slights at his daddy, making him repeat things, implying that what he was saying didn't make sense or ignoring him completely the way she was now, as though he didn't even exist. But David knew, even at eight years old, with a child's intuition he knew enough to sense that he and Bill were unwelcome at the Bracewell's. And it was not easy to understand why because mummy loved daddy and he would have thought they would want to be pleased that mummy was happy. But he was also aware enough to know that he mustn't add to the conflict that existed between them. And so he watched, and said little, and tried to understand.

Bill shrugged and looked at David. "She must be through in the kitchen," he said it as a sort of self justification. "Anyway," he added, "come on, let's go."

David nodded and Bill locked the front door behind them and David took Bill's hand and walked down the road to catch the tram to grandma's.

"You're going to see your mummy today then are you?" Lilly said admiringly. "Well you look nice to go and see her anyway." She turned to the oven for the plates warming on top of the range and carried them into the kitchen.

"What's for dinner grandma?"

"Shepherds pie. You like that don't you." She returned to the living room and David followed her as she carried the pie dish from the oven to the kitchen ready to begin serving generous portions out between them. "Well," she said to him, "go and sit down then while I warms this gravy up."

But here David observed another strange thing. Daddy had said they didn't have to be at the hospital until three. So there was no hurry and they wouldn't need to catch the bus before ten minutes to. And that was nearly an hour-and-a-half away. Yet daddy became impatient and cross with grandma.

"Come on then mother. I thought you'd have had it ready by now."

"It is ready Billy. Just wants serving out that's all."

There was no need to make grandma rush. Apart from them being hungry and ready for their dinner it wouldn't have mattered if it wasn't ready for another half-an-hour; there was plenty of time! It was as though daddy was looking for ways to find fault, the way Grandma Bracewell found fault with him. And daddy took it out on grandma and that was wrong because grandma never did anything to upset daddy, and she always made a fuss of mummy. But grandma was easy to be cross with because she hardly ever answered him back.

It wasn't that grandma was soft. David knew that. In fact she was quite strict about what children should and should not do but she had the warmth in her heart that Grandma Bracewell lacked. And, David thought, it must be because grandma understands that daddy is impatient to go and see mummy, and it is the wait for three o'clock makes him snappy. But he didn't ought to be snappy with her all the time.

At half past two grandma said to David, "Come on, let's wash your face and hands."

"But I washed 'em before we came out," David protested.

"Do as your grandma says and have a bit less." It was the first time Bill had spoken in the twenty minutes that he had been sitting in morose silence.

Dutifully David followed grandma into the kitchen.

"We want you to look nice when you see her don't we!"

David screwed up his face and let her scrub it with the flannel.

"There you are," Grandma said, "Now dry yourself properly. You don't want to get chapped do you."

There was still ten minutes to go before they had to leave.

"Here," Grandad said. "Here's your Saturday money box. I think I owe you a couple of weeks. I didn't pay you last week." He began to fish in his pocket amongst his loose change. David cast a furtive look across at Bill but he was still lost in thought. David took the two half crowns that Harold offered him, said 'thank you' and took them to Bill.

"Will you look after these for me please daddy."

Bill took the coins and slipped them in his pocket. "Remind me to put them in your bank," he said.

"Yes daddy." David looked up at the clock on the mantelpiece. "It's time for us to go."

Perversely Bill replied, "Not yet. I'll tell you when it's time to go."

David looked round but grandma gave him a look that said 'do as your daddy says'. So he stood and waited on tenterhooks, getting increasingly nervous as he watched the clock and saw the final minute to catch the bus approaching.

"Right!" Bill said, rising suddenly, as though he was the one who had been kept waiting by the rest. "Come on. Let's go. Get a move on."

"Go on David," grandma said, "Don't keep your daddy waiting. Will you be coming back to let us know how she's going on Billy?"

"Yes. But I shan't stop."

"Give her our love then won't you."

David was excited as they walked into the hospital grounds. Suddenly Bill stopped and said, "Oh bloody hell!"

David looked up at him and Bill seemed torn with indecision.

"Oh Christ!" he muttered. "Flowers!"

He was looking back along the drive and trying to remember if that shop…?

"Come on." He took David's hand with some irritation and went back down the drive to the corner shop by the bus stop. He was in luck; they had some. They were not very big bunches and they were overpriced for what they were but still, they were better than nothing.

He'd intended bringing a nice bouquet but there had been such a rush to get to his mother's that he'd completely forgotten. And they'd had plenty of time to get here in the end and now he was late. Typical!

There was a reassuring smile of recognition from a nurse in the corridor; a final admonition at the door. "Now you mustn't get mummy too excited. D'you hear?" David nodded and they went in.

Dorothy turned and her face lit with a smile; "Ohhh!" she held her arms out and David ran to the bed.

"Come on then." David scrambled up onto the bed beside her and received a hug and kiss. "Only mind my tummy."

A wave of relief swept over Bill and the tension melted away. Dorothy was clearly so much better in spirit than she had been yesterday. She was smiling readily and the drawn expression had lifted. Somehow she looked less grey, less downcast.

David moved aside and Bill leaned over and kissed her.

"You look tons better."

"I am better. I think it was just the disappointment. You look forward to something and then, right at the last minute they tell you it isn't going to happen."

"I know. But they know what they're doing love."

"I know." Dorothy reached out to them both. "I miss you, you know."

"We miss you, don't we David?"

"Yes we do. We miss you lots and lots." David scrambled onto Dorothy again to kiss her.

"Careful." And she gave a slight grimace.

"Come on David. Climb down off the bed now like a good boy."

Dutifully David did as he was told and wandered about the room looking at her things. On the table were jars and boxes with tissue paper, balls of cotton wool, lotions. One jar was labelled 'Nipple Cream'. It was all very intimate and feminine and it held a strange sort of erotic fascination for the child. He felt a sense of arousal and the feeling gave rise to secret thoughts, like he felt when he looked at the pictures of ladies in mummy's magazines with their clothes off, just in their underneath clothes and he peered at them to see if he could see anything showing. He turned his head carefully to look back over his shoulder at mummy. She was engrossed in quiet conversation with daddy. He had raised her up higher against her pillows and now he was sitting sideways on the edge of the bed with his knees crossed and his back to David. Mummy had daddy's hand and she was placing it on her tummy, moving it over and down on it with the bedcovers pulled back off her. David felt the arousal again. He didn't know why, there was nothing in what he had seen and what they were doing but it just seemed so very intimate between them, beyond the bounds of normal touching when they were at home. He hoped they hadn't seen him looking at the jars and boxes or they would know what he was thinking and he didn't want them to see him watching them or they would know what he was beginning to feel. He turned back and his eye unconsciously sought out the jar of 'Nipple Cream' again and rested on it. Embarrassed, he moved away, still with his back to them and looked through the window. Outside it looked so bright and welcoming with the sun gleaming on the asphalt path beside the neat green lawn. Here, inside this room it was oppressive and hot. He wished he could go; it wasn't how he had thought it was going to be. Mummy and daddy were talking babies and it made him feel as though he was intruding in something private and shouldn't be here.

Mummy was calling to him.

"Would you like to feel the baby?"

David shook his head, overcome with bashfulness at the thought of placing his hand where his daddy had just been touching.

"Come on. He's just started kicking again. You can feel him. Give me your hand, I'll show you where to put it."

Her words struck him with an irrational fear that she might put his hand where a boy shouldn't touch his mummy. Down there! He didn't want to do it.

"What's the matter with you?" Bill said. "Don't be so silly. Come and feel. It won't hurt you!"

David approached apprehensively.

"Oh you are a little silly." Dorothy said and she laughed. "Come here."

She took David's hand and placed it on her belly.

"Can you feel it?"

David waited and Dorothy moved his hand slightly, overcoming his resistance to moving it at all.

"Oh you are a silly." Dorothy gave his arm a shake to loosen the rigidity with which he was holding himself. "Come on... Oh it was there! Did you feel it?"

Nonplussed David shook his head.

"Wait a minute then... Now! There it was again. Did you feel it that time?"

David nodded uncertainly. He didn't know what mummy wanted him to feel. All he was aware of was the firmness of her belly, nothing more.

"Are you sure."

David nodded again.

Dorothy looked at Bill. "I don't know whether he did you know."

"Here, come on," Bill said to him but David backed away.

"I did! I did feel it. It was... like a movement."

Bill shook his head. "I don't know. Here, come and tell mummy what you've been doing at school."

There wasn't much to tell that he could remember about the week. Reading, drawing, sums. Breaking up for the six weeks holiday. Oh he wished it was over and they could go home and he could go out to play.

"And you're going to Worcester for two weeks to see Aunty Ame with grandma. That won't be long now." Dorothy turned to Bill. "What time are they going?"

"Next Saturday. Train's about eleven o'clock I think."

"Oh." A shadow of disappointment fell across her face. "I might not see you before you go then. Depends what time they let me out. Unless you come back and see me in the week. Do you think you might be able to do that?"

David nodded and looked up at Bill.

"We'll see," Bill said. "Depends what time I can get back from work."

"Well anyway," Dorothy said, "you'll have a nice time down there won't you. And I'll bet Aunty Ame's looking forward to seeing you again. And then when you get back it'll be time for mummy to have the baby. And then we can all be together again. That'll be nice won't it?"

She smiled and drew the covers back over her. "Come here and give mummy a nice big kiss."

He kissed her and sat back in the armchair by the bed to wait until it was time to go.

"I shan't bring him tomorrow," Bill was saying, "but I'll try to see if I can get him over next week."

373

"It's alright Bill," Dorothy replied. "It's not easy, visiting like this."
She turned to David in the chair. "Come on then, come and give me a
kiss, it's time to go home."

David jumped from the chair with alacrity and went for the kiss.

"Now you'll be a good boy won't you?"

David nodded enthusiastically.

"And you'll give grandma a big kiss from me as well?"

David nodded again.

"Alright then. Off you go."

Bill leaned to her and she kissed him deeply. "Thanks for bringing
him Bill. You've got those things to take back with you haven't you."

"Yes." Bill brandished the brown paper carrier bag.

"That's it then. See you tomorrow."

They turned at the door and Dorothy waved to them from her bed
and blew David a kiss. He waved back, then skipped along the corridor
to the freedom and the sunshine outside.

Dorothy watched through the window as another week of the
beautiful summer passed her by. Small periods of activity when they
brought her meals and carried out examinations were bounded by
eternities of boredom. Her magazines and books brought some relief in
the slow passage of time until she tossed them aside and lay back,
staring at the sparse room and the unchanging image in the window, self
obsessed and frustrated. Her visitors arrived, small oases in the endless
ocean of the day, smiling with immediate chatter, lingering as the
chatter faltered until they felt it was time to make guilty excuses, their
duty done, to leave Dorothy to her solitude again.

Another week! Dorothy's dark eyes followed the nurses' activities
minutely, watching their reaction when the blood pressure readings were
taken and recorded, desperate for the reassuring smiles to be more than
passively formal. She needed to see a smile that said, 'Well done
Dorothy, it's turned a corner and you're going home'. But the restrained
politeness of the nurses remained constant, matching the stubborn
constancy of the readings.

On Friday, just as they had the week before, they came to tell her
and Dorothy knew what they were going to say for their brave smiles
were braver than hers. Her eyes held disappointment as they spoke.

"It hasn't shown any sign of improvement I'm afraid. We must
keep you here; there isn't the remotest likelihood of your leaving while
ever it remains at the present level."

Dorothy's face remained impassive. Not with resignation but with
bitter, bitter disappointment.

"Oh well," She gave them a rueful smile that was immediately overshadowed by the quivering of her mouth and she shrugged and lifted her head. "I'll just have to stay here then won't I?"

"Would you like a cup of tea?"

Dorothy was biting her lip to keep her emotions in check. The word, "Please," escaped and she clamped her lips again. She wouldn't cry.

They offered gentleness and kind words until they could see that Dorothy had accepted. Then they checked their watches and prepared to leave as well.

"Soon be time for Bill again," they said brightly.

"Yes. I don't know what he'll say. He'll be as disappointed as me I expect."

"It's a bugger!" Bill rubbed his nose in exasperation. "And they've not said when you'll be able to come out?"

"Well, while ever it's like this," Dorothy said calmly, "they'll keep me in won't they."

Over the preceding hours Dorothy had fallen back on her own professionalism and justified it to herself. Naturally they were following the course they were because that was what her condition demanded. You always think it's not going to happen to you, she told herself. Well, it was boring and inconvenient, but there was no help for it. And getting all het up wasn't going to make things any better either. So Dorothy resigned herself to the possibility of a long wait until the baby was born.

"I'm sorry I won't get to see David before he goes," she said. "Do give him my love won't you."

"Of course I will."

There was a long moment when an unspoken thought passed between them. Bill went and stood gazing through the window. Outside, nothing had changed. The same evening light; the drive, just coming into view from the left and swinging out of sight at the entrance to this block of wards. Then the path running past Dorothy's window bordered by the lawn. The anonymous collection of nondescript buildings opposite. And as always, no sign of life whatsoever. Bill wondered why the path was there at all; he'd never seen anyone on it. Where did it lead? He must remember to look when he left and see if there was another entrance further along past the ward.

"Bill."

Dorothy's voice sounded distant across the room.

"Sorry," he said.

He turned and stood by the window with the light on him and voiced the thought that was troubling them both.

"I hope to God it's not going to be another month like this."

"I know," she said bravely.

"I didn't mean that the way it came out. For you I meant. You know I'll come every day." he pleaded earnestly. "I just can't bear the thought of you lying here like this. There must be something they can do surely."

"This is it," Dorothy replied simply. "This is what they do. Rest, a controlled diet, constant supervision. This is what it takes Bill."

"Oh Dolly I'm sorry."

"But what are you sorry for? We're going to have a baby, our own baby. That's not something to be sorry for. Come here."

Bill returned to her and sat on the bed.

She held his hands. "You are a softy," she said.

"I didn't know it would be like this."

"Of course you didn't," Dorothy reassured him.

"I just wish it was over Dolly. For your sake."

"It will be," Dorothy replied. "It will be soon. It'll be over before you know it. Come on, let's not waste time being like this. You know I spend every waking hour waiting until it's time for you to come. And then when you're here it flies by. You ought to be here all the time. The days would soon fly by then."

Looking through the train windows David became aware that the earth in the fields was red, the colour of rich clay but not as heavy and soapy in composition. This earth was fine, it broke easily and David suddenly recognised that it signified they were getting close to Worcester.

The descent of the bank at Bromsgrove was behind them and the Malverns were beginning to grow on the horizon. Grandma and grandad were starting to get restive; they entered a tunnel and as they emerged grandad said,

"Come on mate. Get your things."

Other passengers in the train around them were reaching up to the luggage racks for suitcases and they crowded at the door as it drew in to Shrub Hill. David was completely happy. It was as if he had never been away.

He scanned the faces on the platform as they passed the window but she was not there. No matter.

They walked the familiar route and for David it was like putting on a well worn, comfortable garment as each corner they turned revealed a familiar sight.

And smells! It smelled the same. He hadn't realised that a smell could colour a place so. Even the canal had a smell, not foetid or stagnant, but the smell of water and healthy, luxuriant growth. It was

376

unlike anywhere else.

The entry between the houses rang with the familiar echo of their feet and he heard the first low clucking of the hens from the end of the garden. They turned into the yard and he glanced along at the living room window but it was blank beyond the curtains. Then into the porch, grandad knocked the door then stood back for grandma to place David at the front. The click of the latch and there was Aunty Ame in the doorway, smiling her smile. "Why," she cried as though his appearance was entirely unexpected, "it's our David!" David grinned back at her, she stooped and they hugged each other with pleasure.

CHAPTER 44

Thunderclouds

The fine summer weather continued into the following week but it could not last. Unlike continental summers with the promise of endless sunny days, after two weeks of unbroken sunshine the British summer had reverted to type and the atmosphere grew heavy with a prediction of thunderstorms.

"Typical ain't it." Lilly grumbled, "You wait all this time while the sun's shining and then as soon as you go on your holidays it starts to rain."

"It ain't raining yet," Amy said.

"Can I go out to play?" David asked. He was sitting at the table with pen and paper and an expression of furrowed concentration on his face. "Before it starts to rain?" he added hopefully.

"No," Lilly said. "You've got to finish that letter first. How are you getting on with it?"

"I think I've finished it." He held up the sheet of paper for her to see. It was blank except for five lines of hastily scribbled news.

"You'll have to do more than that. Your mummy won't think much of you if that's all you've got to say to her."

"Aw grandma. Can't I finish it later?"

Amy and Lilly looked at each other. They understood. David had been quite excited at the thought of writing his own letter to Dorothy until Terry, his new friend from up the road had come to call for him. Now the letter had become an onerous task.

"Go on then. But you've got to finish it when you come in."

In an instant David was down from the table and on his way to Terry's house.

In the small room at the hospital the heat was oppressive and Dorothy was feeling decidedly uncomfortable. The window was open but it made no difference, no air was stirring and the atmosphere was heavy and still. Closing the curtains gave no relief; it only added gloom and she hated the curtains drawn in the day anyway. She was feeling nauseous and her uneaten lunch was on the table by the wall. She had begun to feel sick the previous evening. It was the food, she told herself,

378

and her phrase 'school dinners' came back to her. Sometimes it took an effort to eat some of the food they cooked.

An orderly came bustling in for her tray.

"Leaving your dinner?" she said. "Baby needs his food you know."

Dorothy closed her eyes at the mild rebuke and shook her head with small movements. It gave her some relief to close them and shut out the well meaning chatter.

She heard the orderly collect the tray. Oh why couldn't the woman do it without so much unnecessary rattling of the plate and cutlery?

"I'll have to report you to Sister if you're going to start leaving your meals."

But Dorothy could not bring herself to engage in explanations or comments about how distasteful she was beginning to find it. All she wanted was peace and for the feeling of sickness and the ache in her stomach to go away.

The door closed and she was alone again. Now the room was silent she opened her eyes again and the unremitting sharpness of the light pouring through the window made her blink. She was tired of reading. It made her eyes ache and she had begun to wonder if she was going to need glasses. The trouble was she had too much time to think and dwell on her own aches and pains. She slid down beneath the single sheet that covered her and closed her eyes again against the light and hoped the rising discomfort would soon go away.

When Bill arrived in the evening the sky was dark with thunderclouds rolling over the moors and the air beneath them building to intolerable humidity. Like everyone else it made him feel edgy. He was tired and he was sweaty from his day working in front of the furnaces in this heat, swinging the glowing bars of metal from the furnace mouths. He was looking forward to a drink later, after the visit, or maybe a quick one on the way home. But, 'Oh no, better not,' he cautioned himself, 'don't want to get in the old lady's bad books'.

It was strange how such a bright and healthy girl like Dorothy could be laid low for such a length of time over a natural thing like having a baby. It must be rotten for her, he mused, stuck in that room day after day. At least he could leave when the visit was over. Dorothy had been there nearly three weeks now. And every day he hoped to find her better and every day she was the same.

He was walking along the corridor past the small office to Dorothy's room when the Sister, different to the one he had spoken to before, stepped out and intercepted him.

"Oh I wonder if I might have a word."

She gestured with her arm, an invitation for Bill to step inside.

Mildly surprised, Bill went in and she closed the door behind them as she followed him inside.

"I'm afraid you'll find a change in Dorothy this evening," the Sister began. Suddenly Bill found the tiredness falling from him.

"What sort of change?"

"She's under sedation." The Sister paused to observe Bill's reaction. "She hasn't been well these last few hours," she continued, "and we needed to slow things down a little."

"I don't understand."

"Dorothy began feeling nauseous…"

"She said she was feeling sick last night," Bill said. "We thought it might have been what she had for her meal." He forbore to add Dorothy's previous comments about the food. "Perhaps it was that," he added helpfully.

The Sister shook her head. "I don't think so. We've been monitoring your wife very carefully to keep her blood pressure down. Daily urine tests for example."

"I didn't realise you did other things as well. I mean…"

"It's a lot more then just keeping her in bed you know. Well," she continued, "protein levels in the urine are another indicator and in Dorothy's case they had begun to rise and so she has been placed under sedation in order to slow her down. We need to prevent her blood pressure from increasing. She still has some time to go before the baby is due and she needs a great deal of rest."

"How is she?" Bill asked, suddenly anxious.

"She's fine. You will find that she is drowsy. She may be asleep and if she is I wouldn't disturb her."

"Thank you Sister." Bill started then hesitated. "Is it alright if I…?"

"Yes," she said. "You can go and see her now."

Bill went uncertainly back into the corridor and walked slowly to the door of Dorothy's room. What did it all mean? This was the second time he had come away from a conversation with Sister with unformed questions.

He paused at the door and opened it carefully, quietly. The room was unexpectedly dark and he was taken aback by how stuffy it was. Dorothy was lying under a single sheet but unaccustomed to the gloom he couldn't tell if she was sleeping or not. He thought of switching on the light but its suddenness would be an intrusion and somehow that didn't seem to be the right thing to do so he crossed the room to the window and drew back the curtains. The light that came in had no vitality, it was sulphurous and the first big splashes of rain began to fall from the black clouds in the lowering sky above. He heard a low sound behind him, his name, and turned to see Dorothy lying motionless beneath her cover, looking at him.

"Oh Dolly." He crossed to the bed and sat beside her, looking down at her. He put his hand on her forehead, it was clammy and he stroked her hair back, talking to her. "Dolly love. How are you?"

Her voice was no more than a mumble, as though she hadn't the energy to move her mouth to form words. He had to strain to hear her.

"I... all... right..."

"Have they given you something to make you sleep?"

Again Dorothy's mouth didn't move and she breathed, "Ye... es."

"I'm sorry. I didn't mean to wake you."

A smile almost appeared at the corners of her mouth but Dorothy's eyes remained half closed as though she was struggling to keep the lids open. Again the word came on a breath from the motionless lips. "S'alright."

"Shall I close your curtains again?"

"No... oo." It was no more than a sigh and as he looked at her Dorothy's eyes closed. He remained looking at her in silence but she didn't move, only sinking further back into sleep.

He became aware of another sound washing over the silence. He turned and saw the rain was falling in torrents and had begun to cascade past the window from the overflowing gutters above. The room was growing cooler and fresh air laden with moisture came in from outside. He looked at the single sheet covering Dorothy and found a cellular blanket to put over her then he crossed to the window and pushed it closed. Now the room was silent except for Dorothy's breathing which had become deep and measured. He sat and waited in the strange yellow light and placed his hand gently on her abdomen but there was no response from within and neither did Dorothy move. After a while he left, closing the door quietly behind him and looked into the office on the corridor to tell them he was going but no one was there for him to tell. All thoughts of heat and work and having a drink forgotten, he went home to his solitary tea at the Bracewell's.

By the time Bill got home he was thoroughly soaked. The rain had eased back from the earlier torrential downpour but it was still heavy and the thunder which had been absent at the beginning had caught up with the storm and was rumbling sullenly overhead.

He dashed in and shook his coat off, and tossed his shoes into the hearth and made for the stairs, knocking at the Bracewell's adjoining door as he went.

"I'm back. Just going up to get changed."

The bathroom was free and it didn't take Bill long to get himself dry and fresh. Then he went downstairs and waited for Dorothy's mother to bring his tea through.

He heard her knock and call, "Are you down?"

"Yes," he replied.

After a few minutes the door opened and Enid Bracewell appeared with his meal on a tray. There was an air of suppressed resentment about her. She said nothing and without looking at him put the tray abruptly on the table and prepared to leave.

Bill said, unnecessarily, "I've been to the hospital. Dorothy's..."

"I've been there myself earlier. I've seen her," she said.

"Was she... talking?" Bill asked lamely.

Enid Bracewell drew herself up to answer and remained with her back to him.

"She said very little. I hardly knew her. She was... drugged."

She took another step to leave and Bill, defensively clinging to the words of the Sister said, "It's for the best you know."

"How dare you!"

"I didn't mean..."

"How dare you. In my house, talk to me about my daughter like that when you've seen the condition she's in!"

"I know her condition ma," Bill protested. "I've talked it through with the Sister."

"Yes, well I've spoken to Sister too and I'll take her version of what's going on, not yours."

"Why what's she said?"

"Well she certainly didn't say there's no cause for concern as you seem to think!"

"I never said..."

But again Enid Bracewell cut him short. "We'll see what she's like tomorrow."

And she left the room.

Bill looked at the plate on the tray. Lettuce, a tomato and slices of pork luncheon meat. Three slices of bread and butter. His stomach felt sick but after a while he sat to the table and picked at it with his fork, hardly eating. A tear ran down his face and he pushed the plate away, wiped his cheek and cradled his head in his hands. After a few moments he rose and picked a record from Dorothy's collection stacked at the side of her record player. Then he sat in the armchair listening with the image of Dorothy filling his mind as the sound of 'Tit Willow' filled the room. Outside the thunder rumbled and the rain continued to pour in the gathering darkness.

The following day Bill's visit was more satisfactory. Although she was still under sedation, Dorothy was more aware.

"I didn't see you last night." she said. But her voice lacked its

382

former vitality and there was an air of languid drowsiness in her speech.

"I was here. You were asleep."

"Oh I'm sorry Bill. I wouldn't have been if I'd known."

He smiled at her. It was such a relief to see her sitting up and talking again. "You couldn't help it," he said. "They must be putting something in your tea."

"I'll have to tell them to stop it." she said gently.

"Better not," he said. Then, lightly so as not to give rise to any anxiety, "Did your mum come up this afternoon?"

"Yes. She's been every day so far. She's ever so good."

Bill nodded, with the recollection of last night on him. "Yes. Of course."

"She worries," Dorothy continued in the same dreamy way. "I tell her not to but you know what she's like."

"Yes."

"Anyway she had another word with Sister today."

"What did she say?"

"Same as they've been telling you. Not to worry and it's all for the best."

"Ah."

Bill rose and crossed to the window. Broken clouds were drifting across the sky and everything looked bright and refreshed after yesterday's rain.

"The storm didn't disturb you then?"

"No." Dorothy managed a laugh. "I didn't know there'd been one." Dorothy's eyes were screwed up but it wasn't with the laugh. "Come away from the window will you Bill."

"Yes?" He glanced behind him as he moved but it was just as deserted outside as usual. "Why, what's the matter?"

"It hurts my eyes. Looking at you against the brightness." She squinted again.

"Are you alright?" he asked, suddenly anxious.

"I've got spots before my eyes that's all."

Bill moved back to Dorothy's bedside and sat next to her.

"That's better," she said. "It'll go away in a minute."

She sat back and closed her eyes and looking at her Bill noticed the way her face looked more puffy every time he saw her. Must be the drugs they're giving her, he thought. And then, not for the first time, it'll be a good job when it's over.

After a few minutes Dorothy opened her eyes again, but they fluttered with the struggle.

"Sorry," she said, "it must be the stuff they're giving me. I can hardly keep them open."

"It's alright love. Really. Close them if you want to."

"No," she said, "I want to be here with you."

But her eyelids drooped again. Within a few minutes Dorothy was asleep...

And so Bill's visits continued. As before Dorothy's conversation was slow, her voice was low and languid, and her eyes were heavy with induced sleep. But there was a flicker of pleasure when he walked through the door and she put his hand underneath her nightie and they sat intimately, waiting for the baby to kick. But the conversations were as short as the previous one had been, for lethargy overcame her again and despite her efforts, Dorothy's eyes closed and she lost the battle against sleep. But he remained in the room with her. Bill would rather be here, by her side as she slept than alone at home without her. Later, after a nurse looked discreetly through the door to see if Dorothy was alone, was when he judged it was time to leave.

But Bill's anxiety increased with every visit. Dorothy was now barely conscious and hardly registered his presence. Bill sought out the Sister again and protested that there must be something could do but the Sister resisted him.

"We do know what we're doing and this is the best thing for Dorothy, to keep her quiet and under sedation. You have seen for yourself how slow she is to respond and that is the very thing we are looking for. Quietness and a slow pace. It's the best thing for mother and baby and when the time comes we will know what to do."

"But she won't be like this for another four weeks, surely!"

"No of course not. But it's far too early to do anything else to intervene just yet."

And although Bill tried to be content it left him feeling discontented.

Stubbornly the level of Dorothy's blood pressure remained high. The signs showed, if anything, a tendency for it to go even higher. Dealing with the increasingly ominous array of symptoms pointing to pre-eclampsia the consultant increased the medication and through his staff endeavoured to keep the family reassured.

And Bill found that all he could do was to sit or stand impotently by her bed and watch her as she slept. He placed his hand on her belly, feeling like an intruder violating her modesty now that she no longer guided him, and waited for the responses. And at intervals the baby rewarded him.

But sitting and moving about the silent room watching over her Bill sensed that events were beyond him. And he tried to console himself, 'they seem to know what they're doing; they must know what they're doing. I just wish that I knew'.

The following Monday as Bill arrived there was activity in the small corridor office. Some kind of meeting was taking place; anxious faces turned fleetingly as he passed then resumed their discussion. Bill ignored them and went in to Dorothy. As usual she was sleeping but with the kind of artificial breathing that sedation brings. It was deep and nasal and somehow she didn't seem rested at all but troubled in her sleep. He took her hand as he always did and spoke her name,

"Dorothy."

But her eyelids didn't flutter at the sound of his voice. Just the breathing; slow, and heavy, without grace. He walked across the room and turned, looking at her. "Oh Dolly," he spoke softly, as if in prayer, "I'm so sorry to see you like this. I know you said it's all for the best but I can't bring myself to be content, not with you like this." But his words sounded trite and self-conscious.

Bill had never been a religious man. It wasn't in his background and he didn't have Dorothy's faith, the faith that she had maintained at the Methodist chapel throughout her life. But for Dorothy he would embrace her faith and he returned to where she lay and sat close to her and took her hand in his and bowed his head over them and closed his eyes and prayed.

The meeting in the office had barely started when Bill walked along the corridor. It had been convened hurriedly and the consultant stood with the registrar and listened gravely to the Sister's reports.

"Is that the husband?" he asked as Bill passed by the window.

They all glanced up and the Sister said, "Yes," then went through Dorothy's charts and gave him and the results of her examination half an hour before. Dorothy's urine was showing high levels of protein and her blood pressure had jumped to 190/110; but the baby was now showing signs of distress. Its rate of heartbeat had suddenly increased and although Dorothy showed no signs of convulsing her slumber was not as calm and untroubled as before.

The consultant heard the Sisters brisk professional report. The registrar was looking to him for an opinion and the nurse was hovering in agitation by the door. It was what he had feared and what they had been hoping to avoid.

"Eclampsia," he said. "How many weeks is she?"

The Sister glanced quickly at the charts and confirmed, "Thirty three."

"She'll have to be induced. Come along."

When the door to Dorothy's room suddenly opened Bill looked up startled from where he was sitting with bowed head. There were people entering; a young doctor in his neat white coat, a distinguished looking man whose white coat was loose and flapping open as he moved, the Sister, and another nurse.

He stood quickly and took a step backwards,

The Sister turned to Bill. "Please wait outside," she said.

Bill tried to look past her to see what was happening but the Sister was uncompromising. He left, turning at the door for a last look at Dorothy and saw the consultant leaning over her with his listening trumpet on her abdomen.

What had happened? Bill paced the corridor in agonies of anxiety. He tried listening at the door but then moved away in case somebody should find him there. He resumed wandering the corridor aimlessly, constantly turning to see if anyone was coming out of Dorothy's room. If only they would tell him something. Something real! What the hell was going on?

At last the door opened. The consultant emerged and turned to Bill, gesturing him to follow. He led him up to the office, closed the door and perched himself on the corner of the desk. He indicated the chair and Bill sat, anxious to hear what he was going to say and fearful of what he might hear.

"We're going to induce labour," the consultant said.

"What's wrong? What is it?" Bill's voice was trembling with the implications of the sudden activity.

"It's a condition we've been trying to avoid. Your wife has become rather ill. What we need to do now is to get the baby born. It's alright, she is very lucky, it's well within the time for her to deliver. But we have to initiate it instead of waiting for nature to take its normal course."

"But what about...? Where do I ...?"

"There's nothing more you can do at the moment." The consultant was speaking briskly but reassuringly. "It's in our hands now." He smiled at Bill and rose from the desk and Bill stood too. "You will have to join the ranks of expectant father's I'm afraid." He turned for the door. "It's just a question of waiting. Now you must excuse me."

He turned and walked briskly down the corridor to Dorothy's room leaving Bill with a sense of abandonment.

He waited. Should he stay in the office? Or wait outside? There were papers on the desk. Perhaps they were things he ought not to read. He decided to wait outside in the corridor.

More time passed and Bill fretted. Should he knock on the door? Had they forgotten he was still here? Was he supposed to wait somewhere else?

The Sister emerged and glanced sharply up and down the corridor, looking for him. As she walked up the corridor to him she took in Bill's haggard features.

"Perhaps you might be better at home." She smiled. "Nothing's going to happen now for a few hours. You can come back and visit her again tomorrow of course and we'll let you know how Dorothy is getting on."

"But what if anything…?"

"Now there's no use in worrying is there. We'll let you know as soon as anything happens."

She turned and Bill watched her re-enter the room. He looked at the clock on the wall inside the office. Nearly quarter to eight. Where had the time gone? Turning to leave he saw the Sister and the two doctors in the open doorway of the room where Dorothy lay. He wondered if he could take just a quick look at her. Just to see that she was alright. But the door closed behind the three of them leaving the nurse inside and they dispersed, the Sister into the ward at the end of the corridor and the two white coated men coming along the corridor towards him. Bill gave a slight nod of acknowledgement but they were in conversation and didn't respond to him. Bill turned slowly and walked ahead of them and out through the entrance into the fresh evening air. On the drive he paused and looked back and all the windows were blank, as blank as his mind. But behind that unrevealing window on the bottom row lay his wife. And all that he could do was walk away from her. With a heavy heart Bill turned and began to walk leaden footed down towards the road. Now he had to go home and tell the Bracewells.

Bill didn't expect to sleep; there was too much whirling about in his brain and thoughts kept hopping from one to another without time to think clearly through any of the tumultuous trains of thought to any conclusion. In the darkness he tossed, first on this side, then on the other and then laying on his back staring upwards into the dark. Again and again he almost slipped away but the whirling thoughts wouldn't quieten and in desperation he turned again and tried to sleep but the more he tried the greater the commotion in his mind.

The Bracewells hadn't helped; Ernest Bracewell sitting in quiet judgement and the old lady with her acid reserve. He was a stranger in their home. Oh God how he wished for a place of his own and an end to all this. And Dorothy back. He wished none of this had started.

She was slipping from his memory! The thought jolted him back to full wakefulness. The days of their courtship, their first meeting, Dorothy, dark haired and vivacious. That was in another world beyond the veil of her pregnancy. She was sleeping and he could not. But she was sleeping an unnatural sleep; Dorothy's world of sleep was beyond his and he couldn't reach her. No matter how he tossed and turned he couldn't reach her. Couldn't reach... Dorothy was twisting and falling... Their hands grasped... and slipped... the touch of her fingers sliding through his... she was laid in bed smiling... beckoning... but his lead encased feet wouldn't move... wouldn't carry him to her... with an effort he lifted one leg to walk... but there wasn't time... her smile... her smile... reaching out one more time... now their hands were clasped... and bells were ringing for them... but the bell became a harsh, jangling sound. Bill woke with a head like a bad hangover. 'Oh God!' he groaned. 'That time already'. Grey light on the curtains. Oh let me sleep! He turned over and stopped the alarm and lay for a moment to gather his thoughts. 'Dolly! Oh God Dolly!'

He pulled himself out of bed and hastily dressed and hurried downstairs to wash.

At five to six the morning air was cold under the light blue sky. Summer had returned; it was going to be another hot day. But at this time in the morning it was cold, still sharp from the night and the chill rising from the river. It cleared Bill's mind and cleared his head of the dull nausea from the morning cigarette and stale smoke from all the other morning cigarettes clouding the air on top of the crowded workbus.

He dashed across to the telephone box under the railway arch opposite and phoned the hospital. 'She's in labour. Can you call back later on.' Didn't sound as if the girl who answered really knew very much about it, only where Dorothy was. Call again and demand to know more? Six o'clock in the morning? There'd be nobody there. That's why! Bloody hell! Anger fuelled anxiety. He crossed the road into the timehouse and clocked on.

The new spring, designed for station buffers for Swedish State Railways was still giving trouble and Bill looked at the night shift foreman's inspection reports and swore at him.

"Well what have you been doing all bloody night? Pissing about as usual. Leaving it for me again!" he cried. "You're crap Tommy."

"Aye, well. It's your crap now. See if you can get it bloody sorted. I'm going home!"

"I'll sort it don't you bloody worry," Bill shouted after him as Tommy left the inspection cubicle. "We should never have taken 'bloody job on!"

"Aye well, you're so bloody clever, you'd know." And Tommy strode out with relief into the works yard and the sunshine.

The crew assembled between the winder and the furnace heard the exchange and grimaced with the anticipation of another rough shift ahead. There was no bloody pleasing him lately. Anybody'd think nobody else had ever had a baby but him!

Bill stood in the inspection cubicle and yawned, and braced himself to get the shift under way. Christ, but he was tired. And this was only at the beginning! Twelve hours to go and he wondered how he was going to get through it. And bloody management was going to be on his back all day now because that chuff Tommy had only done eight percent of target. God knows what he'd been playing at all bloody night!

"Come on then!" he said sharply as he approached the crew. "What you hanging about for? Let's get some bloody work done for Christ's sake."

Sullenly they dispersed to their stations.

The first few bars were run and produced scrap. It wasn't that they couldn't produce the spring but for some reason during tempering the coils opened up and the spring finished over tolerance. They got to work altering the gripper on the mandrel and Bill flung the coiling tongs onto the glistening steel floor.

"They're bloody crap these Ronnie."

"There's nowt wrong with 'em!" the blacksmith retorted. "They're spot on to 'drawings."

"Well they're no good anyway. Drawings must be wrong!"

"Well I can't help that!"

They tried again and the men swore at Bill behind his back.

More scrap; almost an hour gone and not a penny piece of bonus earned so far.

Bill looked at his watch again. He was going to have to find time to get to the phone. If only they could get this job running he could slip away and make another call.

The men noticed.

"What's up with him? That's about six times in t'last quarter of an hour."

"Wants to keep his mind on 'job then maybe we could get going!"

They decided on further adjustments.

"I want it coiling tighter," Bill said. He called the blacksmith over.

"You see the problem Ronnie. We can't get enough purchase to twist the end right when the final coil feeds in. Can you just…?"

Bill started to show the blacksmith what he wanted and Ronnie said, "I knew they didn't look right but that's what the drawings said. But they'll be out of specification. It's on your head and it'll take a bit of time."

"Just get on with it will you." Bill said testily. "I'm going to make a phone call."

Bill strode off to the office ignoring the looks that the rest of the

389

men gave him. Again the same message. Your wife is in labour. Can you call back later. Christ! How long does it take? He went back to the job.

"Come on then," he cried, "what you all standing about for?"

The men worked with resentment but the modifications showed some improvement. Bill went over to the tempering bath, an open vat of molten lead and watched the spring approaching as it was swung off the coiling machine by the overhead hoist towards them. The time was critical; the steel coils were no longer glowing with cherry red brightness but the spring would have to be immersed in the lead at the right temperature and for the right length of time for the correct degree of tempering.

"Right Tommy."

The man by the bath of lead, in his lead splashed leather apron and already gleaming with grime, signalled to his labourer who pulled on the chains, hand over hand, lowering the spring into the molten metal.

The spring came out and they rolled it away across the floor and lit another fag while they waited for Bill to inspect it.

It was in. It was very tight on tolerance but it was in, no doubt of that.

"Right," Bill said, "it looks O.K. Let's see if we can do another!"

"Do you want us to start the infeed into the furnace?"

That would mean setting a stock of bars off on their pre-timed passage through the furnace to arrive at just the right temperature for coiling and tempering. But if the spring Bill had inspected and passed was a fluke, the next one would be no good and further adjustments would be necessary and the stock of steel bars in the furnace would be lost. It was a fine judgement. But at this rate they wouldn't produce anything at all.

"Yes," he said, taking a chance. "Start it up."

The man turned and gave a 'thumbs up' signal to the others.

"About bloody time," they grumbled.

So the work began. Bill kept a close watch on the coiling and the operator worked resentfully under Bill's silent observation but Bill didn't care. He had his job to do and he moved restlessly between coiling and tempering, checking, constantly checking and the crew's confidence in the job slowly increased.

The morning wore on. The production manager's girl arrived for work and was vaguely seen through the grimy office windows. She'd be out before long on some pretext, wiggling her hips and walking the long way through the department, pretending not to know the men were staring at her with her 'touch me not' smile about her mouth. Thursday was the best day when she brought the tray of payslips round and they

390

could get close and banter with her, smelling the scent she wore above the smell of oil and smoke and steel scale.

It was getting close to the morning break time and the men's teacans and mashings of mixed tea and sugar in newspaper twists began to appear from their knapsacks in anticipation of a sit down and a smoke.

A figure came out of the office but it was not the girl.

"Hello," one of the men said, "what's he want?"

The rest of the men looked round towards the grimy office against the wall next to the open shutters. Grey flannels, blazer; the department manager had left the office and was walking towards them. He didn't look pleased.

"Expect it'll be another bloody inquest about production figures."

The manager approached Bill and took him to one side.

"Told you so!" the blacksmith said with some satisfaction.

The department manager looked quickly around. The men were watching him. He looked worried.

"How's it going Bill?"

"Well," Bill said, "we're beginning to get some out now." He hesitated, poised on the brink of further explanation.

"Look," the manager said, "I've had Personnel on the phone. Can you get up there right away."

Oh God! Bill looked at the manager's face and saw his concern. "What is it?"

"Leave this. I should get up there right away," the manager said and stopped. There was nothing he could add.

Without a word Bill walked away leaving the men looking after him. By the time he reached the open shutter into the yard he was running.

The Personnel Manager was waiting at his office door when Bill arrived. His secretary was at her desk looking up with concern as Bill walked in. Without preamble the personnel Manager said, "We've had Nether Edge on the phone. You're to go up there as soon as you can."

"What did they say," Bill gasped; his heart felt as though it was rising into his throat and his breathing was in gulps.

"You're to get up there right away." he repeated. "We've sent for a car to get you there." He glanced at his secretary. She hadn't taken her eyes from Bill.

"It's on its way," she confirmed. "It should be here by now."

"Go and see will you," the Personnel Manager said and the girl slipped from her desk and ran downstairs to the door.

"Did they say anything? Anything at all?" Bill pleaded.

The Personnel Manager fought for the right words to say. "It's your wife. She's very poorly."

Bill began to cry.

"Here, come and sit down here. Car'll be here in a second. Is there anything I can get you?"

"No." Bill was sobbing and he turned away.

The secretary came back in, looked at the Personnel Manager and then at Bill and said, "The car's here. Let me take you to it." She put her hand on Bill's shoulder and led him from the office.

"I'm sorry," Bill said, pausing on the staircase. "Just a minute." He wiped his eyes and nose. His breath was a little easier now. "My jacket. I need my coat."

"Where is it?" the girl asked.

"It's in the inspection cubicle. Heavy Department."

"I'll fetch it. Don't worry."

She led him down to the car "Wait here a minute." she said to the driver and Bill sat in the back seat, watching her through the window, praying for her to hurry.

In Heavy Spring Department the manager saw her approach and went out to her. "What is it?"

"His coat. He wants his coat."

The manager looked around vaguely.

"He says it's in the cubicle."

"Ah yes, over here." He led the girl across under the stare of the men. This time there were no wolf whistles, just a shocked realisation that something was seriously amiss as they saw the girl running out with Bill's jacket.

She opened the car door and passed it to him. "I hope it's not too serious," she said, and gave Bill a weak smile. The driver turned to look at her. "Nether Edge," she said and watched as the car drew away.

Bill sat in silence, urging the car to get there. It was interminable. He lit a cigarette and looked through the window. So many uncaring people out there, he thought unreasonably to himself, and not one with any idea what he was going through, what was happening to the passenger in this car.

They drew into the hospital grounds. Bill threw the door open, thanking the driver.

"Do you want me to wait?" the driver said.

Bill shook his head. "No! Thanks."

He dashed inside. In the small deserted entrance hall he hesitated, looking to left and then to the right for someone to announce himself to. He went along the familiar corridor but the Sister's office was empty. Further along the door to Dorothy's room was ajar and a narrow blade of light cut across the floor and onto the corridor wall opposite. He peered inside; the room was empty. Turning, he ran back to the entrance and a nurse was there.

She looked at him in some surprise. He was breathless and his face looked haggard. Beneath his old work jacket he was wearing greasy overalls. Taken aback by the nurse's stare Bill looked down at himself and at his hands. They were still black and greasy; he hadn't had time to wash. He hadn't even thought of it.

"I got a telephone call." He was gasping. "At work. They phoned through. My wife, she's in labour, they said she was ill."

The nurse tried to calm him down but she couldn't get him to stand still, he was pacing about.

"Where is she? Where is she?" he repeated and pushed her hand aside, pacing again. He ran his fingers through his hair and gave Dorothy's details to the nurse. He should have gone straight through to the ward at the end of the corridor, he knew he should. But Dorothy had told him that ward was only for the mums to be. Not those who had given birth. She wouldn't be in there! He looked round for the nurse and she was making a telephone call. "Come on, come on," he muttered.

She put the phone down. "This way," she said and led the way briskly down the entrance hall.

He was shown into an office, bigger than the office on the corridor. There were certificates on the wall instead of clipboards on nails and charts and curtains at the window. The consultant rose from behind the desk to greet him and gestured Bill to a chair.

Bill hesitated, "I'm sorry…" and indicated his dirty hands and working factory clothes. The consultant was without his white coat and Bill felt the distinction between himself and this grave, dark suited man.

He waved Bill's hesitation away and said, "Please, do sit down."

Bill sat and looked up at him with pleading eyes. "Where is she? Where is Dorothy?"

"I'm afraid your wife is seriously ill." Bill nodded and fought to keep his emotions in check. "She has a condition called eclampsia." The consultant paused for a second and sat on the corner of his desk facing Bill. He continued, "It can occur in certain cases. Fortunately it isn't very common and it is brought on usually by a specific combination of symptoms. I'm sorry to have to tell you that in your wife's case those symptoms began to become evident and that is why she had to remain here in hospital under supervision."

"But… how is she? I mean, what about the baby?"

"I'm afraid Dorothy lost the baby."

He paused again to allow the impact of what he was saying to penetrate through Bill's distress. Bill stifled a sob, his eyes expressed disbelief and he lowered them as tears began to form in them.

"Dorothy," he mumbled. "How is Dorothy?"

The consultant continued with his careful words. "Eclampsia is a result of toxins being released into the system. They are harmful to the unborn child. That is the reason we had to induce labour when we did. Fortunately Dorothy was far enough advanced in pregnancy to allow us to do it but," he hesitated, "we were unable to save your son."

At the word 'son' Bill's head sank to his chest and he began to weep softly.

The consultant waited. After a few moments Bill composed himself and looked up.

"You said Dorothy was ill," he said.

The consultant held Bill in a steady gaze. He could see that Bill was struggling to grasp the enormity of Dorothy's ordeal. Finally the consultant sighed and rose from the desk, wandering over to the window as he spoke. "One of the other effects of eclampsia is the creation of blood clots. This is what happened in your wife's case." He paused and turned to look again at Bill. "I'm afraid that Dorothy has had an eclamptic stroke."

Bill sat as rigid as stone. Oh God! How much longer was this going on?

"Where is she?" he stammered finally. "Can I see her?"

"Of course," the consultant said gently. "But first of all you must understand Dorothy's condition. She hasn't emerged from sedation yet. We won't be certain just how serious her condition is until she regains consciousness. But you must be prepared to face the fact that there is likely to be some brain damage."

"You mean… paralysed?"

"There may be some…" he paused then tried to give reassurance. "We really won't know until later. I'll give you a few minutes to gather your thoughts if you like." He moved to the door and turned to Bill, "And then, if you'd like to see her…?"

"Yes. Thank you."

He went out and left Bill alone in the room.

Bill's mind was filled with a jumble of swirling images, half formed out of the words he had heard, strange words that had no meaning for him. He tried to remember earlier words, the words the Sister had spoken just a few days ago. But he couldn't remember! He castigated himself for not knowing and tried to put snatches of memory together but none of it fitted. Oh Dolly! What have we done!

The consultant returned accompanied by a nurse carrying a visitor's gown.

"Dorothy's still in the recovery room," he said. "The nurse will take you down there now."

She held out the gown, Bill pushed his arms in and he saw his hands with shame, his grimy hands emerging from the white sleeves as she tied it securely behind him. Then the consultant held out his hand to him. Bill hesitated and saw the consultant nod and took his hand but it seemed such a futile, final gesture. There was no energy in the grip, just a token dismissal. Bill turned and followed the nurse out and along the corridors.

He held his hands before him. "Is there anywhere I can wash?" he said, as though he needed to wash shame away.

"In here," the nurse replied, and she waited in the corridor while he went in and washed his hands and splashed cold water to wash the tears and freshen his face.

The recovery room was bright and silent, more clinical than Dorothy's room downstairs had been. A nurse was busy at Dorothy's side but she stopped when Bill and the nurse entered and stood discreetly away by the other nurse as Bill approached the bed.

Bill stood and gazed down at Dorothy, looking for the girl he had come to see. She was just as he remembered from…? And realisation hit him with a force that jolted his sense of reality. It was only last night! This is how Dorothy had been last night! And last night he had knelt and prayed but they had come for her and sent him away. Now they had brought him back and she was here, just the same. Breathing in the heaviest of sleep, breathing in a way that seemed as if it would go on forever without changing, just the sound of her breathing, the gentle rasp of her breath. It was as though nothing had happened between that room and here but he knew that Dorothy had undergone some violent trauma and now she was here, just the same. Only… She wasn't the same!

Bill paused and looked around the room and it was incomplete. Somehow, somewhere here, in here or an adjacent room Dorothy had been delivered of a son.

"A son…"

He mouthed the word softly, almost incoherently. The recovery nurse stepped forward.

"We couldn't do anything for him I'm afraid." She spoke with deference. Bill looked up at her.

"How…? Was he…?" But he could not bring himself to say words that were so brutal in their finality, as though he was prepared to cast the child away with no further thought.

"He died before he was born." She placed her hand on Bill's arm, a gesture of sympathy. "I'm so sorry." She looked across at the nurse who had brought Bill in. "We all are," she said.

"Where is he?" Bill asked, almost apologetically.

"Would you like to see him?"

"Can I?" He was weeping again.

The other nurse nodded and left.

He stood without moving, listening intently to the steady, continuous, unconscious breathing of his wife.

In the hospital chapel they had prepared a table with a candle at its head and a child's coffin, placed in its glow. A tiny boy, fully formed, beautiful, with a smooth untextured face. But he was pale and limp. He had no residual vitality. How could he, for all his vitality had been consumed in the womb of his mother and in the womb he had died. He had never known this life, the freedom of life that Bill had shared with Dorothy. And looking at him it was hard to believe that today, Oh God yes, it must have been today, only hours ago this tiny being had desperately responded to the urge for life and struggled to be born. But as he fought his way, after so many careful months of nurturing the mother who carried him was releasing poisons with increasing swiftness... and delivered him to the world dead.

Bill heard a deferential footfall behind him and saw the hospital chaplain come into view. "Would you like to name him?"

In tears of despair Bill nodded, remembering the names they had chosen.

"Robert," he croaked. He reached out to touch the tiny chest and hesitated with his hand almost touching it. The child's skin had the texture of cold chitterlings and he drew away.

"Robert..." he repeated.

The chaplain waited.

Bill wiped his eyes with his handkerchief and said, "It's alright. I'm O.K. I'm alright now." But he flinched as the deferential hand of the chaplain touched his shoulder and he turned away. He was plunged into a void, drifting in the bleakness of his mind between this place, silent and reverential with the lifeless child, and the room upstairs filled with the sound of Dorothy's laboured breathing. Beyond the two there was nothing but emptiness.

CHAPTER 45

An idyllic ignorance

A desperate search for normality began. It had started at the hospital where, after seeing the baby Bill continued to wait for Dorothy to emerge from the sleep into which she had been induced. For hour upon hour he had paced and fretted, desperate for news. Sitting by Dorothy's bed he looked for signs of her well being. Each flutter of Dorothy's eyes sent him into a spasm of watchful anxiety. He was plied with tea until he was sick with the coagulating milkiness of it and the cramp in his belly turned sharp and acid and he lost the taste for the food they brought him. It stood uneaten where they placed it until he threw it in the bin before they should see it and think him ungrateful. Finally, Dorothy began to waken and they sent him from the room. Bill started pacing again, scanning each face that approached and passed him in the corridor for a sign, a recognition of his existence, for someone to stop and take him by the arm and tell him with a smile that Dorothy was alright.

Once more the consultant took Bill into his room. He saw Bill's ashen complexion and the darkness under his eyes. Bill was clearly agitated, he constantly had his fingers around his mouth, nibbling and rubbing his nostrils then wiping his mouth again. The consultant took note of the unconscious activity and looked at him with some concern.

"Are they looking after you?" he asked, motioning Bill to a chair.

Bill dismissed the question. "Yes. How is Dorothy?"

"Thankfully Dorothy appears perfectly normal in her movements."

Bill looked at him questioningly, trying to read the words and understand what he meant.

"Normal?" Bill raised his hand to his brow, hoping but not daring to hope.

"Physically." The consultant trod the path carefully, drawing Bill along with him. "There is always a danger in cases like this, where damage to the brain is the outcome, that it may result in physical impairment."

"You mean… paralysed?"

"In some cases, yes."

"And you're saying that Dorothy is alright?"

"No, I didn't say that. But she doesn't appear to show any signs of paralysis. Not physically anyway."

Bill sagged with relief as the tension left his body. "Oh thank God." he said. "I don't know what to…"

The consultant cut him off. "However, Dorothy is not well."

Bill looked sharply back and he felt the tension snap hold again in an almost unbearable spasm. His back and the side of his ribs immediately resumed their ache and a look of pain crossed his face. "How do you mean, not well?" he asked cautiously.

"She has suffered brain damage…"

Bill let out a cry. It was an involuntary appeal as if to God. He averted his eyes and screwed them shut, slowly shaking his head as if in denial.

"Now it may not be irreversible," the consultant continued remorselessly. "Dorothy is a very strong and healthy girl," Bill looked up in disbelief; the description he was hearing sounded strangely at odds with what the man was telling him, "and our feeling is that it may be possible that Dorothy can recover. But she will need specialised care."

He watched Bill trying to recover his self possession. His face was working and it was clear Bill was trying desperately to trust the words he was hearing.

"Yes." Bill nodded. There wasn't enough air in the room and he felt as if he was gasping. "Yes. I see."

"We will keep her here for a few days. And then I think she will need to be placed in the care of Middlewood Hospital."

At the consultant's words a shadow crossed Bill's face as it might cross the face of a prisoner denied a reprieve. All the prejudices he had ever heard flashed through Bill's mind; Middlewood was a mental hospital. The consultant waited, then continued sympathetically, "We don't have the facilities at this hospital. They have the resources to deal with this sort of thing. You know, Dorothy's case is not unique. Often a quite remarkable progression can be achieved."

Bill nodded dumbly. "Can I see her? I mean is it alright for me to?"

"Of course. You may find her speech is a little… slow. She'll be much better in a day or so when the full effects of the medication have worn off."

Bill left the room to see her accompanied by the consultant.

Back at home, in their room, Bill sought refuge in silence from the recriminations of the Bracewell's. He sat in contemplation trying to grapple with events. And then he realised with a start that David was coming home at the weekend. Oh God! He'd forgotten all about David! Perhaps Aunty Ame would keep David there a bit longer, just to give him time until they knew how it was all going to work out. He dashed off a letter and hurried down to the post and hoped it would get there in time for them to make arrangements...

On the following day at breakfast David was finishing the boiled egg that he had collected from the hen house with Amy earlier that morning.

"What's you doing today then?" Amy asked.

Lilly was in the kitchen mashing a pot of tea. Looking through the window Amy could see the morning sun bright on the garden. It made the living room seem dark by comparison. The day was beckoning with hours of playing stretching ahead. It was the last week of their holiday and in a few days David would be going home again.

"Going up for Terry," David replied. "Then we're making shields."

"Oh." Amy said brightly, as if it was a surprise to her.

David and Terry had been such good friends this holiday. They had met on the first day after David had arrived and they had been inseparable ever since. David and Terry's new game was Knights of the Round Table. They had wooden swords, made from the discarded rails of paling fences and they played desperate games of fighting the Black Knight in the street and along the canal side. Yesterday the boys had arrived with big old corrugated boxes they had acquired from somewhere, and set-to flattening them. Now it seemed they were going to make shields from them.

"You'll have to make the most of it won't you," she said. "Three more days and then you goes away and leaves me again. No more holidays. Boo-Hoo." She put her knuckles to her eyes and cried mock tears and David laughed at her.

"Whatever's you making that row for Ame?" Lilly said, coming in from the kitchen.

"She's crying 'cos we've got to go home soon," David announced. "I've finished." He pushed the plate away and climbed down. "I'm going out to play."

He ran out, pausing only to grab his sword from the coal hole in the porch and charged off down the entry to call for Terry.

The faint sound of the doorknocker rattling over the letterbox came to them from the front room.

"That'll be the post," Amy said. "Pour us a cup of tea while I gets it will you Lill."

"Do you want these eggs putting in now?" Lilly called after her.

"Yes. Time 'em." Amy replied unnecessarily.

Lilly opened the door at the foot of the stairs and shouted, "Is you nearly ready Harold? I'm putting the eggs in," then she went out to the kitchen.

399

Amy came back brandishing a letter.

"Here Lill," she called, "it's for you. Looks like our Billy's writing."

Lilly hurried back into the living room, her face lit with anticipation. "Oh give us it here," she cried. "I bet she's had it!"

Amy gave her the envelope and waited, impatiently watching Lilly study the writing before opening it.

"It's early if she has."

"Come on Lill," Amy said in mock exasperation, "let's hear what he says!"

Lilly tore it open and as she began to read Amy saw Lilly's glad expression turn to dismay.

"Come on Lill, what's the matter? What's he say?"

Lilly raised her eyes to look at her and Amy looked in them and saw disbelief. There was a moment's anguish before Lilly could speak.

"Why whatever's the matter Lill?" Amy said, looking at her sister with concern.

Lilly said simply, "She's had a stroke." Her voice was flat

Amy gave an involuntary cry.

"And she's lost the baby." Lilly spoke the words as though unable to believe what she was reading.

"Oh no!" Amy took a step back. "Oh my God!" and reaching out for a chair she sat heavily. It was unbelievable! "What's he say about it Lill?"

Lilly sat and read the letter through.

"She's... she's..." But Lilly was stunned with shock. She could not find words to express what she felt and she offered the letter across the table. "Here Ame, read it for yourself."

The letter was brief and stark. It told simply of Dorothy having to be induced early because of her blood pressure and the complications which had followed and the stroke, "Eclampsia? What's that Lill?" and her child, a boy, stillborn. "But it don't say anything about how she is, only that they're keeping her under sedation." Amy looked at her sister again. "Oh God Lill. First Daisy and now this! However's he coping?"

"He don't say."

Lilly sat in silence.

The stairs door opened and Harold came in, looked at their solemn faces, laughed and said, "What's up with you two then? Is there any tea?"

Amy said flatly, "It's Dorothy. She's lost the baby. We've had a letter from our Bill."

Harold looked from Amy to Lilly. The realisation dawned that they were both in a state of shock.

He said. "I didn't... How did it happen?"

Lilly turned and slowly looked at him. "She's very poorly. She's had a stroke."

"My God!" He looked from one to the other, suddenly feeling dazed himself. "When?"

Amy scanned the letter. "It don't say," she said but the paper was trembling in her hands.

"Give us it here. Let's have a look." Lilly took the letter from Amy. "It must have been a couple of days ago. Perhaps..." her voice trailed away as she scanned the letter; she couldn't concentrate her mind on the text and Bill's florid script. What did it matter!

For a long moment the room was quiet with their contemplation. Amy didn't know Dorothy, only what Lilly had told her. But she felt she would have liked to have known her. Dorothy sounded like the kind of girl anyone would be pleased to meet. And just right for our Billy by all accounts. It was so awful! But, Amy thought optimistically, with a bit of luck she might not be as bad as what it sounded like; the letter didn't say much more then she'd had the stroke, but as for how she was doing it looked like they would have to wait to find out.

Oh but the baby. Such a terrible thing to happen. And they were both so looking forward to it according to what Lilly had been telling them. "Poor Billy," Amy said. "Not had much luck has he."

Lilly indicated the letter. "He's put something in about our David. He's wondering...?"

"I seen it," Amy interjected. "About him staying on a bit longer you means? Course he can."

"It's only while our Billy can get himself sorted out. Just for a few days longer. 'Till they knows how Dorothy's going to be."

"We'll have him as long as he likes. He knows that."

"Only me'n Harold's got to go back this weekend. He's back to work next Monday."

"Why don't you stay on a bit longer with him?" Harold said to Lilly.

"No it's alright. He'll be fine with us here." Amy said eagerly. "Tell you what, why don't you let him stay down here until school goes back. That'd give you two and Bill plenty of time and Dorothy'll be on the mend by then. There's no point in the kid getting all upset about her is there."

"But you had him all that time before," Lilly protested.

"And we loved having him too."

"What about Al? Won't he want to have a say?"

"Al thinks just the same about him as I do. No, that'll be fine. He might even get a few days hop picking with us if he's lucky."

401

"It's ever so good of you Ame. Oh we'd better write and tell our Billy it's alright then. You got any writing paper Ame?"

"In the sideboard. But we'd better go up and tell Rose first. Oh I can't get over it. Poor Dorothy." Amy rose wearily from her chair. "Better not say anything to David though. What do you think Lill?"

"Oh no. Better not. Not just yet anyway."

An hour later David was back with Terry.

"Have you got a big pair of scissors Aunty Ame? And some string?"

"What's you want string for?" Amy asked.

"For my shield. And Terry's." Why did grownups always ask such stupid questions?

Amy went to the drawer and fished out her large scissors. "Now you'll be careful of these won't you?"

"Course we will."

"Where's you going to do it? In the garden?"

"Yes! Shall we Terry?"

"Yes, alright."

"Well don't go away then. I've got something to ask you when grandma gets back."

"Oh. What is it?"

"When grandma gets back I said."

"Where is she?"

"Up at Aunty Rose's. Now don't go away will you."

"Come on Terry. I'll show you the hens."

They dashed out into the garden with string and scissors to make their shields with string loops on the back for their arms to go through. Looking up they saw Lilly returning down the path from Rose's house and followed her in.

"Now then," Amy said, and she tried to look very serious in front of the two boys but there was a little smile playing in her eyes. "You knows how grandma and grandad has to go back to Sheffield on Saturday?" Like lightning David caught the phrase 'grandma and grandad'. And no mention of him! "Well, grandma and me was wondering if you'd like to stay down here in Worcester for a bit longer?"

David leapt in the air and let out a scream. "Yes." Then he turned to Terry. "That'd be great won't it Terry? Ah thanks. Thanks grandma!"

Amy held back her delight at the exuberance of David's response and said, "You can go back out to play now then."

That was it. All settled. She sat down feeling suddenly weak. Her lip quivered and she knew she was going to cry. All her emotions were in turmoil. What with Billy and poor Dorothy and now she was going to have David for a few more weeks! She gave two sobs and tears began running down her face.

Lilly said, "Buck up Ame. She might not be as bad as we all thinks." But all the same she felt like crying herself when she thought about it.

David felt no qualms at seeing grandma and grandad go back home. He waved them off and turned away as the last carriage disappeared from view and went back home himself with Aunty Ame. Then he called for Terry and they got on with their playing.

Bill wrote to say thank God Dorothy wasn't paralysed but her brain was damaged and she would be under the care of the hospital for the future as far as they could see until the damage was healed. But in the meantime he was very grateful to his aunt and uncle for letting David stay with on them. Of course they could take him hop picking if they wanted to as well. A week off school at the end of the school holidays wouldn't hurt, not at his age. And he enclosed three pounds towards David's keep with thanks.

Amy and Rose talked through all the implications of Bill's letters and decided it was better not to say anything. Poor kid! Better let him have his few weeks in ignorance; there'd be time enough for him to come to terms with Dorothy's condition when he got back.

The holiday with Amy established a pattern that David would follow for the next few years until he passed the eleven plus and went to secondary school. After that the disciplines of the school term were rigorously adhered to, but up until that time David returned each year to Worcester and spent the summer at Aunty Ame's. And the boy's friendship, which on the face of it was only a summer friendship, renewed annually and then suspended until the next year, was a simple and true friendship that endured, unlike so many adult relationships which flower briefly in the hothouse of expediency and then wither away.

Each year upon his arrival at Aunty Ames David ran up the road to Terry's and it was almost as if Terry was waiting for David's knock. They picked up from where they had left off the year before and within half an hour they had disposed of the resume of their activities over the intervening months and the summer of childhood would begin again.

There were more opportunities for imaginative playing than the streets, at first glance, appeared to offer. The canal at the top of the street still carried commercial traffic and majestic shires, rich chestnut or dappled grey, would be seen plodding the towpath with the barge gliding silently behind. David and his friends followed as far as the locks and watched with fascination as the horse was uncoupled and took a rest while the barge went in the lock to be raised or lowered to the next level. Then the great horse was re-coupled. Under the urging of the bargee it leaned into the harness and drew the barge from the lock like the slow drawing of a cork from a bottle until momentum was established and the barge drifted along behind the measured clopping of the hooves along the bank.

Above the locks a long meadow dotted with gorse and hawthorne bushes rose steeply to the rim of a clay quarry. The marlbanks had steep, uneven sides, ideal for mountaineering with ledges built into the soft earth, great for kids to play on. Until the quarry owners chased them away. Until next time!

Across the canal opposite the top of the street the allotments were still under cultivation. They rose up the slope until they ended at the high brick wall running across the top. But at the extreme right end, between the allotments and the steep railway embankment the disused mansion with its neglected grounds offered endless clandestine adventures. It was creepy clambering through the shuttered windows into the gloomy rooms among the cobwebs and the dust. There were rotten floorboards to beware of that creaked and groaned as they crept around. And always the danger of discovery, for the notices at the entrance warned trespassers to 'Keep out'. And it was rumoured among the kids that a watchman kept a surreptitious watch and lurked somewhere in the building, ready to pounce on them. It all added to the sense of daring and excitement.

There were even orchards, and before the holidays were over David, Terry and the rest went scrumping and stole more apples than they could eat. But it was all part of the fun of summer holidays and the scoldings that David received from Aunty Ame and Aunty Rose were delivered with barely concealed benevolence for they also shared in the happiness of his summer.

And then hop picking time arrived! No open topped lorries this time. Now they travelled to the hopfields in a charabanc. And now David was older and he could exploit the opportunities for playing to the full. He had real jungle with hanging vines and foliage to hide in. And there were skulls and other bones lying on the earth that had been killed and picked clean by wild animals! So what if it was just the bones of an unlucky rabbit. It had been killed in the wild, screaming in the jaws of the merciless fox with the gleaming teeth red with its blood, tearing it even as the last quiverings of its life shuddered through its body and continuing as the light died from its eyes. It was no less savage than the tiger or polar bear. The fear was just as real for the hunted in the hopyard as it was in the jungle of the tropics.

404

Now, with his rifle unslung and crooked in his arm the hunter pulls the foliage warily to one side, for there might be snakes looping amongst the vines, and begins to track the great beast of the jungle.

Those were the solitary games, when it was safer to track the animals alone. But there were times when David joined with the other kids in stripping the dead bines from the wires or playing hide and seek, playing war, cowboys or the other games that children's imaginations find when the moveable landscape changes day by day from the density of high forest to the ravaged debris left by the destruction of armies.

When Lilly and Harold arrived home their first concern was for Dorothy.

Bill had spent a further week visiting Dorothy and sitting impotently at her bedside in Nether Edge while behind the scenes consultations about Dorothy's future care took place between the hospitals.

"How is she Billy?"

Lilly's voice had a low air of unctuous solicitude, like someone in a sickroom asking after the dying.

"What are you talking like that for mother?"

"What do you mean? There's no need to be like that Billy. I was only asking how she was that's all."

"She's not well," Bill replied testily.

"Well we know that. That's what you said in your letter. When can we go and see her? We'd like to go and see her."

But he put his mother off. He didn't want anybody to see Dorothy, not yet, not until she was better.

"It's not a good time," he said. Lilly's fussing was more than he could bear. "They might be moving her any day. She's not really up to having a lot of visitors."

"Well I don't know," Lilly said moodily. "There's no talking to you sometimes."

"Mother! Don't you understand! I've got a lot on my mind."

"We're only concerned about her that's all. We think a lot about her."

"I know. I'm sorry. I'm sorry!"

Bill felt the pressure, a sour ache, building in his gut again.

Lilly continued with her questions. Bill sighed and tried to resign himself to answering. She asked so many questions; why did she keep asking questions? Why couldn't she just accept what he told her and leave it at that. There was no rest from it. It was as though people were getting on at him all the time. Wherever he went he had to go through it, the same reports, with so little to report. Time after time. If only he

405

knew himself! But there was so much uncertainty and the sourness in the pit of his stomach never left him. The tension never left him. Only sleep gave relief. He wished he could sleep forever.

By the end of the following week the hospital's arrangements had been made and a few days later Bill went to Nether Edge for the last time to accompany Dorothy on her transfer. Dorothy had a nurse at her elbow, guiding her steadily through the corridors to the ambulance waiting for her at the door. Bill followed behind with Dorothy's belongings carefully packed in her small case. Leaving the ward he paused and thanked the sister and the nurse 'for all you've done'. There was conflict in everything he said and did; watching Dorothy moving down the corridor ahead, 'thank you, thank you, THANK YOU.' He wanted to scream his anger at the kind benevolence in their eyes. But he smiled a sad smile instead and turned away and followed her, sick to the bottom of his heart.

Middlewood. A bleak hospital of smoke blackened buildings situated at the north west edge of the city, sprawling over wooded hillsides amongst lawns and rhododendrons above the Don. With misgivings he watched Dorothy consigned to the hospital's care.

"She'll be kept under observation for a few days," they said. "There are some tests we'll need to carry out of course. And then we can start coming to some decisions about the best course of action. There may be a number of options available to us."

It was all very competent and, contrary to his prejudices Bill found the staff to be efficient and caring. They seemed as concerned for his wellbeing almost as much as they were for Dorothy's welfare.

Visiting Dorothy was not as easy as it had been at Nether Edge. There, the bus outside the factory gate had taken him virtually to the hospital door. But the journey to Middlewood involved going in to the city centre and changing buses and the journey seemed twice as long. But he did it. Even when it meant skipping his evening meal. It was a small price to pay, just to be there and sit with her in the long silences of her ward, to give her reassurance against the unsettling noises that erupted faintly from distant parts of the building.

Day followed day in a limbo of uncertainty. Nothing changed. Dorothy didn't change. The routine didn't change. Bed and work. Bill visited in the evenings, her mother during the day and he avoided her as much as he could. Just going through the motions. Waiting.

Until he was called to attend a meeting with the doctors...

Two days later Bill held a family conference in preparation for Dorothy's first homecoming.

Charlie and Marge came across to the Bracewell's and Jean was sent out to play while they discussed Dorothy's care and their role in it.

"She'll be alright in Middlewood," Bill insisted, echoing the reassurances he had received the day before while bravely trying to hide his own misgivings. "They know what's best for her. They've got all sorts of new treatments they can use nowadays."

"Well I'm glad you think Dorothy will be alright in that place."

Enid Bracewell echoed the prejudices they all felt. It was inconceivable that her daughter could finish up in a mental institution. And it was all through him! She glared at Bill, challenging him to reply. Marge, looking first at Bill then her mother, bit her lip and waited. She knew just how her mother felt about the place; she felt the same herself. As for Bill, well Marge was more sympathetic. You only had to look at him, the worry that never left his face to see what he had been going through. But it was difficult to take her mother's side and blame him. He couldn't help it, nobody could have. Only, why did it have to be Dorothy?

Bill ploughed on, repeating the optimistic words he had been given. "And they think the best thing for her is to come out and be with the family – to have familiar things around her. They want the brain to heal itself, so she's got to be amongst all the things she knows to get her brain moving again."

"And what does that mean?"

To Bill's relief Marge said, "Oh mother!"

Thank God! He might still have allies in Marge and Charlie.

"I only want to know what he thinks it means," her mother responded acidly.

"Well," Bill said, "it's not like a broken arm is it? I mean it's not as though you can put splints around somebody's brain is it. I mean," he began to flounder, "well I don't know. We don't know what they can do. Do we!"

He looked around for support.

Charlie said, "It's like a lost memory I suppose. And if there's enough familiar things around her then what they're saying is Dorothy'll start remembering things again and get back to normal. That's it isn't it Bill?"

Bill smiled wanly across at him, grateful for Charlie's endorsement. It was so difficult. It was like trying to grasp something that wasn't there. When he had heard the doctors at Middlewood talking about their plans for Dorothy it had sounded professional and competent. Now, hearing himself repeating their arguments and trying to remember what they had said, it all sounded so lame. But he was aware that Marge and Charlie hadn't seen Dorothy yet. So far only her mother had shared that privilege with him and seen the reality.

"Well I hope you are all satisfied, because it doesn't sound to me as if there's very much they can do for her at all," Enid Bracewell said bitterly.

"Well let's at least give it a chance!" Bill cried.

She glared back at him. "Oh yes, we'll give it a chance. Because that's all we can do isn't it. All I know is, we gave you a chance and I wish to God we'd never done it. And if it hadn't been for Dorothy's wishes we wouldn't have either!"

"Oh mother that's not fair!" Marge protested.

"It might not be fair but it's the truth. It was the worst thing she ever did, when she set her eyes on him!"

Charlie tried to restore some calm. "Look," he said, "this kind of thing isn't going to get us anywhere. And it certainly won't help Dorothy."

"Thanks Charlie," Bill said and he turned on Dorothy's mother, "And I'd have thought if you had Dorothy in mind at all you'd have learned by now to try a bit of friendship and a little bit of tolerance instead of always getting on at me all the time."

"I gave you friendship," Enid Bracewell retorted, rigid in her seat. "I gave you my home. And I gave you my daughter. Don't you talk to me about having my daughter in mind. I've thought of nothing else these past few weeks!"

Now Marge intervened. "Look you two. I don't care what you think of each other but if we're going to do Dorothy any good then you've got to bury the hatchet. She can't see you like this."

"Marge is right." Charlie reached and took Marge's hand beneath the table.

"Well I've got to bring her out at the weekend," Bill said desperately.

"So soon?" Marge said. She hadn't thought it would be on them so quickly.

"Well, yes," Bill replied. "Well there's no point in hanging about is there!"

"No, I suppose not."

"Of course there isn't," Charlie said.

"And what about the boy? I thought he was coming home this weekend!" Enid Bracewell gave him a look as one might look down at an incompetent.

Bill turned to face her. There were so many things happening all at once. It wasn't easy and she wouldn't make it any easier, not if he knew her!

"Well of course he's coming home. What difference does that

make?"

"Well I shouldn't have thought you could be in two places at once."

"What's the problem?" Bill retorted.

But Enid Bracewell said, "Bah!" and retreated into sulking.

"What time does he get in?" Marge asked.

"Saturday morning. But that's not a problem, my mother'll go and meet him at the station. I'm going up to Middlewood for Dorothy. I thought she could bring David straight up here."

But from the expression on Enid Bracewell's face it was clear that the suggestion was unwelcome.

Marge took Charlie's hand and returned his squeeze of reassurance and said, "Listen, why don't you get your mother to bring David up to our house. You can go and fetch Dorothy straight to us for tea as well. Then you can all come back home here to sleep later."

"What good would that do?" her mother asked sullenly.

"Well, we would all be there and Jean would be company for David as well. Dorothy always liked coming for tea at weekends. It'd be familiar wouldn't it? And that's what they said we've got to do." She turned to Bill. "That's what the doctors told you isn't it? Get Dorothy back into familiar routines."

"Well, yes," Bill concurred. It would also be on neutral ground. Maybe the old woman would be a bit more reasonable at Marge and Charlie's.

"What do you think mum?"

Enid Bracewell pursed her mouth, and glanced at her daughter, and nodded reluctantly.

On Saturday morning Marge took Jean to one side and carefully briefed her.

"Your Aunty Dorothy's not the same as she used to be. So if she does things a little bit different you're not to say anything. Aunty Dolly's poorly and we've got to help her to get better. Give her a nice big kiss. But don't squeeze her too hard mind. She's been very poorly."

Jean's eyes lit with pleasure. Ah yes but she's coming home. Aunty Dorothy's coming home!

"But she's not to get too excited mind."

And meanwhile Bill made arrangements with his mother for David's return. Lilly was glad to do it, despite Bill's cavalier treatment of her. And anyway, Lilly reasoned, it would give her the first chance she'd had to see Dorothy since they got back from Worcester.

Bill regarded the coming reunion of Dorothy with the outside world and her family with some apprehension knowing that the whole family blamed him. He had no illusions. Even though Marge and Charlie had been good friends when he had begun courting Dorothy, and despite their support, he knew they blamed him too. How could it be otherwise? For Bill blamed himself. He cursed himself for Dorothy's condition. But, he asked himself continuously, as he had asked himself ever since it began those weeks ago with Dorothy's first sedation, what could he have done differently?

Clinging to hope, beset with despair and faced with the Bracewell's animosity, Bill prepared to bring Dorothy to Marge's.

CHAPTER 46

The empty home

David's holiday came to an end but it ended without regret. The summer had been fulfilling and now it was time to go. David had an open, devil-may-care air about him and a refreshing, healthy exhaustion from days spent outdoors in fields and water with the scent of the earth all around.

He was journeying on the train alone, another great adventure. He was being put into the care of the guard and travelling in the guardsvan, a position of rare privilege and on Saturday morning Amy and Albert, Rose and Bob came to the station to see him off.

"Is you sure you'll be alright now?" Rose asked for the umpteenth time.

The guard overheard and reassured them all. "He'll be alright with me. Won't you." He gestured to the open door. "He's got his own seat look. Anyway we're going in a minute, better get on board."

"You know where he has to get off," Amy repeated. "He's going to Sheffield. Don't let him get off at the wrong station."

"He'll be alright," the guard replied shortly. It was nearly time and he was scanning the platform for any last minute hitches.

"You got your sandwiches ain't you?" David held them up to show Amy and Amy said, "Better be getting on then."

The carriage doors were all shut and the guard was checking his watch. "Come on, let's have you."

There were hurried kisses and David was helped inside, sitting in the shadow, silhouetted against the light. There were parcels stacked on the wooden floor within the wire metal cage built into the side of the coach and two cycles leaning against the carriage wall. The guard had a tall box against the bulkhead to keep his effects in and David's seat was a sealed drum close to the small window opposite the door.

They peered and craned to see past the guard but he was standing close to the open door, ready to get the train under way. He raised his flag, the whistle blew and the guard stepped nimbly aboard as it drew away. The door of the guardsvan closed and there was no point in staying to wave, but they stayed anyway and watched the train disappear round the curve. Then they went shopping.

The excitement soon wore off. David could see very little through the window and the guard didn't like him wandering about the van. It became a long boring journey. The guard was preoccupied with his own responsibilities. After establishing the discipline of keeping David sitting on his drum, he remained largely uncommunicative. David was in some awe of this remote man and the journey was relieved only by the burst of activity at the stations when parcels were tossed in or unloaded, and the small interlude of eating the sandwiches Amy had made him for the journey.

"Sheffield. This is your station next." The unexpected words from the guard broke the silence and David looked up and saw familiar buildings gliding by. The river and the footbridge across it briefly glimpsed, the sunlit street leading to grandma's. The back of factory buildings, black with soot and smoke. David stood at the window eager for the journey to end. Suddenly he was very happy to be home.

Lilly was at the station to meet him and David ran across the platform to her with his small brown suitcase banging against his legs as he ran. She took his hand and they walked through the bustle of the station to catch the bus.

"Your daddy's not back from work yet," she said. "We're having some dinner and then your daddy's going to bring mummy home. Here give us that suitcase."

"It's alright grandma, I can manage it."

Outside the station David smelled the brewery malting in the air. It was definitely a coming home smell. There was nothing like it in Worcester. There seemed to be more activity about the city too, as though the bustle from the station had spilled out into the streets.

"There's our bus look," Lilly said. "Come on, before he goes."

She needn't have worried, the bus wasn't due to leave until half past and it was only twenty five past eleven now but she was filled with irrational anxiety that it might leave early without them. Surprisingly it was almost empty and they sat in the front where they could see straight ahead through the window next to the cab.

"How did you like travelling in the guardsvan then?"

"Boring," David replied shortly.

"Oh well, never mind," Lilly said comfortably, "You're nearly home now."

"Where is mummy?"

The question should not have been unexpected but its suddenness caught Lilly unawares.

"She's going to be waiting for you at Aunty Marge's," she said and then added carefully, "She's been very poorly."

"What's been the matter?"

The further innocent question shocked her. Oh God, she suddenly

412

realised that David still didn't know about Dorothy's condition. She couldn't even be sure whether he knew that Dorothy had lost the baby. His questions were leading Lilly into dangerous areas and she didn't want to start answering them without Bill being there as well. Anyway, she reasoned, it wasn't her place to and she certainly didn't want to start discussing it on the bus.

"We'll talk about it when we get's home," she said firmly.

"But why are we going to Aunty Marge's? Why isn't mummy at home?"

"I've told you. She's been poorly."

"What's been the matter?" he insisted.

"You must wait until your father gets home from work. He'll tell you."

David was taken aback with the sharpness of Lilly's tone and he resigned himself to having to wait for his daddy to come home.

"Alright," he said, and wondered why grown-ups always made such a mystery of things. He was busy taking in the scene around him anyway. It was nearly six weeks since he had left to go to Aunty Ame's. But it all looked reassuringly the same as when he had left.

It was surprising what a short absence could do and a glow of pleasure came over him. Grandma's house was as warm as it always was, the oven was on and David smelled the familiar aromas in the house as if for the first time. The tea in the caddy, furniture polish on the soft yellow duster, the rich gravy simmering in the stew. Lilly busied herself with getting dinner ready for them all and David had to content himself to wait for Bill to come home. He went into the yard with his tennis ball and threw it against the wall to practice catching.

"Don't go away." Lilly called. "They'll be here any minute and then dinner'll be ready."

"I'm only in the yard," he replied.

Harold was the first in from work. "Hello whiskers!" he said. "You're back safe then."

"Yes. Here grandad catch." David threw the ball as Harold reached the door, but Harold was already unslinging his knapsack and shedding the old gaberdine mac he invariably wore to work, and he missed it.

"Butterfingers grandad," David called. Daddy wouldn't be long now and then, as soon as dinner was over they could go back home to mummy.

When Bill arrived David threw himself at him with a joyous shout.

"Hey mind. Steady on," was Bill's sober response. There was little room in him for abandoned high spirits and the exuberance of David's greeting was more than Bill was prepared for. "Come on in. Your dinner'll be ready. Then we've got to see about going home."

413

"Grandma says we're going to Aunty Marge's."

Bill turned and glared at him. "Grandma should keep her mouth shut!"

David watched his father enter the house in silence. Then he picked up his ball and followed him inside.

Dinner was subdued. There was very little talk around the table. David looked from one to the other as he ate. There was something wrong. It wasn't that dinner at grandma's was an event of great conversations. But neither was there this tension. It was as though each was waiting for the other to speak. And he felt they were watching him. Well, David knew he hadn't done anything wrong so what was the matter?

"Finished," he said. Bill was nearly finished too. "Are we going now?"

"Just sit still a bit." His daddy's reply was unexpectedly brusque. David swung his leg back on the chair and sat waiting.

"Cup of tea Billy?"

Bill looked up at the clock. "You'll have to be quick. I need some water for a wash."

Lilly rose from the table, ignoring Bill's short reply and gathered the plates. "You having one aren't you Harold?"

"Yes."

"What about you David? D'you want one?"

David glanced quickly across at Bill but he was ignoring him for the moment. "Yes please grandma."

Lilly went into the kitchen to put the kettle on and when she returned Bill was moving wearily from the table to sit on the settee.

"Come here David." Bill patted the cushion next to him. "Come and sit down here next to me."

David crossed the room and sat primly next to him. Lilly sat back at the table to wait for the kettle to boil and Bill turned David and said, "You know mummy was having a baby."

"Yes. Grandma says she's been poorly."

"Grandma says a lot of things." Bill looked across at Lilly and a mutter of exasperation escaped him. "Can't you wait until I get home to tell him mother!"

"I ain't said nothing," Lilly protested. "He just wanted to know where Dorothy was that's all."

"I can't trust you to do anything!" he said testily and turned has attention back to David. "Anyway mummy was having the baby but something went wrong and mummy became very poorly."

"Tell me what's wrong with her?" David cried.

Bill glanced at Lilly again but she was pretending to ignore him.

414

God this wasn't easy. "Well," Bill continued, "she had something the matter with her blood and the baby died."

David sensed them all looking at him. "Where is it now?" he asked.

"It's… been taken away," Bill said quietly.

"Oh." To Bill's relief David appeared to accept the explanation without further curiosity. Then he asked. "Is mummy alright now then?"

"I've just said…!" Bill sighed with frustration and bit the rebuke off his tongue.

Lilly and Harold sat and watched Bill trying to tell the story without embellishment and Lilly's heart went out to them both. There was little wonder Bill was so short tempered. It was enough to make him so.

Bill began again then paused. "Well…" He wanted David to know enough to understand but it wasn't necessary to go into a full explanation. "She's still poorly. We're going to see her in a minute. She's… quiet," he said. "She won't want you jumping all over her. Just speak to her quietly. It's made her…" Oh God this wasn't easy. He furrowed his brow in a search for the right phrases. "…she doesn't move about as quickly as she did before. And she speaks slower."

Was that enough explanation? He couldn't start going into eclampsia and what a stroke was, not with an eight year old. All he wanted was for David to be prepared to see that Dorothy was different to the way she used to be the last time he saw her. Bill glanced up at his mother and father. Lilly was looking at him with sympathy and Bill couldn't say why, but the idea of being deserving of his mother's sympathy irritated him! His father gave him a small nod of approval. Bill ignored them both and turned to David again and said, "Do you understand?"

"I think so."

Bill looked at David, trying to decide if he really did. It was so frustrating, there was so little reaction, just answers in monosyllables! It was as though the boy was being deliberately perverse. Or else he couldn't grasp the seriousness of what he was being told and didn't care enough.

"Well, mummy's in the hospital," Bill continued, looking at David's serious face watching him. Bill sighed. Why couldn't David make it easier for him!

"The hospital will be looking after her. But she's coming home to stay with us at the weekends. I've got to go and bring her home in a minute. But we're all going to Aunty Marge's first. Grandma will take you there while I go and fetch mummy. Then we're going home together."

"Why?"

415

"Why what?"

"Well you said the hospital's got to look after mummy."

"Yes."

"Why has she got to go back to hospital?"

"Because she needs to, that's why! Stop asking so many questions. Mummy's poorly, I've told you. You're not to be like this when we get home. Mummy needs peace and quiet. To help her to get better."

Again, an expression of wide eyed comprehension. "Oh."

"So you'll have to be quiet when you see her. No running about."

David continued to grapple with what Bill was saying and tried to make sense of it. But it was only about what mummy was like. It didn't really tell him what had happened. He wished he could picture what it meant, about mummy being quiet! And being slow! For David didn't really understand the implications of what Bill had said to him at all. How could he? Mummy was slow. Slow in her movements and slow to speak. What did it mean? They had said she was poorly. But 'slow' wasn't poorly! There were questions he wanted to ask but he couldn't work out what the questions were.

He heard his daddy saying, "Come on then, I've got to go. I'm not bothered about that tea mother. Can I have that water for a wash!"

"If you want to," Lilly replied. "We haven't got to go just yet anyway."

Bill disappeared into the kitchen and David said, "Can I go out to play then?"

"Go on then," Lilly said. "But don't go too far away. You've got to get ready to go to Aunty Marge's don't forget."

David went out with relief. There was so much to think about and he went up the road and through the privet onto the river bank, watching the slow water in the concrete channel bubbling down the shallow brick water falls. Why wasn't daddy more pleased to see him? Perhaps something had happened with Grandma Bracewell. But daddy ought to be happier now that mummy was back at home. Even if it was only for weekends.

After a while, when he had scrambled down the concrete from the bank to the lip of the water and followed it to the end of the culvert where the river resumed its natural course under the little wooden bridge David went back in to grandma's. He didn't want to be late and get into trouble again.

"Come on then, wash your face then it's time to get your coat on," Grandma said.

Grandad pulled a handful of loose change from his pocket and passed half a crown to David and grandma picked up David's case and said, "Here, carry this."

"Give her my love won't you David."

"Aren't you coming grandad?"

"No. Grandad's staying here. There's too many for tea as it is."

"Goodbye then David. Be a good boy won't you!"

Marge and Charlie were welcoming when Lilly and David arrived. Enid Bracewell was less so. The tiny living room was crowded with the table opened out to its fullest extent to get them all round.

"Here, come and sit next to dad," Marge said and Ernest Bracewell moved into the corner of the settee to make room for Lilly to sit down. "We'll have a cup of tea when Dorothy gets here."

Jean was filled with excitement at the thought of her Aunt Dolly coming. She was dashing about the room and David got caught up in the excitement too. It was great to be able to jig about without getting told off. Then they started playing hide and seek, getting under the table and around people's legs until Charlie said, "Go outside. There's no room to play that here. You'll have to be quieter than that when your Aunty Dolly arrives."

Marge started preparing tea and her mother began laying the table with plates and cups from Marge's cupboard in the wall beside the chimney breast.

"Can I do anything?" Lilly offered but Marge declined.

"You just sit there and talk to dad. There's not really the room when we've got a houseful."

She brought out a bowl of salad from the cellar head and then started picking the soft bones from tinned salmon, ready to put onto the dainty tea plates. Enid Bracewell began buttering bread.

"There's enough to feed the whole street I should think," Lilly said politely.

"There's trifle for after," Charlie said proudly. "Nobody makes trifles like Marge."

Marge smiled down at him, pleased to receive his compliment.

"Then we might have a sing song later. Like we used to. If we get cleared away and I can get to me piano."

There was a commotion in the yard, the sound of squeals and much running about. Marge pulled the lace to one side and peered through the window.

"Go and see what they're up to will you Charlie."

Charlie went to the door. Jean was jumping up and down and David was running back from the street at the bottom of the passage.

"It is!" he screamed. "It's them!"

"They're coming, they're coming!" Jean shouted, jumping and stamping her feet in excitement.

"Come here!" Charlie ordered sharply. "Calm down! Stop it."

"But it's Aunty Dolly!" Jean cried.

"Stop it!" Charlie repeated. "She doesn't want to see you like this. Remember what you've been told. She's not to get excited. Come on, in the house both of you and wait until she comes in."

Charlie turned to the family inside. "They're here. Just coming down the street."

"Oh!" Marge cried and pulled her apron off. She dashed to the mirror and put her hands to her hair. "How do I look? Here Charlie, stand to one side, let me see her." And Marge joined him on the doorstep, ready to greet her sister.

Charlie stepped down to the head of the passage between the houses and met Bill and Dorothy just as they were coming along it.

"Hello Bill," he said with a grin of welcome for Dorothy. "You got her here safe then."

"Look," Bill was saying to Dorothy, "there's Charlie, look."

Charlie stood back to let them pass and Marge threw her arms round Dorothy in a hug.

"Here you are then love. Welcome home. Come on, come on in. Dad move them cushions up a bit. Make room for her to sit down then. Come on Dolly. Come and give us a kiss then."

Lilly stood to make room for her. "Hello Dorothy," she said. She was unsure whether to kiss her or shake hands. In the end she did neither but indicated the seat she had vacated. "Come and sit down here love." With a rush of zealous love Marge and Charlie took Dorothy from Bill, led her across the room and sat her down.

Enid Bracewell stood at a little distance apart. She had been visiting Dorothy every day. Now she stood and stared coldly at Bill. And Bill, uncomfortably aware of her, busied himself with getting Dorothy comfortable in her seat. And through all the bustle of Dorothy's arrival they all, each in their own individual way, appraised her and tried to discern the difference in her.

Dorothy was wearing her lime green costume with the full pleated skirt and short box jacket. It was well cut and stylish and when Dorothy had worn it before she became pregnant, the skirt had swung provocatively about her as she walked. Now it didn't seem as though it fitted her properly. It was nothing to do with size, or that Dorothy's weight had altered dramatically. But now, even seated it was clear she lacked style in some way.

Marge stooped before her. "Now love. Would you like a cup of tea?"

Dorothy was looking without expression from one to another of the faces before her. She didn't answer and Marge looked up at Bill.

"I'm sure she'd like a cup of tea," Bill said.

There was a momentary pause as Marge rose to put the kettle on.

"Well what do you think Bill? Is she getting any better?" Charlie asked.

"It's difficult to say," Bill replied. "She's a little better I think." He turned to Dorothy. "Aren't you love?"

Enid Bracewell said with an expression of distaste. "How can you say you think she is better! She's the same as she always is!"

Bill tried to ignore the tone of her reply as best as he could, but it depressed him. And it hurt his pride and undermined his dignity the way 'the old woman' wasn't making any attempt to disguise her feelings in front of his mother and David.

And Dorothy was looking up at them too but it was a look without anticipation, just a reaction to the sound of conversation.

Lilly stepped in to lighten the tension which had suddenly arisen in the room.

"Where's David then? Where are you?" she called to him. "Why don't you come and say 'hello' to your mummy?"

David was standing at the table with Jean, trying not to stare. His feeling of excitement had evaporated. This was nothing like what he had expected. Mummy was different! Silent. Aloof. He felt nervous of her and it was making him feel ashamed.

"Yes! Come on." Bill turned and ordered David forward. "Now then Dolly. Look who's here then. Aren't you going to say 'hello'?"

Reluctantly David felt himself being pushed forward and he heard the sound of Dorothy's voice in reply.

"Hello." Her voice had no resonance; it was low and toneless, lacking the energy she used to have.

Bill drew David further forward. "You know who this is don't you?"

Dorothy looked at David but there was no recognition. Those dark eyes which had once been so beautiful were now blank and impenetrable. A deep sense of shock passed through David. She didn't know who he was! And then, with dismay came further realisation; neither did David recognise the person sitting in the chair. It was Dorothy's face but inside it wasn't his mummy. The rest of the family stood carefully watching.

Bill was saying to her, "This is David. Your little boy."

David rebelled at the words. He was not her little boy. That had been a dream for him and his daddy but this wasn't the dream. Something had dashed the dream away! He heard his name repeated and repeated again, two different sounds.

"It's David, come on, you know, your little boy. Say hello to him."

419

"David." He heard her voice but Dorothy wasn't looking at him. She was looking up at Bill and mimicking the sound of his name.

"David." She repeated his name and again he heard the empty voice. A glimmer of pleasure briefly lit her face with the success of repetition and then it disappeared and she sat passively with David watching her. He wanted to go away but the people all around were beaming their encouragement and he knew that somehow he was going to have to join in the slow and ghastly dialogue.

Slow! That word again. His daddy had said 'slow'. Now the realisation was beginning to dawn. It wasn't just 'slow'; it was distance too. There was a measureless void between the mummy he had seen in hospital the week before he went to Worcester and this remote, unknown person sitting in front of him. He felt another pang of guilt. Perhaps none of this would have happened if he had stayed close to her and not gone away. She might have kept the baby; she might not have become ill. And then she might not have forgotten him. But David didn't know how to help her to reach for the recognition that she lacked. The gulf of understanding was too great and the journey to span that gulf was too long. Was that what they meant by 'slow'? It wasn't just the physical activity, the speed of movement, alacrity of wit and comprehension. With a child's insight David knew there was not even a starting point for the journey from which to begin to span that gulf.

Bill was urging him forward again.

"Come on David. Come and say 'hello' to mummy."

David's heart cried out within him. Oh daddy why don't you see? She isn't my mummy now, she isn't! David felt the world reel about him. She was staring at him but there was cold detachment in her stare and he didn't want to go any closer but daddy was urging him on.

"Come on, come on David, hold hands, say 'hello'."

The others added their encouragement too, a cacophony of voices overwhelming him. "Come on Dolly, you know David."

"Say hello to him. He wants you to say hello."

"There, that's it, hold hands. See, he wants to hold your hand."

Bill was prompting Dorothy, lifting her arm and drawing it forward, insisting. "Come on David, take her hand, take mummy's hand, say 'hello'. Say 'hello mummy'."

David reached out and she clasped his hand in hers. It was dry and slender, and her fingers closed around his. He said, "Hello mummy."

Her head inclined forward as though with remembrance of something lost and faintly heard again, but the light of remembrance died, her face clouded and she frowned, searching for what had been there. All around them the family smiled their encouragement and Dorothy clung to David as though the touch of the child was a conductor

420

for her memory and she squeezed his hand and pressed it in hers with the intensity of her desire for remembrance. David tried to free himself from her but she grinned at him and increased her grip as he tried to withdraw his hand.

"Hello," she said, inclining her head again, desperate to cling to the memory that eluded her. "Hello."

"It's David," he heard his daddy saying to her. "Say David."

"David…" she echoed in the same dull voice. David turned with his mouth open in silent appeal to his daddy and tried to pull his hand free.

But so preoccupied was Bill with trying to force David and Dorothy into some sort of reunion before that audience that he insisted, "She won't hurt you. Say 'hello' to her. Ask mummy how she is."

The pressure of Dorothy's grip was increasing, she began to hurt him and David tugged at his hand to get free of her but she seemed unaware and held him tighter, drawing him to her, smiling at him and grinning.

"David," she repeated.

"Daddy she's hurting me!" David cried, tugging and tugging but the fierce grip was implacable and she wouldn't release him. David started to cry and Bill intervened and separated them.

David sprang from her, nursing his bruised hand and whimpering, out of reach and snuffling back his tears. He heard Bill admonish her for hurting him; he heard her saying, "Sorry," and repeating it with futility in the same toneless voice but there was neither understanding nor remorse in her eyes. Now David wished he had never come home.

CHAPTER 47

The trolley song

The weeks passed. Each weekend Bill brought Dorothy out and installed her in the family and they watched for signs that she was 'making progress', some indication that she was connecting with her past, restoring her intellect, returning to what she used to be. And each Sunday evening Bill returned her to the care of the hospital and reported any of the desperately sought for signs of improvement in Dorothy's condition. And the weeks became months and the months grew into a year and none of the signs amounted to any real change in Dorothy's condition at all. But still he continued to persist, obsessive in his determination to restore Dorothy, to see again the girl she had once been, the girl he had loved.

The antagonism of the Bracewells became unbearable. Bill went to his mother and tried to confide in her and Lilly tried to comfort him. She told him to 'try not to worry' and the futile platitudes increased the strains between them too.

"Well what can I say?" Lilly cried. "Every thing I says to you is wrong! If I could do anything to make her better I'd do it. You know I would. Me and your father. But what can we do?"

"Oh just leave me alone mother!"

Dismayed, Lilly and Harold saw that Bill was the one who changed. He became remote, an introspective figure. His irritability with David increased, and he became less tolerant of other people and their opinions. And meanwhile he continued to parade Dorothy amongst them each weekend.

His life became a round of 'bed and work' as he put it, with visits to the hospital sandwiched in during the week whenever he could make it. The signs of strain became permanent and he was beset with stomach pains. He became unable to enjoy a meal without recourse to Rennies and the chalky white tablet, which had always been Harold's standby for heartburn, became Bill's antidote to every meal he took.

"You ought to go to the doctors you know," Lilly said one Saturday. Bill had given up going back to the Bracewell's after work on Saturday morning. Instead he kept a change of clothes at his mother's and David caught the tram to join him there for dinner at grandma's.

Now Lilly had found Bill retching over the sink. But her well meaning concern met with rebuke.

"Oh shut up mother will you. Something I've eaten that's all."

"I seen you doing that before," Lilly continued. "Your dad was like that when he had his ulcer."

"Give over mother. You burned that meat. No bloody wonder we get heartburn. Ask me dad if he's got any Rennie's left will you." He leaned over the sink again.

"You ought to go across the yard to the lavatory if you're going to be sick."

"I'm not sick," he retorted. Another bout seized him and he bent heaving over the sink again, then looked up ashen faced. "Don't worry mother," he snarled at her, "I'll swill it down."

Lilly turned away and accepted her son's rebuke. She knew she hadn't burned his dinner. Not today nor any other day; she was too good a cook for that. But he just wouldn't listen. He'd always been the same. Not like George. You could have a sensible conversation with George. He didn't snap your head off all the time.

But the 'heartburn' grew more persistent and the retching turned to vomiting and Lilly insisted. "It's no good Billy, you'll have to go and see a doctor if it's that bad."

And Bill replied irritably, "Oh give over fussing mother! Go and make us a cup of tea."

But although Bill disdained to take his mothers advice he knew that she was right. It had happened at the Bracewell's too, only he didn't get the sympathy from the old woman that his mother gave him. All he got there was looks of disapproval when she caught him at her sink. It was becoming unbearable and he knew he would have to see the doctor sooner or later.

It was no surprise to the doctor. He knew the background with Dorothy and he sensed that Bill's temperament and anxieties would only aggravate the condition.

"You should have come to see me before this," the doctor said.

"I didn't want to trouble you. Not for a bit of indigestion."

The doctor sniffed his disapproval. "That's what we're here for."

"Well," Bill apologised lamely, "I know how busy you must be."

"Nasty things, duodenals," the doctor said, writing on his prescription pad. It would call for a strict regime.

"Are you sure that's what it is?" Bill asked with a sinking heart.

He had heard what his father had suffered as a young man; it had led to surgery and his discharge from the Light Infantry, the 'Shropshire's', before the first war. And a good job too, he thought on reflection. Still, Bill didn't relish the thought of an operation.

"Yes, there's no doubt. But," the doctor continued in a lighter tone, "it doesn't necessarily mean the operating theatre. Not these days. If you treat it right and look after yourself you can live with an ulcer."

"What do I have to do?"

"Diet. Oh I don't mean slimming or that kind of faddy thing. But you must eat food that won't aggravate it. Fish."

Bill's spirits lifted. He enjoyed fish and chips so that wouldn't be a hardship.

"But you must have it boiled, not fried. No chips, cut out fatty fried foods. Boiled in milk, that would be nice and bland. Tripe, but be careful of the onions. Do you drink?"

"I like a drink. Occasionally." Bill could see what was coming. Soon there'd be no pleasure left.

"You must cut out the drink. Anything you do have must be taken in moderation. You don't want to aggravate it. If it bursts, and you'll know if it does, you must get to a hospital right away." The doctor peered earnestly at Bill over the top of his glasses. "And in any case within twenty four hours."

Bill left the surgery depressed. He could just see the old lady's face when he told her. Oh his mother would be alright but Ma Bracewell would kick up an awful fuss about having to prepare meals to a special diet…

Marge and Charlie had a new television set, a Cossor with a nine inch screen and Dorothy became quite content to sit watching any programme that was on.

David's confidence around Dorothy had slowly recovered after the first disastrous reunion. She didn't make any effort to reach out and touch him, in fact she seemed to have no desire for physical contact with anybody. Neither did she attempt to join in conversation unless she was primed. She was quite content within her own limited world to sit and watch and smile incomprehendingly.

They had also learned after the first tea-time with Dorothy that her meals would need to be carefully thought out and supervised. The problem was that Dorothy had lost physical co-ordination. Watching her as she dribbled her cup of tea and spilled it they felt embarrassment and a rising sense of helplessness. Marge had leaned across and tried to hold Dorothy's cup to her mouth to prevent it spilling but Dorothy turned away and resisted Marge's hand, which only made matters worse. David and Jean shifted uncomfortably in their seats and tried not to look as she spooned her trifle clumsily and trailed custard and fruit across the tablecloth.

424

"Never mind," Marge said bravely. "It'll wash. It's only a trifle."

Marge's unconscious joke gave David and Jean an excuse and they laughed, not at Dorothy but out of a sense of relief.

"Hey you two," Charlie said sternly, "get on with your tea. It's not funny."

"I'm ashamed of you!" Lilly said to David. "You should know better at your age."

So on Saturday nights Dorothy sat with David and Jean with cake or a slice of pie if Marge had baked, or any other form of solid food that Dorothy could handle herself, oblivious to the talk around her while she watched a panel game or variety show.

David had begun to realise that provided Dorothy's attention was occupied she wouldn't trouble him and he could sit close by her without feeling nervous. He also knew that this was what his daddy wanted, to see the two of them sitting together like a happy family.

Over a few weeks they became increasingly aware of how much Dorothy looked forward to it. The first thing she did when she walked in to Marge's was to take her seat on the settee where she could see the television set, oblivious to whoever else was there. Perhaps this was the link they had been looking for, a connection to the days when she and Bill used to go to the cinema together.

Filled with trepidation one Saturday Bill and David took Dorothy to see a film. She walked with them into the cinema foyer without a qualm. Bill's anxiety about what might happen when the lights dimmed were unfounded and Dorothy sat in the darkness quite content. And when the film was over she stood to leave with the rest and at long last Bill felt the tension inside him lift. Here was something they could enjoy together as far as Dorothy was capable of enjoying anything for all they knew. And it took the pressure off Marge and Charlie too. The occasional Saturday visits to see a film became part of Bill's regime for Dorothy.

One Saturday evening, on their way back home to the Bracewell's from the cinema on the tram, Bill started to feel queasy. It had been raining earlier, a light autumn drizzle but now it had stopped leaving the wet pavements reflecting under the gas lamps. Despite the light breeze that was blowing along the street the tram was uncomfortably hot. It was full and most of the passengers were wrapped in raincoats and scarves against the earlier rain. The air was stale, it was jolting about more than usual and the claustrophobic atmosphere was aggravated by the strong dry smell of hot electric motors beneath the floor. Bill and David were sitting at the front on the long slatted wooden bench with Dorothy between them, rocking gently to the motion of the car, face to face with the passengers opposite and endeavouring to avoid direct eye contact.

Dorothy was answering in monosyllables as Bill and David tried to engage her in conversation.

"Did you enjoy it Dolly?"

"Yes."

"Wasn't the ending good?" David said eagerly, "Especially the bit where he fell off the cliff into the sea."

"Yes."

Dorothy's toneless replies carried above the small conversational murmur of the other passengers and both David and Bill were aware of the furtive glances of the people around them. It happened each time they were out and it was the only thing that marred the enjoyment of being able to go out with Dorothy together. Neither Bill nor David had ever got used to this prudish curiosity.

"Would you like to come and see another one next week? Dolly! Shall we come again next week? Would you like that?" Bill said.

Dorothy looked straight ahead at the passengers sitting opposite and they quickly lowered their eyes as she replied, "Yes."

David saw their eyes drop and he sat erect with emotional pride and all the defiance of a nine year old. It wasn't defiance of Bill or Dorothy but defiance of the other passengers and their sidelong looks. 'What do you know!' David silently cried. 'This is my mummy! She was lovely once and we are trying to make her well again. What are you looking at?' And he looked from one to another, staring them out. 'Well! – what are you…?' He moved closer to her side and stared round the car again as Bill continued to prime her with questions.

Suddenly Bill rose from his seat.

"Come on, bring your mummy," he muttered and he began to hurry off along the car towards the platform under the curious gaze of the other passengers.

David looked up at him with surprise. This wasn't their stop but he stood and tugged at the sleeve of Dorothy's coat.

"Come on mummy, we've got to get off."

Dorothy resisted and began shaking her head vehemently. She also knew instinctively that it wasn't the place where they usually got off.

"Come on," David insisted. The tram was at the stop and Bill was standing at the platform beckoning.

"No." Dorothy was quite implacable. Her toneless voice rose alarmingly and she began waving her arms in the air and pushing David from her. The other passengers stared and the ones nearest to Dorothy shuffled away in nervous disapproval, averting their eyes as David stood looking desperately to Bill for help. He ran to the platform leaving Dorothy where she was. Immediately Dorothy became quiet and sat composed, waiting for them under the watchful glare of the other passengers.

"She won't come daddy. She won't get off," David cried.

The conductor started to become impatient.

"What's going on? Are you getting off or staying on?" he demanded belligerently. He didn't know how to deal with passengers like Dorothy and he didn't want to have to. Besides, he had a timetable to keep and his driver was peering down the tram from his window at the front and gesticulating. The conductor reached up to push the bell.

"Wait, wait a minute, we're getting off," Bill demanded.

The conductor was about to tell Bill to make his mind up but there was something in the mans expression that was wrong and his voice had a strange, almost strangulated sound.

"Go and fetch her," Bill said desperately to David. He didn't feel as though his legs would continue to support him, he felt ill and hot and he pushed David roughly back into the car then stepped down into the road. Undecided, David hesitated then he ran back to Dorothy. She was still in her seat, sublimely oblivious to the muttering and stares of the passengers. The conductor reached for the bell again.

"Well are you getting off or what!" he called irritably. This situation was beyond his control and he wanted them off so that he could get on his way.

"Wait a minute!" David called anxiously. He was terrified in case he was left alone on the tram with Dorothy. "Come on mummy," he cried, "come on we've got to get off." She resisted him again and David tugged at her sleeve, coaxing and pulling at her as though she were the child instead of him, pleading with her and looking around desperately.

But the other passengers had seen enough; this young woman wasn't right, she was clearly mental and although she was only a slight thing nobody wanted to tangle with her. Well, you could never tell and she might turn nasty. So they looked on, and lowered their eyes with embarrassment as the child drew her down the car between them. At the platform Dorothy hesitated again and the conductor began muttering and moved onto the staircase, watching until David had her safely down the step and into the road under their disapproving eyes. Then the tram burst into chatter and condemnation and the conductor rang the bell with relief and it went on its way leaving them alone in the road, David with Dorothy in his care and Bill doubled up against the wall vomiting uncontrollably…

After six more months Dorothy started to become incontinent and after a couple of near misses in town the trips to the cinema ceased. If they were honest with themselves they could see that she wasn't making any progress; indeed if anything… But they wouldn't permit themselves to think about that.

And so they persevered even when, sitting at home amongst them with her air of bland innocence Dorothy soiled herself. And no-one was aware until the smell hit them. Then with a groan they sent David from the room and undressed her and washed her down and changed her underwear, stripping the covers from the cushions and carrying it all off at arms length in the bucket to soak.

They admonished her with increasing impatience.

"Why don't you tell us when you want to go? Dolly; Dolly! listen to me. Come on, be a good girl now. Look! You must tell us. You must know when you want to, eh. Why don't you? Just tell us."

And Dorothy, comfortable once more beamed at them and nodded, blank behind the brightness of her eyes.

And they said to each other, "I think she's got it this time. I'm sure she understands."

And they smiled encouragement at her and Dorothy smiled back at them. Until it happened again. And so the year went by and another Christmas loomed with tinsel sentimentality but without the joy it promised.

A conference with the medical staff at Middlewood was called. Enid and Ernest Bracewell sat with Bill and listened as the case for Dorothy's full committal to the hospital was outlined to them. They heard themselves congratulated on the dedication and patience they had shown. Enid Bracewell listened with her lips compressed. Then she watched the doctor address himself directly to Bill, persuading him that, despite the efforts by everyone concerned – and here there was an all embracing gesture to the parents and a sigh of resignation towards all three of them – there was nothing to be gained by continuing the visits home.

"Dorothy's treatment," he said, "ought to be continued solely within the confines of the hospital."

"I see."

Bill turned to look at Dorothy's parents but they made no gesture, no acknowledgement of his presence as they sat rigidly absorbing the impact of the pronouncement. Bill saw Ernest Bracewell's hand move and rest on his wife's upon her knee.

"Is there nothing we can do?" Ernest Bracewell asked.

Again the sweeping look across the three of them. "I think you have done – you have all done – as much, and more than most people are capable of."

Enid Bracewell murmured, "I see!" It was an echo of Bill's response, filled with bitter disappointment but it was no more than a breath.

428

The doctor inclined towards her.

"I beg your pardon?" he said.

But Enid Bracewell shook her head, small movements like tremors of pain, biting her lip against the quivering of her mouth and her eyes closed tightly to shut out the tears. She released her hand from her husband's and brushed her nose with a small white handkerchief.

"Is there nothing then?" Dorothy's father asked. His strong aquiline face looked drawn and defeated.

"Visits are important. She mustn't lose contact of course."

"I'll come every day," Bill said.

"Of course."

There was optimism and reassurance in the irresistible voice as it continued to ease the burden of the decision from Bill, from all of them. After all, new developments were taking place in neuro-surgery and psychiatric care and, "...who knows? Perhaps we'll see a breakthrough in Dorothy's case."

But the advice of the doctors on Dorothy's behalf was also heightened by their concern for Bill and his ability to continue caring for Dorothy outside.

Bill left Middlewood with the Bracewells, and they walked down through the hospital grounds as strangers. There was nothing he could say to them. There was nothing they wanted to say to him. They journeyed home in silence.

Bill sought refuge from them and went straight into his living room, the room he and Dorothy had set up as their home. He hadn't used it as a home for two years. Not a real home to relax and be happy in. Oh he'd taken his meals and shared the room with David and sat in it, out of 'her' way when he wasn't at the hospital, visiting. He looked around him. It was a place in limbo, devoid of life's colour, waiting for the time when Dorothy would return and life would begin again. The room was filled with their things, but they were just things. In reality it was empty. And so it would remain. He rebelled against the thought but... it had been Dorothy's home. Now it would never see Dorothy again.

The door from the adjoining rooms swung open. There was no preamble, none of the respect for privacy which until now had been preserved. Bill looked up as the door swung hard against the shelf bracketed on the wall with Dorothy's record player on it and Enid Bracewell walked in.

She stood looking at Bill with a calm steadiness that belied her feelings.

"I'll go and see her every day," Bill said gently. "She'll have whatever it takes, gifts, books. A television if she wants..."

"Get out of my house." Enid Bracewell's words were spoken

slowly and evenly, without threat or malice.

Bill felt an overwhelming sense of relief. He saw the years of unspoken hatred in Enid Bracewell's face. Now at last he could be honest. No more pretence; no more innuendo and the strain of living with unremitting disapproval.

"It was nobody's fault ma," he said. Calmly. Sadly.

Enid Bracewell's stare continued but her self control began to waver and her breathing started to become heavier and she screamed in uncontrollable rage, "Get out!"

Bill raised his arms as though in an involuntary act of self defence.

"Don't you raise your hand to me!" she cried. "How dare you! How dare you in my house. Get out…!"

"I wasn't," Bill protested. "David'll be back from school…"

"I want you out! Do you hear me? Out! Out! Out!" she screamed and the scream became suffused with tears and she leaned upon the door sobbing.

"Get away. Don't come near me…"

Ernest Bracewell appeared behind his wife and she turned and he held her and supported her against his shoulder. He looked at Bill.

"Did you…?"

"I never went near her," Bill protested, "I'm sorry," shaking his head. "I'm sorry. I'm sorry…"

"You've got to leave."

"I know."

"We want you to leave now."

"But David…"

"Gather his things and take him with you. You can come back for the rest later."

Ernest Bracewell turned and led his wife sobbing from the room.

Bill packed their clothes and went to the school to wait for David coming out.

"Come on," he said. "We're going to grandma's."

"What for?"

"We're going to live there."

"Oh we're going to go back to grandma's?"

"Yes."

There was no disappointment in David's voice. Kids! Bill thought. They just take it as it comes. This place one day, that place another day, nothing seems to matter when you're a kid. It's all play. That's all it is. Playtime all day long.

PART FOUR
JUDITH – 1957

CHAPTER 48

Visi d'arte

Lilly turned as the back door opened and saw David running in and heard his unexpected cry of, "We're coming back here grandma."

It was followed by Bill's voice calling to him from the yard. "Will you wait a minute!"

She was expecting Bill but not until after tea; he was due to come and tell her the latest news about Dorothy and what the hospital had said. Now she saw with some surprise that he had a suitcase and bundle with him.

"Why Billy!" she exclaimed. "Whatever's going on?"

"I'm coming back mother."

"What!" Lilly exclaimed, "Now?"

Bill tried to put a brave interpretation on it. "I can't live up there any more. I've had enough! We'll sleep in the back bedroom."

"Well you might have given me a bit of warning. 'Bed's not aired or anything." Clearly something had precipitated this sudden exodus but she thought better than to probe too deeply. She knew. For hadn't Bill been bringing his troubles home to her for too long now. There had been a row, there must have been and it wouldn't surprise her if the old woman hadn't thrown them out. And if that was the case Lilly was wise enough to know that Bill wouldn't want to admit it.

"Well you'd better take that stuff upstairs then." She said it with an air of inevitability both for herself and for the change in her son's circumstances.

"And what about Dorothy?" she asked when he was downstairs again.

Bill was standing against the mantelpiece, looking not at Lilly and David sitting at the table or Harold in his usual armchair, but at his own reflection in the mirror in a kind of narcissistic self examination. "She's going to stay in the hospital. Up in Middlewood." He spoke with resignation. "There's nothing we can do for her out here." Then he paused, conscious that David was listening attentively. "They've got some new treatments they're going to try," he said by way of reassurance but his expression belied the hopeful statement.

"Come on love." Looking at him Lilly saw the grief and

433

disappointment written in his face. He looked so exhausted. She was at a loss for anything to say to drive it from Bill's mind, to give him some respite. "I'll put the kettle on. We'd better get some hot water bottles in that bed to get it aired. Then we'll have a nice cup of tea."

"What about the rest of your things?" Harold asked. "What you doing with them?"

Bill's mind was in turmoil; things were moving too fast for him again and he hadn't had time to think it all through properly but some things were obvious.

"Furniture'll have to go into store until I can get something worked out. Perhaps our name'll come up on the housing list. God knows we've had it down long enough."

He sighed, a hopeless sound, almost like the expulsion of the last vestige of hope. He despaired of his life and it warped the self absorbed view he had of himself as he stood, with his son and his father and mother around him and mourned. Denied a home of his own, Bill mourned for the loss of wife, family, children. His ulcer was gripping him in pain again, incessantly nagging away at his spirit, flaring into bouts of vomiting and reducing him to a bland diet of boiled fish, tripe poached in milk, anything to keep it under control. It wasn't fair.

Within the following three months they were ready to try a radical form of treatment on Dorothy. David overheard grandma telling Mrs Short in the queue at the pork butchers.

"They're going to give her electric shocks."

"Oh, what's that for then?"

"They want to see if they can shock her into recognising things. You know."

"How d'you mean?"

Mrs. Short wanted all the facts and, as Lilly looked around to see where he was David pretended to be absorbed in something outside the shop.

Lilly shook her head slowly with the pain of the recollection and lowered her voice to a discreet stage whisper for the benefit of the people in the queue listening around her.

"Well the last time we saw her there she didn't know where she was poor soul, or who we were or anything."

"Ahhh." Mrs. Short shook her head in sympathy, prompting Lilly and ready to hear more.

"It's the latest treatment for this kind of thing." Lilly took Bill's translation of what the hospital had told him and added her own interpretation, gratified with Mrs. Short's attention and the attention of the queue. "They couple 'em up to wires. You know."

434

Mrs. Short nodded in incomprehension and said, "Oh!"

"Then they switches the current on."

"It's a wonder it don't kill 'em."

"Well of course they don't leave it switched on. I mean it would if they did that wouldn't it. Stands to reason."

"Its amazing what these doctors can get up to nowadays isn't it."

The queue shuffled forward towards the counter and Lilly continued, "If this don't work they don't think there's very much more they can do for her."

Mrs. Short muttered commiseration and asked again how Dorothy was.

"About the same. There's not much change. Our Billy goes up to see her every Saturday without fail. Never misses. I do feel sorry for him. He's had it rough."

Mrs. Short nodded in sympathy and there was a silent, discreet shaking of heads all around.

"And her mother," Lilly continued. "She's given Bill a terrible time. Blames him for everything. You should have heard some of the things she's said to him. And after all he's been through. He's been as good as gold he has." The queue surged forward again. "Still we might see some progress with this new treatment now. Six ounces of boiled ham Mr. Phillips please…"

David hadn't really expected to pass the eleven plus. Nobody had thought he would get to secondary school, let alone grammar school. Grandma had not said, 'You shall have a bike if you passes.' No-one had any expectation of him, least of all David himself. But unexpectedly David did pass and their pride in him knew no bounds. They insisted he had to write and tell Aunty Ame and David, who hated writing letters, dashed off a few unwilling lines then threw down the pen and set off to go out to play.

"Aint you got more to say than that?" Grandma demanded, looking at the few careless words on the page.

"But I'm going to be seeing her soon."

The summer holidays were imminent and David would be spending them at Worcester as usual. And at Aunty Ame's there would be no talk of Dorothy. She could be put from his mind, the mummy he knew he would never want to see again. And what a relief it was each summer to be away from grandma and grandad and the imposition of their rigid disciplines. And his dad, returning morosely from the never ending pilgrimages to Middlewood and demanding to be loved but now so mistrustful and incapable of showing love himself.

"I'm going out to see Earnshaw," David protested.

435

"Come and finish it off properly," Lilly insisted. "She'll think the world of it, come on."

"Aw whats up with it?"

"Well its not very neat for a start. And why don't you put her a few kisses on the bottom."

David obeyed sulkily and then dashed out to play leaving Lilly to fold his letter into the envelope with her own. Then she went round to tell the neighbours that David had passed his exams.

None of the other kids in the street had managed to pass and, as a consequence Lilly found hitherto unacknowledged scholastic achievements by which to explain David's success.

A few days later when Lizzie was returning a mixing bowl that she had borrowed, Lilly said, "Of course he's ever so good at history. Ain't you David? Knows ever so much about it."

David was reading with the total absorption he had cultivated that enabled him to become quite oblivious to what was going on around him but he heard his grandma's words of praise. Basking in the glow of the unexpected tribute he looked up and nodded.

"He can tell you all about different kings and queens," Lilly added, "King John and Henry the Eighth and all that."

"Fifteen o' nine to fifteen thirty six." David responded dutifully and both women beamed at him in benign incomprehension.

"Good isn't he," Lizzie offered and Lilly smiled down at him.

And as he looked at them smiling their approval down on him David realised with a shock that he could have said anything and neither of them would have known whether he was right or wrong; they hadn't a clue. It felt as though grandma was smiling at him for performing some kind of duty, a trick to impress the neighbours. His sense of pleasure vanished; he returned to his book feeling, in some strange way, insulted by their ignorance, and grandma claiming the credit of some of his knowledge for herself.

In a perverse way David's winning of a place at Secondary School was sufficient achievement in itself as far as the family was concerned; it was an end rather than a means to a different end. But they made David feel that he was lucky to be there at all amongst the clever kids and in a strangely insidious way it undermined his confidence.

He began to feel out of his depth, unable to keep up and he struggled at lessons and lost interest in those he couldn't understand. He had always been competent at drawing and the family had remarked constantly upon it. Now he found himself amongst others who were equally competent artists and draughtsmen. David no longer excelled where he expected to and to this insecurity at school was added the latent insecurity deriving from all the changes at home. It wasn't

436

sudden; it evolved. Grandma was good. She was fair but old fashioned. And her house, in which as a younger woman she and Harold had brought up their own two boys was now too small and cramped to share with a young family.

"No, you can't have the kids in from out of the street to play. If you wants to play in, go to their house."

On reflection perhaps it was only right and David tried to reason it out to himself. The house, two up two down, was small and grandma and grandad had had it to themselves all these years and didn't want it invaded by all the kids in the street. But the other kids noticed.

"You never let us come into your house to play. Well clear off. You can't come in our house either."

David became sensitive to innocent remarks; and jokes about mental illness and lunatic asylums, which in other circumstances he might have shared in, now goaded him into angry protests. The other kids picked this up and taunted him even more until the self inflicted torment became unbearable. It carried echoes of ten years earlier, forgotten memories buried deep in David's subconscious mind, the little kids in a ring on the pavement surrounding the dirty child with the rash on his face and the unwashed smell of stale urine, screaming at him, pointing their fingers and taunting…

"Shut up! Shut up will you!" David yelled at the gang with futile anger mounting in him. "It's not fair. You wouldn't like it. You wouldn't like it if your mother was in an asylum."

"Aw shut up yourself. Can't you take it? Nobody meant owt did they? Mardy arse."

"You wouldn't like it if it was your mother."

"Aw shurrup. You're always going on about it."

"No I'm not. It doesn't matter. Anyway, there's no need for you to go on like that. So shurrup yourself then."

"Who are you telling to shurrup?"

And when the challenge came, as it usually did David subsided into resentful silence. He pushed the anger away.

"I'm not telling anybody. I'm just saying that's all."

"Come on then! Want to tell us to shurrup do yer. Eh! Eh!" Then the pushing started as they tried to goad him into fighting. He had tried fighting but they were all better fighters than he was.

"Give over will you. I were only saying. Get off Earnshaw! Tell him Cartwright. Get him off – get off will you…"

And occasionally it did end in an unsatisfactory fight where no-one really hurt anyone else. Apart from a swollen lip, or a bruised eye. But the loss of his self esteem had to be regained and that was the greatest hurt of all.

Enduring the taunts of the other lads at school was more difficult for there David was subject to the imposition of greater discipline and self control. And his tormentors indulged themselves whenever they chose where he was most vulnerable.

The class was moving down the corridor, filing along in pairs with prefects and masters posted at intervals to enforce their silence en route to the next class. David was paired with Styring with whom he had little in common. And Styring began to whisper in a sing song way, "Whose mother's in Middlewood? Who's mother's in Middlewood?"

David turned to him and Styring was grinning as he repeated the jibe, challenging David to try to make him stop. David clenched his teeth and muttered, "Stop it!" and Styring did it all the more.

"Shut up there," a prefect called.

The two boys looked straight ahead and Styring began again.

"Shut up or else…" David hissed.

"Or else what? Mummy's little boy! Little tinky boy."

David clenched his fists and Styring, knowing he was safe from attack turned the taunting into a continuous, sibilant mantra, repeating and hammering into David's brain. David looked straight ahead with the grinning Styring hissing his insults at his side. And David knew, although he had never really hit anyone, that all he had to do was turn with his clenched fist and punch Styring in the face with all the force within him to send him sprawling unconscious to the floor. For the pent up years of anger would all be released in that one blow at the tormentor at his side. He turned and Styring paused at the expression in David's eyes; it was a look he hadn't seen before in anyone and Styring knew in that instant that David was going to hit him hard. And David realised it too and had a picture of Styring sliding across the floor of the corridor from the force of the punch he was about to unleash. And David also saw clearly the masters' reactions and his father's, and the retribution that was bound to follow just for the pleasure of that one annihilating blow. And that ultimately he, David would be the loser. And he said to Styring instead,

"Just shut up, that's all."

And he continued to walk, trying to block out of his mind Styrings gleeful resumption of, "Who's his mummy's little boy then? Mummy's little tinky boy! Mummy's little tinky boy…"

What did the other kids know? Sometimes David felt special as though he had been chosen like a hero of old who must survive against insurmountable odds and fight through great adversity to win fame and fortune. For somewhere deep within him lay a bright and burning optimism carrying him forward to his destiny. David's was a land where play blurred reality and his layers of fear were hidden beneath this landscape. He created a world about him, nurtured by his imagination; a world of heroes and true knights, populated by the force of evil where dragons stirred in the darkness of their lairs and you must forever be on guard. For he had seen things and done things which others had not. He had confronted evil and seen what the malicious hand of fate could wreak upon the innocent.

But to those who bothered to look, David's world appeared to be one of blithely rushed homework, forgotten homework and playing his way through school without any serious thought except when, as periodically happened he was brought before the masters for poor work. Then the unsympathetic world fell about him with detention and lines and trying to catch up and ever falling behind...

Bill decided that it was time David learned to defend himself.

"Come on." Bill got down on his knees on the hearthrug. "I'll show you how to box." He put his hands up in a boxers attitude but with open palms instead of fists. "Come on, try and hit me."

David tried. He raised his fists but his reach wasn't long enough and he couldn't get close enough to land a blow. And meanwhile Bill inflicted sharp, snaking slaps to David's head and arms while he taunted him to 'Come on, hit me, hit me. You're not trying.' Slap! And then another.

"I am trying," David cried and rushing forward again he received further jolts and slaps.

"No wonder the other kids push you around." Slap! Another hand found its mark. "Aw come on, don't give up! You'll never get anywhere if you give up that easily!"

Another futile rush, repelled with ease.

"Oh I give up. I can't be bothered with you. You're no good."

Bill climbed off his knees and returned to his chair.

"But I want to dad. I want to learn how to fight."

David wanted above all to know the secret of being able to inflict instead of perpetually receiving.

"Perhaps tomorrow." And Bill ignored him.

There were more attempts and more humiliations. The defensive posture that his dad showed him didn't ever seem to work for him. No matter how David held his arms crossed in front of his body Bill always shot an arm through and landed another humiliating slap with a laugh and a cry of, "Come on then, do as I showed you and then you won't get hurt."

And then a chance shot of Bill's caught David on the nose and drew blood. David stood in surprise with his mouth open, his nose filling and an ache rising behind the bridge of his nose. Even the lads, when they ganged up, didn't draw blood, not like this. He looked at his hand as he drew it away from his face and the blood was running on it.

"Oh Billy you should be more careful," Lilly said and she led David off into the kitchen.

"He should learn to defend himself properly and then it wouldn't happen," Bill called after them without remorse. "That's what this is supposed to be all about."

Lilly stanched David's nose with a cold cloth and made him hold his head back. After a short while the bleeding stopped.

"There now," she said to him. "That's better. It's not bleeding now. How do you feel?"

"I'm alright thanks grandma," David replied nasally. And an overwhelming anger rushed over him. How dare his daddy hit him and hurt him like that! David turned away from Lilly's hand and rushed into the living room. Bill was back in the chair by the fire. Before he had chance to look up and see the figure coming at him David punched Bill in the face. Bill recoiled with a cry and Harold looked up at the noise. David's punch had caught Bill full under the cheekbone. Bill nursed his teeth gingerly; he looked at David and there was anger blazing in his eyes.

"How dare you come and hit me like that!"

David began to cry at the enormity of what he had done. "But you made my nose bleed daddy."

"You shouldn't come rushing in like that, lashing out! You could have had my eye out or anything."

Harold, watching the two of them wryly said, "Well you wanted him to learn how to fight didn't you?"

But, waiting somewhere, there was bound to be retribution.

David didn't get the bike for passing the eleven plus. That was just another unfulfilled promise. He had to wait another year for the bike but it was worth it when it came, a black drop handlebar racer. But why did they always have to go on at him about cleaning it all the time! Lilly had been on at him for days.

"It's a disgrace, a nice bike like that. Your father'll be mad when he gets home if you haven't done it. Lovely new bike like that and you don't care about it."

"Grandma I've got my homework to do."

That had to be dashed off or there'd be trouble again. Not that he was keen to get to grips with it. He hated it. Chemistry and Physics. Boring! He wasn't any good at it anyway. And he couldn't understand the maths and Old Todge just kept going on and there was never any time to see how he'd reached the answer. English was alright but History? That was just dates. What about all the reasons why all those different things happened to people?

He got the rag and pushed it resentfully over the accumulated grime on the wheels and round the pedals. It wouldn't shift, it was too bound up in oil and now his hands were all greasy. He should have done it before when grandma told him to but it always took so long and there wasn't time when the lads were waiting. He pushed and rubbed harder, the metal pedal spun and took the skin off the knuckle of his finger joints. God that bloody hurt! And blood was running into the oil on his fingers. Despite the pain he watched the interesting mixture of the red over the black grease. David sucked his teeth and shook his hand. Oooh! It did hurt! But at least he could pack up cleaning it now.

"What've you done?" Lilly asked seeing the grimace on his face as he walked in.

David shook his hand and held up the finger, now freely running with blood to show her.

"Careful," she said, "You'll have blood all over. Here, you'd better wash it."

She made a space for him in the sink.

"I'll get you a piece of clean cloth to wrap it with."

"Thanks grandma."

After a few days the finger was no better. Normally his grazed knees and the sundry other minor injuries he accumulated while out playing healed up quickly. The finger did not and the area around the finger joint started to become red and inflamed. David was wearing a sticking plaster over it but the plaster was an obscene looking thing, grimy and frayed and hanging loose over the wound.

"Come on," she said wearily, "let's have a look at it."

She peeled the plaster off and David winced. Beneath it his finger joint was an open wound congealed with puss.

"Here. Let's get it cleaned up and I'll get you a clean rag."

David winced again as she went to wipe it. "I'll do it, I'll do it," he yelped.

"You'd better show it your father when he comes in," Lilly said and got on with cooking their tea, leaving David gingerly dabbing at his finger...

"It wants sterilising," Bill said when, under Lilly's insistence, David showed it to him.

"How do you mean?" David asked with trepidation.

"Salt's the best," Bill said. "It's what they used to put on sailors backs after they'd been lashed."

441

David's heart sank. He remembered seeing a pirate film where, after a mutiny a sailor had been tied to an upright grating, his shirt torn from his back and then lashed with the cat o'nine tails. The man sagged onto the deck after the punishment and had needed to be carried below deck for treatment where a shipmate had scattered a handful of salt over the man's bleeding stripes. The man had immediately arched in pain and raised himself on his elbows and let out a shriek.

And Daddy wanted to put salt on his finger!

"I don't want you to do that daddy."

"It's got to be done or you'll get a poisoned finger."

David shook his head vehemently. "Don't! I don't want you to do it!"

"But it'll have to be cleaned first," Bill went on relentlessly. "Is there any water in the kettle mother?"

"I'll have a look."

Lilly went into the kitchen.

"Put us some on if not," Bill called after her.

When she returned to the living room Bill asked her for a needle.

"What are you going to do?" David asked fearfully.

"I've told you. It's got to be cleaned."

"No daddy don't."

"You'll have to have your finger off if you don't!"

David's breathing started coming in gasps. What was daddy doing? What was going to happen? He didn't want to be hurt. He shook his head, repeating, "No daddy. Don't. Let me do it. Let me. Please."

The kettle was boiling and Lilly passed Bill a needle from her sewing box.

"Come on," Bill ordered. He took David into the kitchen and stood him by the sink while he poured the boiling water into the bowl.

"Come here, let's have another look at it."

Bill raised David's hand to peer at it and David flinched away.

"Come here!" Bill ordered testily. "I'm not going to hurt you."

He took David's finger between his own and touched the area of inflammation around it. David bit his lip, sucking in his breath with the anticipation of pain.

"Don't be so silly!" Bill admonished him. "I haven't touched you yet."

"I'm scared of what you're going to do."

"I'm not going to hurt you. You don't think I'd hurt you do you?"

David looked down at the sink. Steam was rising from the water in the bowl and he could feel the severity of the heat rising from it.

"But that water. It's hot," David pleaded.

"It's got to be hot to kill the germs."

442

Bill took a cloth, dipped it into the steaming water and wiped it across the puss filled wound. David yelled and tried to pull away but Bill held his finger firmly in his grip.

"Don't do that," Bill said, "or I will hurt you! Keep your finger still."

David winced and whimpered and although his finger was still the rest of his body was writhing. "Oh oh oh oh…" he cried.

"Oh stop being silly," Bill said.

They both peered at the finger but despite wiping the cloth across it the puss had barely been disturbed and was still in the wound, covering the healthy flesh they could see over the knuckle bone below.

"Ah. Mmmm. Right," Bill said with the air of one coming to a decision.

He took the needle and lit the flame on the gas ring.

"What you doing?" David asked fearfully.

"It's to kill the germs."

David watched as the needle tip briefly glowed red then incandescent white as Bill removed it from the flame.

"No, no!" David cried. "It's hot."

"It won't be. It cools down straight away."

"Let me feel!" David begged.

"No! Don't touch it! Or I'll have to put it in the flame again."

Delicately Bill inserted the tip of the needle in the yellow matter and began to puddle and tease the puss out. David screamed at Bill to stop as the needle pricked into the live wound, pressing against the bone.

"Nearly done," Bill said and David shrieked and danced in his grip.

David could not believe the delicacy of the torment as Bill pricked and probed with admonitions to David to, "Stand still then I won't hurt you."

Now the salt. David watched, stricken with the pain in his finger as Bill reached for the salt cellar.

"No don't," he whimpered again but Bill poured a liberal sprinkling over the bleeding red wound and David cried out again…

At last it was over. A clean dressing was put on and David nursed the throbbing finger and prayed that it was going to get better.

"There," grandma said. "You should have washed it nice and clean when you first done it."

443

CHAPTER 49

Into the shadows

David was thirteen when he ran away.

He was outside in the backyard cleaning his bike while Lilly got tea ready. It was early spring and a cool March wind was blowing along the back of the houses in the yard. Through the lace curtains behind the steamed over windows David could see grandma moving about in the kitchen. There was an air of enviable comfort within, seeing the kitchen like that with good food being prepared and grandma, competent, warm and secure. Yes! The thought made David pause – that was it. Grandma was secure in her life. And seeing her at that distance, indistinct through the glass and steam he suddenly realised a great sense of isolation and he wanted, oh! how David wanted someone to hold him securely in their arms and cuddle and kiss him and take all his cares away. But grandma would laugh at him. Not because she was insensitive or unkind, but because she was matter-of-fact and practical and it would make them both embarrassed.

Cleaning the bike was always such a fiddly, tiresome job with his bowl of cold water and the bit of rag that got more and more oily going round the rims, round the spokes, round the frame, round everything! And he couldn't do the job properly and thoroughly because he remembered how treacherous the bike was and how capable of injuring him. And the spring light was fading and the evening was growing gloomy and cold.

It wasn't that having to clean the bike was the last straw. No it was nothing like that. It wasn't that David was afraid that his father would come home and find the bike hadn't been cleaned. But he was lonely in the cold backyard with the dirty water and the rag in the failing light.

And it wasn't that a conscious decision was suddenly taken. It was more like the inevitable unfolding of events. He didn't want to leave grandma. He didn't want to leave his dad, for despite the edginess of his father and the constant irritability David still loved him and wanted to be loved. But David's life was filled with shadows and he couldn't escape from them here. He had one-and-three in his pocket and the lamps were on the bike. So David left the bowl of water and the oily rag where it was and pushed the bike out of the yard and into the terrace with a careful backward glance at the kitchen door and simply rode away to Worcester.

How brisk and suddenly refreshing it was. Within fifteen minutes he was at the outskirts of the city, passing the road where the Bracewells lived and breasting the climb to Meadowhead and the woods in the park where the Secret City used to be, where he had roamed when they had all lived there together. Now David faced the open road and the tyres were singing beneath him and the breeze was rushing by his head, clearing it of anxiety and worries.

Won't Aunty Ame be surprised! Wonder what she'll say? David pictured her welcome, the look of delight and the warmth in her smile as she holds out her arms and hugs him.

'Why look who's here then! What brings you here?' No anger, no criticism, only love and shelter. And he will talk to her and tell her of his fears and the problems he has left behind and she will make arrangements and he will stay and dad will come to see him sometimes and the world would be – could be – a happy place again...

Soon Chesterfield will be coming into sight and then where to? On the train they used to go through Derby so that must be the route. Just as long as he kept going south and when he got to Birmingham he would know he was nearly there. David gave no more thought to grandma or dad except, when he got there he would write and then they would know that he was alright. Anyway he hadn't been gone long yet; they would probably think he was round at Mick's or somewhere.

Steadily David pedalled away into the night preoccupied with his thoughts. Mummy and all the plans they had made together had vanished as though they had never existed. Normality had been snatched away despite all that they could do. A cruel intervention by fate. Now the reality was a warped continuation of an earlier theme in his life but more shattering in its intensity. David pedalled to escape, as though physical distance was all that was needed. But although the road was long and the distance from home was increasing, the phantoms of his past were following. He was certain he could still see them in the darkness just beyond his shoulder, swooping over fields and hedges, grinning at him from the roadside ditches; at his heels and at his back, cold and ever present within and all about him, images and memories he rejected and tried to push away but they were always there unbidden, haunting him. Mummy was gone! All her love and gaiety was gone too, only the dreadful shadows remained.

At Chesterfield David had his first doubts. He should have stayed and had his tea first; he was getting hungry. The temperature was dropping and although the pedalling was keeping him warm his hands were numb with cold. He wished he had gloves. But at least he had

445

reached Chesterfield. Now he was well on his way. The streets of the town were deserted and the shop windows had a cold and lifeless air. David remembered he had been here once with his dad and Dorothy, to the pictures. It had been a real treat, something special, worth catching the bus all the way from Sheffield for a night out at the pictures. It had been cold then too, just like tonight but they had been cosy in the warmth of each other's company. David relished the memory and pressed onward with renewed heart. Why, he could continue like this for hours before he needed to rest.

A signpost flashed by and from the corner of his eye David saw a sign that said Birmingham. Birmingham? Wow! He must have covered more distance than he thought. It took longer on the train. Perhaps the train went on a more roundabout route to call at other cities on the way! It won't be long now. There was another signpost ahead. David didn't want to break the rhythm of his pedalling but he had to know for certain how far he had to go. He slowed as he approached the finger post. 'Derby 28'. What! Disbelief filled David's mind. Derby was miles before Birmingham! Another 28 miles? But what about the sign for Birmingham he had seen? He wished he seen it more clearly then he could be sure. Uncertainty dogged him as he pedalled on. Perhaps he'd read the figures wrong in his haste. Was it 18 to Derby? Or had it been a 12? Another signpost showed beneath a street lamp. It read, 'Derby 26'. And beneath it, although he didn't have time to register how many miles it said, the word 'Brimington'!! He should have known. Now the slopes began to tire him and the road ahead seemed endless in the dark. Never mind! He tried to bouy himself up with anticipation of the welcome he was going to get from Aunty Ame. It was going to be worth it.

Now David was getting hungry. He should have stopped for some chips in Chesterfield but it was too far behind for him to turn back now. There was nothing in sight on the solitary road and with the dawning realisation that Derby wasn't even half way David wondered how long it would be before he could get anything to eat.

There were lights up ahead but a long climb to get there. It was Clay Cross. The distance was diminishing slowly as David slogged up the hill and he was cold and hungry. Again the town looked empty and deserted as he entered the main street as though it was closed for the night. But there was a chip shop and the smell filled the air. David felt a surge of relief. Wearily, stiffly he climbed from the saddle and rested the bike against the grimy paint of the window. He checked his one-and-three again and worked out what he could afford from the price list chalked above the steaming pans. The chip shop owner served him his fishcake and chips and a buttered breadcake with sullen disinterest. Trade was slow; always was on a Wednesday night. It was almost worth not opening at all on a Wednesday; it hardly covered the cost of the gas. Meanwhile along the road, in the shelter of a shop doorway out of the chilly breeze with his rapidly cooling parcel of chips, David was considering his future.

All he ever wanted was to escape from his troubles and go back to Aunty Ame's and the sunshine days of summer. But now it was getting late and the way was long and dark, he was tired and Worcester was so far away. He felt disloyal and confused. He knew that Aunty Ame loved him. But didn't dad love him too? And grandma? And now there would be more trouble. What would they say! And what about Aunty Ame? Would she open her arms to him and keep him or scold him and send him back? What would...? what would...? There were so many imponderables and no way forward only back. Back to Sheffield and to his past, to grandma and grandad, stern and just. Back along the dark road to dad with his duodenal and overwork and worry and his pilgrimage every Saturday with no end to it and now his son had run away from home. Ingratitude added to tragedy! David filled with guilt. He loved his dad. He wished he could love him more, as he used to love him when they were just the two of them planning for the future they would have together. But Dorothy's misfortune had come between them and dad had been changed by the strain of maintaining hope in the face of hopelessness. And meanwhile David had begun to slip away, the living forsaken in pursuit of a remembered dream year upon weary year.

And in their goodness of heart grandma and Bill had wanted to protect David so they tried to carry on as normal and they deflected his questions and refused to discuss Daisy with him – "One day. When you're old enough." But what about Dorothy – "my mummy. My new mummy." He wasn't old enough to understand, they said. They refused to consider the possibility that a child of David's age might have some understanding. How could they know that knowledge, not ignorance, was the healer? And a gulf of silence had descended.

Now David stood in indecision in the cold shop doorway and his thoughts increasingly turned to home. But every milestone back along the road seemed to carry him back into the memories so carefully hidden in his mind, those memories of three years ago, like a landscape shrouded in mist where things known cannot be seen. 'But they are there,' David cried wretchedly, 'they are there! Only why won't someone explain them to me...'

After three sessions of electro-therapy some new social stimulus had been considered beneficial to reinforce Dorothy's treatment and although Dorothy wasn't well enough to leave the hospital she was able to receive visitors so they had decided that Dorothy would benefit from a visit by David. After all she had loved David and perhaps a connection might still be made. Besides, David was now ten and it was almost a year since he had seen her. If left much longer she might forget him entirely. The time had seemed appropriate and he was to make the visit in the company of his father.

Hand in hand with Bill, David walked through the extensive hospital grounds, along drives that seemed to meander through lawns planted with laurel and rhododendron bushes. Signposts at intersections guided visitors to the different hospital departments. The buildings were low and David looked about him at the sheer diversity of disciplines carried out in the hospital.

Bill entered the reception area with the air of one who was familiar with both the establishment and its staff and they nodded to him in familiar greeting. "Won't keep you a minute. This your little boy then? What's his name? David? Oh that's a nice name. Hello David. Shan't keep you a minute."

They were ushered through a door, then a second, and the doors were re-locked behind them and the atmosphere of the hospital closed around them, pale and unsympathetic, lacking the colour of the world outside. Intermittent sounds came to them from solitary rooms, vague sounds, indistinct as though not just the people but the building itself had forsworn its identity and entered a timeless limbo from which there was no return.

David gripped Bill's hand firmly and followed him along a shining corridor into a waiting room, long and rectangular with fixed benches running the length of the cream painted stone walls. Some patients were already seated, waiting in the care of discreet white coated staff for their visitors to arrive. As Bill and David passed along the front of the bench they leaned out, sometimes with a low unintelligible sound, peering at them with angular inquisitiveness, momentarily distracted from their otherwise passive indifference.

David felt panic rising. He was trapped, locked inside this strange malevolent room. He tried to fight the panic down and looked only ahead, not looking round or making any sign of contact, clinging to Bill's side. They reached a vacant area on the bench and David sat cringing with Bill's arm around him, making himself as tiny as possible and keeping well away from whoever else was sitting near him. Keeping his head lowered he stole a furtive look around the room.

The people were strange and disfigured; some were unable to make a coherent sound and made odd gutteral noises while others, driven to movement, were rocking like metronomes, obsessed by some inner rhythm. The whole room seemed to be filled with disconcerted sound and movement, alien to anything that David had experienced. He felt uncomfortable and hot, the whole room was stuffy and hot! There was no freshness, just the stale smell of the institution, vaguely reminiscent of an abandoned kitchen. Terrified, he lowered his head and retreated further into the shelter of Bill's arm.

A nurse was bringing Dorothy across to them. She was shuffling along in carpet slippers and a long white hospital gown that reached down to her calves. David quickly raised his eyes to her as she approached and looked away again, and then sat transfixed with dismay. There was no recognition in her dark eyes, just a vacant lifelessness as she came across the room towards them.

"Sit down Dorothy," the nurse ordered in a tone that was gentle but uncompromising and Dorothy turned and looked at her nurse. David held his breath; there was a moment's reluctance. "Dorothy, sit down. Sit down, just here. That's a good girl."

The hesitation passed and the nurse sat Dorothy next to Bill on the side opposite to David.

"She looks a little better this week Bill. What do you think?" the nurse said brightly with a smile at Dorothy.

"Yes I think so," Bill replied and it was a voice of denial, a voice that tried to deny reality, a voice that tried to say, 'tell her she is well and she will become well'. David had heard Bill use that voice before in reply to people who asked him how he was. "I'm fine!" The answer was made in a way that defied the enquirer to take issue; short barking phrases. 'I'm coping really well, really well! They can't get me down. Not me! I'm coping, I'm doing better than that, I'm fine, just look at me. Fine! Look!' And here Bill would draw himself erect in the manner of someone showing off their physique And the people looked and saw the strain that he denied; they saw the stubborn refusal to accept that he couldn't cope and that he was one who needed help as well. The nurse gave him a knowing look and, retiring a little distance away, hovered discreetly.

Bill turned to Dorothy. "Hello Dolly. Hello love. Look who's come to see you then; look who's here. It's David. You remember David don't you?" He coaxed her earnestly. "You know him; of course you do. Yes you do."

Bill turned to David and eased him forward from under his arm. "Come on David, say hello to mummy."

David held back.

"Now come on, don't be silly," Bill insisted, "she's alright, she just wants to say hello to you." But David turned his head away.

Dorothy was shaking her head slowly and she began swaying slightly from side to side in rhythm to the movement of her head. Now her face had an anxious expression and on each sway Dorothy

449

murmured, "NO… no… no…"

Bill became more insistent. He was desperately aware that this was probably the only chance he would have to bring David out to see her.

"Yes Dorothy," he said. "Come on. Now don't be silly." He half turned in his seat and tried to ease David forward again. "Say hello to her," he commanded. "Say hello to your mummy. She's alright!"

"Hello mummy," David muttered and retreated back under Bill's arm again. But there was no recognition, only Dorothy's vacant look and the steadfast repetition, "No… no… no…" as she rocked back and forth and gazed fixedly at somewhere beyond their comprehension.

David felt oppressed by the room and the people in it. He was in a nightmare world beyond his control. He felt his dad start to move his arm around his shoulder to bring him forward from his hiding place.

"Now come on and stop being silly," Bill said and there was the hint of impatience in his voice. He pushed David and held him forward. David looked up at Dorothy and immediately recoiled in horror. Dorothy's hair, once so sleek, once so carefully set and curled, had gone. All that covered her head was a mat of short hair; it was dark and spiky like a brush and David was shocked at the clarity of her hairline, so precise across her brow. But what shocked him into retreating, distressed and whimpering beneath Bill's arm, were the two scars on narrow strips of Dorothy's shaven white scalp either side of her head above her temples. The wounds were red and vibrant against the whiteness of her skin. It seemed to David that they were throbbing. Horrified, he tried to look again as if he needed the reassurance of seeing what he had seen but he couldn't bring himself to look at her. Where was the mummy he had come to see? Why had he been brought here? He was afraid of this place and its people. He was afraid of what they had done to his mummy, the mummy who had once loved him so. But now she looked at him without seeing him, making sounds he couldn't recognise.

Dorothy was growing agitated. She wanted to take her slippers off. Bill tried to put them back on for her but she resisted and pushed his hand away and her swaying became more insistent. David leaned forward and peered at her, filled with dismay as Dorothy's wilfulness grew.

The nurse stepped forward and said sharply, "Stop that Dorothy. Put your slippers back on." And Dorothy subsided and did as she was told.

Shrinking back into anonymity beside his father David wished desperately that the visit was over and they could leave this awful place where nothing at all triggered responses of defiance and baleful interest. He was terrified that one of them would come and sit close beside him,

450

terrified of their reaching curiosity. He wanted to look at his watch but he didn't want to attract attention to his presence by making any movements. Afraid to look at Dorothy again David listened in rigid fascination as Bill tried to coax words from her. But once more she became restless and started to rise.

"No Dolly; sit down. Come on, sit down. Sit down love."

Bill took hold of Dorothy's arm but she pulled herself free and stood. Bill reached for her to pull her to the bench again and the nurse came briskly forward.

"Come on Dorothy. Sit down!"

But Dorothy was too agitated; she refused and began murmuring tonelessly and putting her arms wildly about her, fending off the nurse.

"I'm sorry," the nurse said to David's immense relief, "I'm afraid she's had enough for today. Perhaps she'll be better next week. Come on Dorothy, come along. Say goodbye. That's a good girl."

Dorothy walked away, content to be taken from them, away from the strain that the visit involved and returned to a world with which none but she was familiar. David felt the oppressive heat of the place. Or was it panic growing within him again. He was glad that she was leaving and he was ashamed of himself for feeling like that. But now they could leave too, avoiding the gaze of the other patients and retracing their steps through the locked doors. But David saw nothing of their exit. He was carrying the awful image of red scars throbbing lividly on white temples above her dark, empty eyes. That night, much to his shame and Bill's discomfort and anger, David began to wet the bed...

Inside the cold shop doorway David stirred and raised his eyes to the bike. He wanted to ride away for ever to put the images of his past beyond the reach of memory. But the road was too long and the night was too dark and he remained confused. But somewhere inside he had a concept of home only he didn't know which it was, dad or Aunty Ame. The only person left was Aunty Ame and happy images beckoned to him but he couldn't go on. Which was the way forward? He couldn't tell. He was bound to his past and the confusions waiting, like his dad, to confront and defeat him again. David pushed his bike onto the road and cycled back to Sheffield, his father and the shrinking world waiting for him there.

CHAPTER 50

Rebellion and 'Reformation'

Childhood was giving way to the confusions of puberty and the confusions were founded on a rich mixture of David's experience and insecurity. He longed to rebel and throw over the constraints that were binding him but his attempt to run away to Worcester was his only open attempt at rebellion. On the evening following that attempt when, on his late return, David had been sent sternly to bed to fret for twenty four hours over the retribution in store for him, Bill had summoned David and sat in stern judgement on him.

"What the chuffing hell do you mean by it? Running off like that?" Bill demanded and he glanced up quickly then back at David and added sourly, "You twat!"

David had heard Bill swear, of course he had, but never before had he been addressed like that by his father. Waiting for the inevitable punishment that was bound to follow, David lowered his eyes and mumbled, "Sorry. I'm sorry."

"Who the bloody hell d'you think you are? You been seeing James Dean films or what?"

"Course not."

"Well what is it then? Don't we look after you? You've got a nice home here. How do you think grandma feels?" Bill was working himself up with verbal prods of indignation. "Eh? Eh?"

"Don't know."

"I can't hear you!" Bill said, sneering at the sight of David cowed before him. "What's the matter with you? Can't you speak?"

David took a sharp breath and looked up at his father. He wouldn't cry, not for anything would he let his dad see him cry. "I don't know."

"Well where in God's name did you think you were going to get to?"

"I wanted to go to Worcester."

"Worcester!"

David nodded.

"What the bloody hell for?"

"To see Aunty Ame."

Bill was dumbfounded. It was a hundred and twenty bloody miles away! "Whatever for?"

"I just wanted to get away for a bit. Just to think things through." David snuffled. "Everything's so…" He broke off and waited. He couldn't explain it. Nobody knew how he felt. It was no good, they wouldn't understand. But suddenly Bill's tone changed.

"What about me?" he said, "Don't you ever think of anybody but yourself?"

David looked up at him, and Bill continued, "Don't you have any idea what it's been like for me?" He looked sharply round again but they were still alone. "I've had your mummy to try and look after all these years. And then having to come back here to grandma's, sharing a bed again with nowhere to be on our own. D'you think I like it?"

David shook his head sadly. Now he was being made to feel ashamed for bringing more trouble to his father. "No," he mumbled.

"And now you try and run away from me after what's happened to mummy. I should think you want to say you're sorry."

"Sorry dad."

"And you'd better say 'sorry' to grandma too when she gets back."

David nodded with relief as well as acquiescence; it looked as though he wasn't going to be punished after all, or at least not physical punishment.

"I'd never have bought you that nice bike if I'd thought it was going to lead to this…"

Here we go, David thought resentfully, now I've got to have the lecture and he braced himself to put up with it until it was over.

He was lucky to get away with it, he knew he was, but why did they have to keep going on at him all the time? Didn't they know that was what he wanted to get away from? He sat and listened, nodded, mumbled the words his father expected to hear; anything just so long as his dad would get it over as quick as possible.

Looking at him Bill shook his head The boy was such a disappointment! Well, he'd have to be kept under control. He wasn't going to have David causing him additional worry on top of everything else! For Bill was coming under increasing pressure from Middlewood and the authorities at the hospital were counselling him repeatedly.

"You must understand," they said, "that Dorothy will never get well again."

Bill heard their words and his heart rebelled against them.

"How long has it been now?" the consultant pursed his lips and sought the answer from the ceiling. "Oh it must be close on – let's see – five years? There really is no hope you know."

It was said with the greatest sympathy but Bill obstinately reasserted his devotion to Dorothy. He would not abandon her now.

How could he? She needed him! And given the opportunity for his own freedom, Bill rebelled against it. No! Divorce was out of the question!

"But," they said, "she doesn't know. She's not the Dorothy you married. Not anymore. She won't get well and you have no hope of anything like a normal life with her."

Slowly Bill's devotion to Dorothy began to erode and he hated himself for it. He recalled the pretty wedding at the chapel with David in the white satin pageboy suit, Jean thrilled to be a bridesmaid and Marge as Maid of Honour. It was a lifetime ago! And he had lost contact with Dorothy's other friends, the people she had known before he met her. Those friendships had slowly foundered on Dorothy's illness...

For better, for worse; for richer, for poorer; in sickness and in health. And a promise is a promise and he had loved her so.

"But David, what about David?" They began pushing Bill from another direction. "Doesn't he have a future too? Doesn't he deserve one? Your life with Dorothy is at an end."

"No, no, no," Bill cried, "she was more to me than that and I won't cast her aside now."

They looked on with sympathy as Bill desperately fought against their reason, and they tried to prise him from the world he had chosen to inhabit, to free him to live again. They offered him freedom without remorse or recrimination.

"Think of your son; think of your future together; think of yourself. Give yourself a chance. You deserve it. You can do no more, believe me, no more. You are still a young man remember."

Their reason finally prevailed leaving Bill heavy with guilt. He tried to set down conditions.

Dorothy would be cared for, the best conditions; and he undertook to provide regular payments for treats and privileges.

"I will still come and visit her."

"Of course."

"Every week."

They nodded sympathetically.

"If I can't make it every week then as often as I can. I want to see her, I want to keep in contact. I must."

"We understand," they said. "You can come as little or as often as you like. Dorothy will be cared for. You'll always be welcome."

Bill walked away from the hospital with his emotions tearing at him and started proceedings for divorce. He never saw the Bracewells again. Or Charlie and Marge. No more Sunday evenings with them round the piano with a jug or two of beer from round the corner. All that remained were echoes of the family he had once tried to belong to, Charlie's bony fingers straddling the keys, the distant sound of their voices singing…

He thought about taking up dancing again, anything to take him out of the house, to get away from the stultifying evenings, waiting for tomorrow and next day's work whilst bitter memories paraded across his empty mind. And people who met Bill heard him say with forced joviality, as though to convince himself, "I'm OK. I can cope, there's nothing wrong with me! Come on let's have a good time, life's too short, come on, we must!" And his laughter, they heard, was brittle, a veneer over his personality. He wouldn't share his past with others. "That's all put away now and I don't want to think about it. I must be strong! Right, what's next? Good. Let's get on with it! I must be strong, you won't find me sat about moping. Whatever's up with you? You don't know what life's about yet!"

David, the adolescent idealist, didn't argue and said he understood. Only – why couldn't dad have stayed married to her?

Nobody cared for nobody and the world was a rotten place!

He stopped going to Worcester for holidays, he had other things to do. Besides, Worcester had changed, they had all changed. Everybody was older. Miss Fieldew had died and he hadn't been to see her or written to her. David felt rotten about that too and he thought of the reproaches he would have to endure. Even Worcester wasn't a place of refuge any more.

When the 'Teen Bar' opened next to the post office under the wall by the railway bridge it became an immediate mecca for the local youths. David and his pals had seen it from a distance on their way to the pictures, crowded with young men in drape jackets and greased back hair, swaggering around the door in front of the girls. David and his special pal Richard were immediately attracted.

Richard went to the same school, he was a year younger than David but with a greater air of worldliness than David possessed. Richard was already affecting the heavily greased slicked back hairstyle and had got his mother to make the legs of his trousers narrower for him. But such bowing to the dictates of current fashion was totally denied to David.

"You don't want narrow trousers," Lilly said with an air of distaste. "That's what them Teddy Boys wear."

"Anyway he's not having 'em!" Bill ordered. "Wide trouser bottoms are far more fashionable. When I was young we used to have 'em sometimes up to 24 inches wide. They looked really smart."

David walked away, resigned to having to look like a schoolboy even when he went out in the evening.

"And don't be late!" they called after him.

Don't be late! David was filled with dejection. When was he ever late?

"Come on," Richard said, trying to raise David's spirits, "let's go and try it."

David pulled a wry face. "I don't know. I'm not dressed for it."

"Aw come on. It'll be alright," Richard said. "I'm going anyway."

He set off down the road and David reluctantly allowed himself to be taken in tow.

Inside the Teen Bar it was noisy and smoky. Music was playing on a juke box, not the usual Light Programme melodies but Bill Haley and Freddie Bell and the Bellboys. The room was alive with jostling and laughing with some of them dancing, rock n'roll wherever a small space appeared.

"Wow it's great!" Richard was immediately in his element. "Come on let's go and get a drink."

"I've got no money."

Richard always seemed to have enough money to do what he wanted to do but David didn't have pocket money; he never had been given pocket money of his own. 'What d'you want money for?' Bill had said to him when David asked for it. 'You know you can have anything you want; I'll buy you what you want, you only have to ask, you know that.' And David had had to resign himself to the answer.

"Come on then," Richard said pushing his way to the counter. "I'll get you one. Just this time. What d'you want?"

"Thanks Rich. What they got?"

The bar offered the usual array of soft drinks; lemonade, Tizer, Pepsi Cola; Vimto. "Or coffee. Or you can have a cup of tea if you like."

They chose Vimto, in the bottle and without the straw! Now David felt he was entering a different world, a world of casual sophistication. He took a pull at the bottle and looked around, trying to imitate the swaggers he saw around him, trying to forget his schoolboy style of dress. There were familiar faces all of a sudden! Lads he knew from school, a couple of fifth years who normally disdained to have anything to do with fourth year or below. And girls too, only now they were out of uniform they looked more like women than girls; they were wearing lipstick.

Richard was over at a table, talking to a couple of youths, one with a pair of Woodbines in a small white paper sweet bag and David sat down and joined them.

"Are you buying it then?" the youth was asking.

"How much did you say?" Richard asked.

"Threepence."

"But you can get 'em up the road at that little shop for twopence."

the other lad protested.

"Well go and buy one then! And see if he'll serve you."

"I'll give you twopence halfpenny."

"Threepence."

"Aw, go on."

"Tell you what. Threepence and you can have two matches."

The sale was made and David watched with fascination as the lad at the table, little older than himself, lit up and sat back with a swagger, puffing smoke.

Richard said, "I'll buy the other one. Here." He produced threepence and the deal was done.

David looked on enviously as Richard began to puff and blow the smoke, selfconsciously trying to imitate the youths around him.

"Give us a puff Rich," David said eagerly.

Richard turned and blew smoke straight into David's face.

"Go on Rich. Give us a puff."

"Only a little one then."

He held the cigarette to David's mouth, David tried to puff it but forgot to suck on the smoke and Richard took it away.

"Aw come on Rich, I didn't get it properly. Let me hold it for myself."

"Only a little one then." Reluctantly Richard handed David the cigarette.

David took a drag and without thinking breathed the smoke down. Immediately he began to cough and splutter, gasping the smoke from his lungs. He felt sick and dizzy, so sick he thought he was going to throw up. Around the table they were laughing at him but it didn't matter.

"I've never done it before," he said.

For a week the Teen Bar became David and Richards favourite rendezvous. It was a good place to congregate and listen to teenage music and, if you had the money, to treat yourself to a bun or sausage roll if you felt like it. Despite his initial nausea David learned to smoke, buying the cigarettes one at a time with money that grandma gave him to buy sweets. But on the Wednesday of the second week as they were sitting in the crowd round the table with their Vimto Richard's attention was caught by one of the lads nodding towards the window. He looked up and gave a smile of surprised recognition at Bill's face, staring in at them from among the crowds outside on the pavement.

He turned to David. "It's your dad!" Richard said.

David's heart sank. Only a second before he'd had the cigarette in his lips and was in the process of exhaling smoke. His dad must have seen him!

"What you going to do?" Richard asked. The rest of the gang were laughing.

"It's not funny!" David said desperately.

"Are you going out to him?"

"I don't know!"

"You'd better go," one of the others put in, "He'll be waiting for you." And they all laughed again.

"Is he still there?" David asked without turning, surreptitiously dropping the cigarette onto the floor by his chair and putting his foot on it.

"I'd have had that," Richard said.

"I'd better go I suppose." David took a swig from the bottle to mask the smell of tobacco on his breath.

"He's not there now," one of the others said.

"Perhaps he didn't see me. Perhaps he doesn't know I'm here."

"Course he's seen you. He was looking straight at you."

"Go and have a look and see if he's still there will you."

"I'm not going," Richard said. "He knows me!"

"Go on somebody," David pleaded.

One of the lads went out while David sat apprehensively, not daring to look up until he returned.

"He's still outside. He wants to see you."

David felt his spirit sag. He knew it meant trouble but he wasn't doing anything wrong. Only smoking. And his dad smoked! So…? He put a brave face on and said, "Better go then. See you."

Outside, David paused at the door and looked around the crowd and saw Bill near the pavement edge, scowling at him.

"Why didn't you come out when you saw me?" Bill asked sharply.

"I didn't know you wanted me," David replied lamely.

"You've been smoking haven't you?"

For a split second David wondered if his dad knew; if he had really seen him with the cigarette. But it was no good, he'd been caught out and he knew it.

He replied, "Yes."

Bill slapped David hard on the face. The sound of the slap made those nearest to them look round, then they looked away again. David stepped back sharply, feeling his cheek begin to colour and it wasn't just the force of the slap but shame too at being treated like a child in front of everybody.

"Come on home!" Bill took David's upper arm and dragged him away and when they were clear of the crowd David pulled his arm free and walked sullenly at Bill's side with his eyes rimming with tears.

"What do you want to go to a place like that for?" Bill snarled.

"There's nothing wrong with it," David said and flinched as though

458

he expected his answer to precipitate another assault.

"And what's that you were eating?"

"It was just a scone. That's all."

"What the bloody hell's the matter with you? Don't you get enough to eat at home?"

"Course I do," David protested.

"Well what do you want to buy that for then?"

David was confused at this line of Bill's intolerance. There was nothing wrong with it. "It were just... well the other lads had one and I had one as well."

"And where did you get your money for cigarettes?"

"It were only tuppence."

They were nearly home and David knew he would have the same inquisition all over again from grandma and grandad. Oh God! He felt frustrated anger rising in him and he gritted his teeth; he knew he daren't show it, that would only make matters a lot worse, so he put up with his father's sarcasm.

"Who told you to smoke?"

"Nobody. Just... all the lads smoke. You smoke."

"And I suppose if 'the lads' told you to put your head in a bucket of water you'd do it?"

"No! Just leave me alone, leave me alone," David cried. "Of course I wouldn't."

They were home and Bill pushed David inside.

"You found him then?" Lilly said as they entered. "Was he where you said?"

"I don't want you giving him any more money mother. He's spending it on cigarette."

"Oh you naughty boy. You shouldn't do that," Lilly said sternly.

"You should just see 'em all down there," Bill said. "Smoking. Girls like tarts in lipstick."

Lilly saw it all starting again, the whole sorry cycle. That's how it had started with Bill and look how he had finished up! She knew she should have been more strict with him.

Lilly fixed David with her sternest look. "You mustn't go with girls," she said. "You must keep well away and have nothing to do with them."

A year went by, a further year of frustrating loneliness in which David, locked in his own solitary world of unique tragedy carried his anger and resentments concealed beneath compliance. He spent hours in the cellar beneath the living room with the old blunt axe, chopping the orange boxes that Harold brought home into firewood. In his imagination the panels of wood from the dismembered boxes represented enemies to be executed with ruthless efficiency. He amassed victims in the form of strips of wood piled up from the boards as he split them, then he took each one and placed it on the gritstone paving slab at the foot of the cellar steps and derived a primitive satisfaction as he swung the axe and chopped each piece in two, adding them to the growing pile of bodies. Lilly and Harold rejoiced in the willingness with which David performed what was, to them, an irksome chore, never realising that it was providing David with an unwitting release for his pent up anger.

And David had also entered into a weekly Saturday evening routine with his father. After work and an hour's rest in the afternoon when lunch was over Bill shaved and changed into a suit or blazer and went off into town to console himself. He had found that milk stout was tolerable provided he stuck to an otherwise bland diet and now that he no longer had the obsessive strain of Dorothy gnawing at him his ulcer gradually became more tolerable, helped by the medication he was taking. He met his cronies in city centre bars, 'getting on with life' as he put it and occasionally joined by women for whom steady drinking through the day offered pleasurable escape from grinding reality.

For David the routine began after tea. Then he abandoned his pals and changed into something more suitable to meet his father and went into the city to join the queue which, without fail, was already forming outside the Gaumont to wait for the start of the Second House. Bill normally timed his arrival for when David had reached the head of the queue just before the programme was due to start. It saved Bill the boredom of having to wait and meant he could stretch his time out with his own mates until the last minute.

The consolation for David, standing outside in the silent line of people each week, sometimes for half an hour or more depending how long the queue was when he arrived, was that over the period of that year and well into the next, he saw every new film that was released almost without exception. And there was a kind of cameraderie between them, a papering over the cracks as they journeyed home together afterwards to collect the fish and chips for their late night Saturday supper with grandma and grandad. But it was no more than a truce and deep inside David continued to feel constrained by the narrow bounds of living with Lilly and Harold and their apprehensions, and Bill's domineering control. David sought escape in pursuing other interests...

Down by the lineside on the quiet road behind the factory the gang was waiting. There were about ten of them and on some evenings there were more, covering a range of ages from David and Richard at fifteen to Rooarp at twenty three. Sometimes a group of youngsters tried to join them, eleven and twelve year olds attracted by the glamour of the gang's maturity and their huge collections of locomotive numbers. But the gang ignored the little 'uns and tried to discourage them. They got in the way when girls, also attracted to the gathering of teenage boys came along for some flirting and kissing and casual petting. But when the horseplay started the little 'uns made a run for it and the girls stood at a discreet distance, just in case.

By common consent the tall and skinny Rooarp was the acknowledged leader because of his age and propensity for bullying the younger ones. He was pale and repressed, constantly rolling a ball of spittle round his tongue and spitting random shots whenever one of the youngsters came within his range. He was given to de-bagging and took great pleasure in getting the game underway, standing back until the crucial moment and then, the chosen victim having been caught by the rest of the gang, Rooarp came forward and took a personal hand in the removal of the victim's trousers. Then the game of 'catch your trousers' followed and if the victim was lucky they were fairly easily retrieved. But there was always the danger that Rooarp, getting carried away, would get them tossed onto the track and then stand back to enjoy the sight of the victim scrambling up the embankment in his underpants to retrieve them from the line before the next train was due. Nobody felt themselves safe alone with Rooarp but the gang paid court to him because he was excellent at organising trips to exotically located railway sheds. The Carlisle trip for example, for those who had been able to afford to go, was generally acknowledged to have been a resounding success. It was rumoured that Rooarp, who had been spotting for longer than anyone could remember, needed less than 100 numbers to complete his collection of every locomotive in Britain.

David and Richard were sitting astride the fence waiting for the daily ritual of the evening 'fitted', a long distance express goods to Scotland with each of the long line of vans coupled to vacuum brakes, 'fully fitted' for express running. Each evening they lived in hope of copping an engine they hadn't seen before.

"It's here!" one of the youngsters called from his vantage point on top of the embankment adjacent to the wires alongside the rail.

Over the distant rooftops where the line curved between factory walls to the south a brief cloud of white smoke appeared, vanished and reappeared again. Then the train burst into sight with the smoke billowing over it and down the line of freight vans. It was greeted with boos and a chorus of disappointment from the gang as the locomotive bore down and pounded by them.

"Never get anything good on it lately," Richard complained.

461

But David was watching as the youngster, now down from the edge of the track, furtively noted the number in his book. "You copped that?" he asked incredulously. "Everybody's seen that!"

Rooarp looked up; here was an opportunity to complete the youngster's humiliation.

"Go on then! Get him," Rooarp cried and the gang made a rush as the youngster scrambled back over the fence and started to zig zag up the embankment like a startled rabbit.

Richard and David gave token chase but it didn't seem fair on him. Anyway, that was it for tonight; the rest of the rail traffic would be local stuff. Rooarp was leaning back against the fence with the hand in his pocket furtively moving inside his trousers, watching the pursuit. Neither of them wanted to spend time alone in his company and David said to Richard,

"What you doing now then?"

"Dunno," Richard replied. "Might go up to the shed." Then he added, in a reserved, offhand way. "In a bit."

David retrieved his bike from against the wall and began riding lazy circles in the road. "Come on then," he said, "if you're coming."

"Where are you two buggers off to then?" Rooarp asked sullenly as Richard mounted his bike.

"Shed!" David replied, and he called up the road to where the rest of the gang, having tired of the chase were lounging against the fence further up the line, "Going to the shed. Are you coming?"

But there was no response except from the repressed Rooarp who suddenly made a lunge at Richard, circling close by him. "Come here! Come here you bugger!"

David and Richard sped off throwing taunts back at him from the safety of the accelerating bikes, leaving Rooarp to call impotently, "I'll get you, don't worry."

He heard their laughter in the distance and rolled a thin ball of spittle round his tongue. "Spastics!" he muttered and spat a thin stream into the gutter and turned his attention back to the rest of the gang along the road.

"Where are we going?" David asked as Richard turned off the road and took the narrow bridge across the river.

"Just got to go and see this girl."

"Ah. Right. Who is she? You're not going to be long are you?"

David had the normal teenage interest in the opposite sex, admiring and taunting them from a distance but his grandma's stricture about girls lay in his mind like a conscience and he felt shy in their presence and didn't know how to initiate a relationship beyond awkward conversation. With Richard it was different. He was good looking

462

already, with a handsome Robert Taylor profile, his thick dark hair greased and slicked back at the sides, and an easy manner born of confidence in girls' company. But if Richard was planning on spending the rest of the evening with this girl then, David decided, he would go up to the shed alone and meet the others up there.

"We shan't be long," Richard replied. "I might take her to the pictures tomorrow. We'll go up to the shed in a bit. Come on!"

David began to hang back, undecided. "Where you meeting her?"

"We're calling for her."

David looked at Richard in surprise. "What! At her house?"

"Yes."

"What about her mum and dad?"

"What about 'em?"

Here was something novel, David thought, grandma warning him not to even talk to girls but this girl being allowed to have Richard call for her at her home!

"What's she called?"

"Jennifer."

The house, an Edwardian villa with bay windows stood on its own with a car parked on the hardstanding where the front garden used to be. David stood holding their bikes while Richard walked boldly to the front door and rang the bell. He turned and gave David a grin of superiority, 'look at me, am I a man about town or what?'

The door opened and Richard spun round to face the girl standing there holding the door half open, a white towel in a turban round her head and another draped across her shoulders.

"Oh hello," the girl said with great composure. She was young, certainly no older than fifteen, with an air of self assured prettiness which, if anything, her appearance in towels only served to emphasise.

Richard managed to swagger his shoulders from the back for David's benefit and said, "I just thought I'd call round…" but the girl interrupted him.

"I thought you weren't taking me out until tomorrow." And then before Richard could reply she added, "Who's your friend?"

"Oh. It's Dave," Richard said, and as the girl raised a quizzical eyebrow he stepped aside, made an awkward gesture and added with a slight air of embarrassment at having to make a formal introduction on the doorstep. "And this is Jennifer."

"Hello," David said.

Jennifer ignored him. "Well anyway I can't stand here all night like this." She stood back and opened the door to them. "You'd better come in."

She led the way into the hall. A staircase rose along the right hand wall beyond the coatstand and David could see along the end of the hall into a kitchen with somebody moving around inside. From somewhere beyond them David could hear music playing. Jennifer pushed open the first of the two doors on the left.

"You'd better wait in there a minute. I shan't be long."

Richard and David stood and peered selfconsciously into the room but it was empty.

"Go on in," Jennifer said, amused at their deference, "make yourselves at home! I shan't be long."

She darted upstairs and they entered and sat talking in subdued voices.

"What do you think of her then?" Richard asked David with pride.

"Alright," he answered, impressed that she hadn't seemed at all embarrassed at being caught in the middle of washing her hair. "She seems nice doesn't she!"

Richard gave a smirk of self satisfied superiority.

The door opened and Richard looked up expectantly but a different girl entered the room, a little older than Jennifer by about a year and wearing what looked like a bluey grey nurse's uniform, black stockings and flat walking shoes. Her auburn hair was cut short and her smiling mouth carried a pale shade of lipstick. She was carrying a belt and had an air of busyness. David heard the music again, an orchestra playing a theme of great majesty and compassion.

"Oh I'm sorry," the girl said, momentarily startled, "I didn't know anyone was in here." She crossed the room, selfconscious under the boy's gaze. "Are you waiting for Jennifer?"

Richard nodded but David sat completely still, observing her and listening to the sound she had brought in with her. It was unlike anything he had experienced before.

"Well I shan't be in your way." She hunted in a cupboard and pulled out a workbasket, rummaging in it for black cotton. "Jennifer's nearly ready. I don't expect she'll keep you long."

She turned to leave.

"What's that?" David asked, suddenly anxious to detain her.

"Hm?" the girl answered.

"That music."

"Oh," she said. "Mendelssohn. Do you like it?"

Mendelssohn! It sounded terribly classical and highbrow, the sort of thing that his dad and grandma would turn off when it came on the radio. But this was beautiful music.

"I've never heard it," David said.

"Oh you must come back and listen to the rest. Sorry, I must go now."

464

The door closed and she left, taking the music with her.

David turned to Richard. "Who was that?"

"Don't know," Richard replied.

They sat in silence waiting. David strained to catch the music again but it was shut out.

Jennifer re-entered; the towel was gone from her shoulders and the wet turban had been replaced by a carefully arranged dry towel.

She took a chair opposite them and asked artlessly, "What brings you here then?"

"Just thought it'd be nice to make arrangements about tomorrow night." It was a lame excuse for an opportunity to see Jennifer again and they both knew it.

"We're going to the pictures aren't we?" she said.

"Yes," Richard replied. "I thought that's what we'd said. What's on?"

David sat with them and yet apart from the proceedings feeling slightly uncomfortable as they made their arrangements. He was completely out of the picture and they were both ignoring him. He didn't know why he'd agreed to come now and he cast about for an excuse to get up and leave without looking completely foolish.

The door opened and the older girl walked in again gesturing with the needle with its tail of black cotton and said, "Sorry. Just wanted to put this away."

Her words were addressed to Jennifer but as she spoke her eyes rested on David.

"Oh," Jennifer said, "don't mind us. This is my new boyfriend."

"Which one?" the girl asked with a hint of mischief in her voice.

"Richard. And this is his friend…" Jennifer paused.

"David," David said, looking up at her. The girl smiled at him and the smile made him feel as if all the cares he had ever known were melted in its warmth. Looking at her David could find nothing to say; he wanted to be able to keep her in the room longer but his tongue was tied and his mind refused to work.

"This is my sister," Jennifer continued, "Judith."

"Hello Judith," David said, feeling ridiculously formal.

"Hello," Judith replied.

There was a moment when neither knew what else to say. Finally Judith moved across to the cupboard. "I'd better put this away," she said. "I'm the tidy one in this family, not like my bohemian sister."

David said, "I see you're a nurse then."

It sounded such a clumsy, stupid thing to say. Why couldn't he have come out with something smart and clever. Mentally he berated himself for being gauche and obvious.

"Not yet," Judith replied. "I'm still a student. I'm at PTS at the moment."

"Oh."

"That's Preliminary Training School."

"Oh I see."

"Anyway," Judith went on, "I'm afraid I've got to go now. Nice to meet you."

"Right. Well... bye then."

She smiled at him again and David's smile lingered at the corner of his mouth long after he had watched Judith leave. Judith. He mouthed her name silently and rolled the consonants round his tongue, oblivious to the sound of Richard and Jennifer talking. It was a beautiful name, a classical, ageless name and he longed to be able to speak it aloud and hear the sound of it again. Suddenly the shed and the 'fitted' and the rest of the gang didn't seem important at all.

CHAPTER 51

A kiss in Chelsea

And Bill, meanwhile, met Betty. There was not the passion he had known with Dorothy, nor was there the deeply felt love. But here was a woman who would care for him and bring comfort into his life. She was a spinster whose mild flirtations as a girl had failed to woo her from her job, first as typist and then as a secretary in one of the steel firms. An unglamorous job that suited an unglamorous woman leading a life of limited aspiration. Each month Betty silently and carefully set aside a little money from her wage, paying it into the slowly accumulating bank account while living with her equally abstemious parents. The romance that she did allow came from the black and white heroes of television, the infatuations of the nurses for the fictional doctors of 'Emergency Ward 10'. But she was becoming aware that life was passing her by and, fed by the fictions of television Betty started to realise that if she wasn't going to become a lonely spinster then she needed to find herself a husband.

She idealised him as a man who would not make physical demands or expect children from her but who would be content to provide an unostentatious home with comforts. She enrolled with an introduction bureau, the same discreet bureau that Bill, with many initial misgivings, had finally approached and in the fullness of time, a meeting of the two had finally come about.

Bill was careful and tentative, Betty was smilingly undemonstrative and neither one was in a hurry to push demands upon the other. It was a perfect match and they settled comfortably into a groove with no expectation beyond a tacit recognition that inertia would, on some future day, bring their marriage about.

Bill was reticent about his past, beyond admitting that his previous wife had become incurably ill and he had been forced to seek a divorce on the advice of the hospital. And of course there was already a child, well a grown up son actually, almost ready to leave school and start work. And Bill too was living with his parents and was looking for the right partner to share a home with and settle down in life. Betty looked and listened, weighed and balanced the things that Bill told her and saw that here was a good looking man with responsibilities and good intentions. She could hardly believe her good fortune and she settled down to wait for his proposal.

David had used Richard's friendship with Jennifer to see Judith again. They were to meet again at her home and David left grandma's with Richard looking smarter and neater than he would otherwise have been if they were only going out with the gang. But he tried not to make it too obvious; mindful of grandma's strictures about 'girls'.

"Going somewhere special?" Lilly asked.

"No. Just out," David replied, hoping it sounded as casual as he tried to make it sound. Oddly, his greatest worry was Richard. Although he was younger than David, his parents took a more relaxed view of Richard having a girl friend. At fifteen they almost expected it of him and David wanted to get out of the house before grandma got too inquisitive and Richard let slip some casual remark about meeting Jennifer.

"Come on Rich. Going grandma."

"Well you look nice the pair of you," Lilly said, watching them leave and she left it at that.

David was nervous as they approached the door again. He wasn't sure what he was going to say to Judith. She was about the same age that he was but she seemed to be so much more self assured and in charge of her life. According to Richard, Jennifer had told him that her sister was soon going to leave home and board at the PTS nurses home. It made the G.C.E's that he was going to receive at the end of term prizegiving when he left school to start work as an apprentice look a bit paltry.

Richard rang the doorbell and David paced the area round the parked car nervously. A shadow appeared at the frosted glass panel in the door; it opened and an attractive, petite woman in her thirties smiled at Richard and stood aside to let him in.

"Hello Richard. And is this David then?" She smiled and showed them into the room where David had first seen Judith. "They won't be long, my daughters. Actually we're more like sisters really. At least that's how I like to think of them. Sharing the same interests. Like a family should really." She smiled again and David noticed that a smile was never far from Mrs Crawford's mouth. "Well I'll go and see what's keeping them shall I?"

Richard seemed quite at ease while they waited but David didn't know whether he should stand or sit and he picked at his fingers nervously, trying to be interested in a picture hanging on the wall. He sensed change in the atmosphere; he glanced across his shoulder and then turned round to see Judith standing in the doorway.

468

She was wearing a green sweater of fine wool with short sleeves, scalloped at the edges. It contoured the beautiful curves of her body, the pale green complementing the red skirt flowing out from beneath the belt around Judith's slim waist to the calves of her shapely legs.

David's breath was taken away. He had been struck by her on first seeing her in the loose nurses uniform made of some kind of stiff blue cotton material, carrying the belt in her hand. But now, standing before him, she was a vision beyond belief, beyond his expectation. Her short auburn hair was softly curled and David realised as he looked at her that the glasses Judith was wearing complemented rather than detracting from her appeal.

"Hello again." Judith came in and sat on a chair. "Jennifer won't be long. Where are we going? Anywhere in particular?"

Richard looked over to David and grinned. "Thought we'd just go for a walk. It's nice and warm out."

"Is that alright with you?" David asked earnestly.

"Yes," Judith said. "It sounds nice."

David searched for more words to say, but each set of words he formed seemed to lead nowhere and he held them back and they waited in awkward silence. And what he could not know, and didn't learn until much later, was that Judith felt just the same as he did, sitting and hoping that she looked alright. For she had sensed on the first chance acquaintance that David held an attraction for her that she couldn't explain. He was good looking, although not handsome and dark with Richard's romantic profile; a nice looking boy. But he had a reserved intensity of manner that Richard lacked and Judith had wanted to look her best to meet him, so she had decided to risk the new sweater that was so flattering. Now she sat and smoothed her skirt across her lap and hoped that she hadn't overdone it.

When Jennifer arrived they set off without preamble. "Where are we going?" she asked as they turned along the road. The sun was still high in the June sky and the evening was balmy after the humidity of the afternoon.

"Millhouses," Richard suggested. From the footpaths in the park you could still see the main line descending into Sheffield and you never know, it would be a shame to miss the 'fitted'.

"Chelsea," Jennifer countered, "Millhouses is too far."

"Where's Chelsea?" David asked.

"Don't you know where Chelsea is?" Jennifer asked, incredulous. "It's a nice little park."

"I like Chelsea," Judith added.

So Chelsea Park is where they went to…

Jennifer and Richard were walking ahead in the warm evening shadows leaving David and Judith to stroll back deep in conversation at their leisure. With Judith, David's tongue tied embarrassment with girls disappeared. He talked to her freely about his dreams and what he would like his life to be, not in a heavy, confessional way but with vigour, unafraid to share his thoughts. And Judith reciprocated. She shared her ambitions with him; her desire to complete her training and get her SRN and then to specialise in children's nursing. She told him about her current boyfriend, a youth with whom she had been 'going out' without any thoughts beyond the occupation of a few hours leisure whenever they met. But from that evening with David, Judith dismissed the studious Andrew from her life.

Within two hours David felt that his life had moved onto an entirely different plane and he knew that he would want to continue seeing Judith again and again. As they approached the road where she lived David wondered if he should kiss her on the first date. They paused by mutual consent in an area of shadow and he bent to kiss her and she responded to him, a kiss without passion, a polite kiss. But it thrilled him! She hadn't said 'no' and turned away or made a fuss about the 'first date', neither had she shown herself to be expert, a girl who had spent a lot of time with different boyfriends, falling in and out of love. She had respect for herself and equal respect for him. David wanted to hold her closer; he could feel her body pressing against him and he wanted to place his hands on her breasts. But she would push him away for being 'too forward' if he did that now; it was too soon and David knew it and meanwhile he felt the overwhelming ecstasy of Judith in his arms and he wanted to be able to see her again. They turned and continued to walk and paused again for the innocence of her kiss. David felt light headed with happiness and the pleasure of the evening shared with this beautiful girl by his side. Now at last there was tomorrow to look forward to...

Bill decided that he would tell David of his engagement to Betty on the night of the school speech day. They sat in the packed school hall with all the other parents and pupils, listening with anticipation as each examination success was announced. Then the recipient's names were intoned and they slowly filed up onto the stage where the staff and dignitaries led the applause as each ribboned certificate was presented. David walked slowly forward in the line and mounted the steps onto the stage. Mr. Cooke held him back until the boy ahead had received his certificate from the Lord Mayor and shaken his hand, then it was David's turn to walk across the stage in the waves of applause that rose. David heard the headmaster prime the Lord Mayor with his name as the certificate was passed across for presentation; he heard the Lord Mayor say something that he couldn't remember as he received the certificate and shook his hand, and then the applause subsided as David left the stage, only to rise again as the following pupil's name was called.

At the end of the ceremony the hall rose in a buzz of excitement and congratulation. David saw his classmates with their parents and there was a deal of dashing about and comparing their experiences on the stage during that great occasion.

Bill was anxious to get away. There was news to tell and a tram to catch and there was this huge crowd who would be wanting to catch it too. Besides, he had to see Betty home and there was work in the morning. Reluctantly David called 'Goodnight' to his mates and they set off to leave. What a night it had been!

They reached the tram terminus well ahead of the crowd following them and sat in the front bay of the tram upstairs. David sat proudly holding the certificate, so that other passengers could see it.

"We've got something to tell you," Bill said.

David turned to him expectantly. Betty was next to Bill, looking at him with an expression of prim benevolence on her face. Perhaps, David thought, they've got something for me. For getting the G.C.E's.

"We're going to get engaged. To be married."

"When?"

"Next year. April."

David greeted their news with resentment and his face fell. This was his day! It was the biggest day of his life, going up before the whole school to collect the award for his achievements! He'd done it, nobody else but him! David! They should be pleased for him. They should allow him to enjoy his pleasure, just for this one day, but all they could think of was themselves and their news. It wasn't fair! Everything he did, every time, nobody took any notice. He might as well not bother.

"You just don't care!" David cried. And in his misery David looked aghast at Betty and in her saw someone trying to usurp the place he held sacred to the memory of Dorothy, his mother, the mother that was to be and who had been denied him. Dorothy, cast aside and languishing in that hospital, that asylum, without visitors, without hope, without any connection to the reality of her past, discarded, replaced and here was his father with the woman who wanted to take her place. Well she wouldn't take her place, nobody could take Dorothy's place. Oh no! And turmoil rose in him again, anger and disappointment at the way they wanted to usurp his night and sever him from Dorothy! Only, he hadn't seen Dorothy for so long, not since the dreadful day of his last visit and he didn't want to see her again, and he felt rotten about feeling that way but he tried to cherish good memories and David knew it was

471

no good but his heart cried out within him. He knew that his father had needed the divorce and that was betrayal enough but now he was going to compound the sin.

"What do you mean, 'don't care'?" Bill said, frustrated at David's attitude to him. And in front of Betty too.

Betty sensed a looming confrontation. It was just what she had heard about teenagers and she placed a restraining hand on Bill's arm.

"Of course we care." she said. All it needed was a little reasoned explanation. "We thought that you'd be happy for us. It's our big day too."

"But… but…" David spluttered, "you could have waited." How could he make them understand? "You could have let me have this day for myself." He was on the verge of frustrated, angry tears, "You even had to take that from me!"

A number of passengers turned their heads to look and quickly turned away again.

"We thought," Betty continued, "that is, your dad and me, well… your dad would like you to be Best Man."

Why now? Why now? David looked at them with disbelief. I don't want to be, I don't want to help you!

"That's right isn't it Bill?" he heard Betty say.

"But what about Uncle George? I thought he would be," David tried to marshal arguments. "I mean, he's your brother. You'll be having Uncle George won't you?"

"No," Bill said. He had been intending to extend the invitation to David later but, well, now it was out and David seemed to have calmed down a bit. Perhaps it was having the desired effect. He reached out for David's hand but David withdrew it.

"Well anyway," Bill continued, suppressing the impatience he felt, "he's not. You're more important to me than our George is. You're old enough now and I'd like you to be my Best Man."

It was more of an instruction than an invitation and David found himself accepting with bad grace.

With pride they showed David the house they were proposing to buy and renovate with their combined savings and a loan from Betty's parents at a nominal rate of interest.

And David contemplated another new beginning with someone he refused to call 'mum' despite – or maybe because of, his father's earnest instruction to do so – in an unfamiliar part of the city, remote from his friends and, more importantly, at some distance from Judith.

And so the following year Bill settled into the marriage he sought with Betty. It soon became empty, a sterile relationship based on her balance sheet of disadvantage weighed against possible advantage without the light of love to illuminate the shadows that descended on their home. Betty was ill prepared to give of herself except in duty; a clean house, regular meals and a timetable for visiting and for receiving visitors. Her idealised view of marriage was not matched by reality and her spinsterish ideal of home and family, gleaned from the pages of the magazines which she devoured had nothing in common with the real demands of a husband and an inherited teenage boy. Their marriage sank with remarkable rapidity into an unforgiving relationship riven by attrition.

It was remarkable that Judith grew to love David at all. With insight she perceived his vulnerability and the emotional turmoil boiling beneath the manner he adopted with his pals. And the more Judith saw of him, the more apparent David's confusions became. But when they were alone together she saw the sensitivity he was capable of and it proved to be the cornerstone of a relationship that would last, despite the enormous strains put upon it at the outset.

They fell in love with all the intensity and passion of late adolescence. They loved each other consumingly, dreaming and yearning for the day they could marry and be alone at last to make love, finally, completely and without guilt. They dreamed of the home they would make, sheltered from the storm outside in the warmth and fireglow of their room, content in each other. Supper, hot chocolate, soft bread, rising passion, warmth and the freedom to love and be loved safe together in the darkness. And in Judith at last David found someone he could confide in and reveal the troubles of his past without the fear that she would laugh or, worst still, run away or close him out of her life. All his days were spent in yearning for the evenings when work at the shabby little engineering company his father had found for him was over. He was jealous of the time spent apart from her and immediately tea was over David rushed across the city to be with her. But the conflicts within him manifested themselves in nights of utter boorishness.

It wasn't that he set out to hurt Judith. The weekends were glorious, when he and Judith devoted the two uninterrupted days to each other around her pattern of duty at the hospital. But it was on Sunday night with the weekend drawing to a close and another week looming at the lathe that it became unbearably bad and all the repressed rage fell onto Judith. David's mood changed inexorably from irritability to murderous ill temper and Judith watched dismayed as David sat consumed with self pitying, introspective hatred. He wasted golden opportunities to spend the last hours of the evening in pleasure by sitting in intense silence, her slightest word provoking outbursts and finding fault with her.

Judith tolerated his moods and consoled herself with the knowledge of how good it was the other times they were together, such golden times of loving tenderness. With increasing understanding she loved him completely.

Bill watched David with feelings of dismay. Was David going to repeat it all again? Could nothing that was learned be passed on from father to son? Did all the learning have to begin anew with each new generation? Bill watched and waited for the friendship to end.

Betty said, "There's plenty more fish in the sea." in the naïve expectation that her silly little homily would encourage David to leave Judith for someone else. She offered what she regarded as friendly advice and confided the names of other girls but whatever she thought that was supposed to achieve heaven only knew and David regarded Betty with increasing disdain.

What it did achieve was the opposite of what they sought, for David became even more resentful of life at home, their opposition and their interference. Relentlessly he pursued happiness with Judith in the warm solitude of the front room of her home, playing records and smooching. It was always against the background of voices in the next room and the knowledge that Mrs. Crawford might snap the light on and walk in at any time under the pretext of, "Kettle's on. Would you both like a cup of tea?"

Then David and Judith would spring apart blinking sheepishly in the sudden light, David trying to look as though he had been interrupted in a discussion of deep and profound significance and Judith exchanging knowing smiles with her mother.

For three years David courted Judith relentlessly, even jealously when, finding David's moodiness intolerable she had dalliances with other fellows. But they were never far from each other's thoughts. David pined and became an object of ridicule amongst his mates on the occasions when, because of a tiff they parted and he was inconsolable until they made up. And, once they were back together again Judith wondered why ever she had done it…

It was shortly after David's nineteenth birthday, and few weeks before her own, that Judith detected something in his manner as she stood at the mirror applying a final brush of eyeshadow and watching him looking at her.

"Don't watch me," Judith said bashfully, "it's putting me off."

"Sorry," he said, and then as she concentrated on her makeup again he crept up behind her and his reflection suddenly appeared and startled her.

"Go on," Judith said and she elbowed him playfully aside. "Whatever's the matter with you?" There was an edge to Dave's playfulness as though he was excited about something.

"Come on," he said, fidgeting with impatience.

Judith pouted and inspected her lipstick. "Why? Where are we going?"

"Nowhere," he said, filling her with exasperation.

"Well what are you rushing me for?"

"Nothing. Just thought we might go a walk that's all."

"Where to?"

"Oh I don't know. Park. Millhouses woods. Where d'you want to go?"

"Park if you like," she replied.

They walked to the park in the warmth of the July evening sun, talking of their plans and dreams together. David had changed firms and was working for a bigger engineering company who had put him in the drawing office for a period as part of his ongoing apprenticeship. They looked at the houses, dreaming of the one they would one day have.

"I could be chief draughtsman one day," David said. "That'd be a thousand a year! Just imagine what we could do with that! And when you get your SRN…"

Vistas of comfort and a place in the community opened before him.

They lingered by the garden of a bungalow, half of stone and half of brick, long and low like a ranch with a biscuit coloured stone chimney climbing up an outer wall and huge picture windows. The long garden was lawn with islands of flowers and a broken shoreline of dense shrub borders.

"Oh just imagine," Judith said with envy, "driving home to that in your own car."

David looked at his twenty odd pounds a month as an apprentice, wondering what their life together was really going to be like.

By the time they reached the park the afternoon glow was fading from the air and a sunset was building high in the west. They sat by the stream where all afternoon children had played at floating their sticks and pretending to catch fish with ninepenny nets. Now the park was becoming deserted. A small family group was packing up to go home, their children still kicking a ball about and there was a scattering of other courting couples. In the distance, by the deserted tennis courts a park keeper was fussing about the tiny pavilion and swallows began to swoop erratically over the shallows of the stream.

They walked further. Behind the park across the railway line that bordered the stream the woods rose up the hillside, deserted.

"Come on," David said and they made their leisurely way to the steps back onto the road and crossed the railway bridge to the woods, dense with foliage and ringing with the calls of invisible birds. They found a grassy bank under the trees away from the path and shielded from the road behind, overlooking the meadow in the park which they had just left and the kissing began.

Then David turned and looked about him, seeking to ensure solitude for them both. Judith was watching him and he averted his gaze and lowered his head, examining his fists clenched before him. Judith waited.

"Judy," he began, "I've been waiting for the... er... right moment." His voice was low, hesitant.

"What for? What's the matter?" Judith's voice carried a hint of anxiety.

"Nothing. Nothing's the matter." David lifted his head and turned to look at her and he felt his heart racing. She was so pretty, sitting on the grass with her slim body erect, the collar of the deep blue dress open above the rise of her bosom and her legs folded beneath her with her skirt spread around her on the ground.

"Judy." He appeared breathless and faltered again and then he said, "Judy, will you marry me?" And immediately he thought how pretentious his words sounded. "I mean, I know we can't marry now, well not for a bit anyway. But... Oh hell this is all coming out wrong. What I mean is... can we... shall we... sort of... well unofficially get engaged? I mean..." Oh God! he berated himself, this was awful! All his carefully prepared words were faltering away! It wasn't at all how it should be. For days he had been preparing the scene in his mind, carefully planning where he would bring her so that it would be right! So that he could ask her the question, the most important question. He didn't want it to be an engagement they casually drifted into. It had to be a decision they made with great awareness, consciously reflecting the importance of Judith's answer on both their lives. And the setting, the occasion, above all the words had to be right. He couldn't go on his knees in her mother's sitting room. But here, in the solitude of the woods, the two of them alone in the sunset... How silly and pretentious he suddenly felt!

"Oh David," Judith said, "Of course I will."

David was quite incredulous. "Do you mean it?"

"Of course I do. I'll marry you anytime. Anywhere."

He looked earnestly at her but there was no trace of mockery in Judith's voice or her expression. She threw her arms around him and they clung to each other and kissed until they were both breathless. And then she broke away from him and said, "We can't. They won't let us, your dad I mean. He wouldn't let us would he?"

She was right. He was only just nineteen and Judith was barely that. He'd heard his father say it. 'Twenty five, that's plenty soon enough to get married.' And the others in the drawing office too, Terry and Mick, they were both well into their twenties, courting but determined not to marry 'for a long time yet'. But they didn't feel about their girlfriends like he felt about Judith; they couldn't do or they would not talk like that! If only everybody else would take them as seriously as they took themselves. But David knew that Judith was right; his father would never agree to them getting married and he needed his father's permission, at least until he was twenty one! Well, they would just regard themselves as 'unofficially engaged' anyway and wait…

They fell into each other's arms and lay beneath the canopy of trees and the darkness enclosed them as they kissed. David's fingers were clumsy on the brass buttons of her dress and Judith helped him, opening it to her waist. She looked round but the shadows were dense and silent and she slipped it from her shoulders and lifted off her brassiere and lay back on the dewy grass.

David kneeled by her side and looked at her, reluctant to touch the virginal purity of her body. "Oh God, you're so beautiful," he breathed.

He reached out gently, carefully and her skin was cold beneath the rising moon and Judith shivered at his touch and closed her eyes. "Oh God Judy." He bent over her and she quivered again as his lips touched her and she felt his breath on her skin as his mouth hovered delicately over her breasts. "I love you… I wish we were married…"

"I love you…" but her reply was smothered in David's kiss.

But it wouldn't do, this unofficial engagement business. It was like that song of Elvis Presley's; 'Won't you wear my ring around your neck'. What's the point of trying to pretend you're engaged if you can't tell anyone. And that's surely the whole point of it! To tell the world and for the world to be pleased! And David's motivation was just as strong as before. Engagement to be married, a betrothal, was an important step, one of the landmark decisions in anyone's life. It had to be seen as such and the earlier declaration, he decided, was not enough. It was wrong and premature.

And anyway, David reasoned, an announcement of your engagement didn't mean you were getting married straight away so what if his dad did object? They would just wait until they were both twentyone and then get married anyway! So David and Judith continued to love each other with unconsummated passionate.

And they waited another year.

The Millhouses Hotel had a nicely appointed cocktail bar, tastefully decorated in deep red flocked paper and David reasoned that if they got there early enough it might not be busy.

Judith knew what he was going to do. She knew, by the strong romantic streak in David's nature, exactly what he was going to do as soon as he suggested going there. She dressed in her dark charcoal grey tailored suit; a slim fitted skirt and bolero jacket over a white blouse and a pair of high heeled shoes. She looked stunning. David called for her in his new grey wool herringbone suit, and looked at her and smiled.

And because she knew the game Judith smiled back at him with a light hearted smile and said, "Are we still going to the Millhouses?"

"If you like," David replied casually.

"Alright then."

The Cocktail Bar was empty when they arrived. It was lit discreetly with low overhead lighting and hidden lamps reflecting off the glass in the fitment behind the bar. The barman, in a white shirt and burgundy waistcoat too short in the waist with his shirt hanging over his belt was leaning in the door adjoining the Smoke Room bar waiting for the evening's business to begin. David ordered a Cherry B and a pint for himself.

"We don't generally serve beer in here sir." The reply was made just this side of civility. "This is a cocktail lounge! You'll have to go through to the Smoke Room if you want a pint."

David hesitated.

"You can have a half pint if you want."

David settled for the half pint in a stem glass with a round bowl. It didn't feel like half a pint at all.

"Thanks," he said. "Actually we shan't be staying long." And he carried the drinks across to the table in the corner by the bay window where Judith was sitting. They took a first sip of their drinks and David put his hand on Judith's arm.

"Judy."

She looked across at him intently and seriously, without a glimmer of the smile that was bubbling behind her lips.

David glanced quickly across the room but the barman had gone through to serve in the Smoke Room. He looked into Judith's eyes, looking with such frankness back at him and put the question formally.

"Judy. Will you marry me?"

"I knew that's what we'd come here for." She laughed with pleasure, not unkindly and without embarrassment. "Of course I will."

David felt in his jacket pocket and produced the box, opened it and showed Judith her ring, a tiny cluster of diamonds surrounding a ruby.

"Oh David it's beautiful."

She took it and slipped it on her finger. It fitted perfectly.

When David told Bill that he had become engaged to Judith, Bill

478

was aghast. They were only just twenty for goodness sake! How was David going to manage without him there to take care of things? Bill's first question was,

"Is she pregnant?"

"Course she's not pregnant!" David cried in indignation. "What sort of a question's that?"

"Well," Bill said, "That's why a lot of people get married..."

"Well it's not why we're getting married!"

"Are you sure?" Bill fixed David with a keen eye.

"Of course I'm sure! Oh I'm going out."

"Now wait a minute..."

"Your dad's only thinking about you," Betty said.

"No he's not!" David riposted. "You're thinking about what the neighbours'll say. That's all you're thinking about. You're just thinking about yourselves!"

"That'll do," Bill said angrily. "All I've ever thought about is you."

"You've never liked her and she's never done anything wrong and now I want to marry her and all you can think about is, 'is she pregnant'! Well, she's not!"

"And when's it all supposed to happen?" Bill said sarcastically.

"I don't know! We've got to work all that out. Maybe find somewhere to rent. There must be lots of places. Anyway, we want to get married and it doesn't matter if we get engaged now or later. We'll just wait until I'm twentyone that's all to get married."

David stormed out, his temper fuelled by disappointment at their response. It wasn't as though he was asking for anything! All he was doing was letting them know!

Judith's parents were much more relaxed and to their delight they gave them their blessing. Mr and Mrs Crawford's respect for their daughter enabled them to trust in her judgement. Besides, they could see that Judith was happy with David and that was the important thing as far as they were concerned. They admired her ring and settled down to watch, and wait for a wedding day they suspected would come sooner rather than later.

Judith and David sat and thought through a strategy together.

"What if we show my dad that we are old enough to be responsible for ourselves." Bill's experience of living with the Bracewells was still strong in David's memory. "He just thinks that once we're married we're going to come to him looking for a place to live."

Within two days Judith met David with the evening paper. She turned to the classifieds. "Look, look at all these houses and flats." She had circled three probables for them to look at. "But we'll have to be quick," she said. "They soon get snapped up."

479

By the end of the week they had been rejected by one, been put 'on our list' by another and a third had accepted their provisional offer to rent a small house, similar to Harold and Lilly's close to the city centre.

Together David and Judith went to see Bill and Betty. They didn't plead, but presented their opportunity with a budget based upon their joint earnings. It was tight! It barely left them with anything at the end of each week but it was feasible.

"I want to think about it," Bill said. "Go into the front room while I talk it over with your mother."

Like applicants for a job they went into the front room to wait.

"I mean why doesn't he just say no!" David lamented. "What's he have to go through all this for?"

The door finally opened and Betty's head appeared. "Are you coming back through," she said.

"You're determined to get married then!" Bill began.

"Yes," David said. "I mean if this house falls through then I expect we can get another. We just wanted to show you that we know what's involved. We can stand up for ourselves. We're capable of living our own lives."

"What about furniture?"

"It's part furnished. That's why the rent's as high as it is."

"But we'll still have to buy some things of course," Judith said. "But my mum and dad can let us have a couple of chairs."

"What do your mum and dad think about it?" Betty asked.

"They're fine about it, aren't they," David said, turning to Judith.

"Oh, so you've been to them first," Bill said.

Oh hell, can't I do anything right, David thought wretchedly.

"It's just that we were down there when we heard that we've got a chance of this house that's all," David protested.

Bill was silent.

"Supposing we buy you a three piece suite," Bill said finally after exchanging a glance with Betty. "Is that what you need or is it part of the furniture that's included!"

David was astounded. "No. That'd be fantastic. Wouldn't it?" he turned to Judith then back to Bill. "Aw thanks dad. Does this mean that…? Aw great!"

"Doesn't look like we can stop you does it," Betty said.

In many ways David's ambitions were born from the experiences of his past. With Judith he endeavoured to build a secure future for them both and the two children that followed. The childhood of his own son and daughter was particularly precious to him, as it was to Judith. But his own experiences had taught him that the buffetings of the adult world have a profound effect and children, no matter how young they may be, are not immune to them. With Judith he worked to build a happy world within which their children could grow free and happy. And whether David really understood it or not, there would have been a different outcome without her, an outcome with far more tragic results. In the latter years of his adolescence David had been labouring under the increasing pressure of his repressed experiences and it was a pressure that needed an escape. The torment that Judith suffered in the early years of David's courtship of her was the manifestation of a slow release of anger. It could never be completely dissipated but with Judith's love and forbearance it was at least brought down to a manageable level, enabling David to emerge through adolescence intact and take his place in the kind of society he aspired to.

Their wedding on a bright September day was a happy affair and the reception was held in the Hall and grounds of a large Victorian villa belonging to friends of Mr and Mrs Crawford in the western suburbs of the city. Amy and Rose came up from Worcester and Judith basked in the warmth of their approval. Amy took David to one side and congratulated him.

"She's a lovely girl David. She's going to make you very happy. You only has to see the way she looks at you to know that. Anybody can see it. And her family's nice too."

"Thanks aunty. We do appreciate you coming up. You and Aunty Rose. I know you don't get up here very often."

"We've always been used to your gran and grandad coming down to us. It's nice for us to come up for a special occasion like this. You will come and see us again now you're married won't you."

"Course we will aunty."

"You ain't been for so long David. Not since you were a little boy. We misses you."

"I know aunty. I'm sorry. It's just that… you know… things happen." The excuse was lame and he knew it.

"You'm always welcome. You knows that."

A cry arose in the garden around them.

"Where's David? His missis has lost him already!"

Bill came over amid the laughter. "I think she wants you to have your photo taken."

"Thanks dad."

He went back inside through the french windows and joined Judith, resplendent in her white wedding gown at the table, ready to cut the cake. Her wedding bouquet of deep red roses lay on the table before her.

They stood with the point of the knife in the icing and smiled, and kissed and cameras flashed and cheers rose from the hundred or so of their families and friends all around them.

EPILOGUE

1977

The bells of St. Mary's...

i

The past is always with us and no matter how we try we can never escape from it entirely, for it remains, even though concealed behind the thin veil of memory. But sometimes the veil draws back and then the past comes bursting through despite the passage of innumerable years, to confront us once again. Sometimes it comes with benevolence, but at other times it is like a demon and capable of taking a different form.

The summer of 1976 was hot and dry and quite unexpectedly so, for spring had been a season of disappointingly cold winds, culminating with snow in May. Judith and David had contemplated their holiday plans with some despair for they had made arrangements for an early June break in Cornwall with their children Philip, ten years old and his little sister Julia who was almost four.

"Next year," David said magnanimously, "we'll go abroad. Get some sun, somewhere you can rely on. Julia'll be old enough. We'll go to Majorca, somewhere like that."

Besides, the job was going well and he was confident of his prospects to advance further in the sales hierarchy and take the next step into management. David was buying a home on a mortgage, a nice new semi detached house on an exclusive small development; a promotion with a rise in his basic salary would ease some of the financial pressures. He had come a long way after a succession of false starts with dead end firms and now he was well established with a blue chip chemical company who placed greater emphasis on interpersonal skills than on the 'smart Alec', slick style of salesmanship he had experienced previously. And, if you had the aptitude and ambition, the company was prepared to invest in talent. The future was looking good and so was his life with Judith and the family they were raising around them. And then, as though to underline the benevolence surrounding them, the week before they were due to go away the weather broke and winter fell away. June came in with clear skies and the temperature rose sharply and with it the spirits of David and Judith rose as well.

"Shall you go and see your Aunty Ame while you're down there?" Lilly asked during their visit the week before they were due to go.

"Don't think so grandma," David replied. It was a long journey from Sheffield to Falmouth especially with the family in the car and David didn't like to extend it by unnecessary stops. He wanted a prompt start to keep ahead of whatever traffic there might be, with minimal breaks for the kids to have a quick stretch and something to eat on the way.

"She's not been well you know," Lilly persisted. "I had a letter from her this week. And she's had a terrible cold. I ain't surprised, rotten winter we've had."

She fell into a mood of thoughtful reminiscence. It was ages since Lilly had seen her sister. Harold had retired at sixty-five with the annual free travel concession the railway granted to all its retired railwaymen but once he ceased working they had felt reticent about applying for it and the annual trips to Worcester had ceased within three years of his retirement. And then, two years ago, late one September afternoon while Lilly was in the kitchen preparing some fish for tea and listening with anticipation to the announcer giving details of a boxing match to be broadcast on the radio later that evening, Harold had died in his armchair with his pot of tea on the hearth beside him after a retirement that had lasted barely ten years.

Despite her widowhood Lilly had retained a sturdy outlook on life. She maintained her independence and kept in regular contact with Rose and Amy and letters passed between them twice a month. But it was so long since they had all seen each other and Lilly nursed the hope that David would find time to call on his great aunt.

"It'll take us out of our way," David protested, "We'll want to get the journey over." But he felt a twinge of misgiving as he said it, knowing that the motorway passed within fifteen minutes of where his aunts lived. "Besides," David tried to justify his reasons to ease the conscience that was pricking him, "we can't just call unannounced and then dash straight off again. It wouldn't be right."

All the same it was very sad, Lilly mused to herself, especially when she remembered how much Amy had meant to him as a child. He didn't seem to be bothered about Amy at all now. But Lilly was old enough and wise enough to know that life was seldom meted out in balanced measures of good and bad, obligation and reward.

"Oh well," Lilly said with resignation, "I hope you all have a very good holiday. Looks like the weather's picking up a bit for you anyhow."

Amy's cold had persisted beyond the winter; she just couldn't shake it off even with the improvement in the weather. She recalled how she was used to seeing Lilly with her perennial summer colds when she and Harold had come down in the past for their holidays, and Amy remembered how she had teased her sister about it. But it wasn't much fun really and this one had persisted now for months. And even though she no longer had the runny nose it had left her with a persistent sore throat so that, by the end of April and at Rose's insistence Amy had taken herself off to the doctor. He had laid his glasses on the table and carefully dropped the wooden spatula into the wastebin underneath and leaned back and said,

"It doesn't seem to be getting any better does it?"

"No," Amy replied with her handkerchief to her mouth. She was becoming conscious of her breath and the odour that seemed to accompany the soreness.

"And how old are...? Hmm." He mused, inspecting Amy's record card again. "Your teeth? They're still your own?"

Amy nodded. She still had most of her own teeth at seventy four. Perhaps they were something to do with it. 'Oh Gawd', she thought, 'it'll be one thing after another now. I'll have to lose me teeth.'

"How long have you had it now?"

"Well it's ever since I caught the cold this last winter. I had this awful runny nose and sneezing. I was ages getting rid of it. Well now that's gone but I've still got the sore throat. Sometimes it really hurts, you know, like a stabbing pain sometimes when I eats. Not all the time, but it's always there. I can feel it now when I swallows." Amy swallowed in an involuntary demonstration and a grimace passed fleetingly across her face as she did.

The doctor leaned forward comfortably, reassuringly. "I think we ought to have another opinion. Get the ear nose and throat specialist to have a look at it."

Amy regarded him, looking for shades of meaning and nodded slightly, almost imperceptibly and smiled a little.

"Shall we? Eh?" The doctor nodded encouragement at her. "Get to the bottom of it?" He turned back to his desk and began to write. "I'll make an appointment for you and let you know when. Shouldn't take long. Couple of weeks perhaps. Maybe sooner."

"Thank you doctor."

"And we'll have it cleared up in no time. Everything else OK? Good, good. And you'll come and see me when the specialist has had a look at you? There we are then."

Rose was waiting to hear what the doctor had got to say. It wasn't like Amy to be poorly. Not that she was poorly. In fact she was as fit as a flea but some days for no apparent reason it seemed worse than on others.

"How'd you get on Ame?"

"Got to see a specialist," Amy said in as non-committal a tone as she could manage, the way she felt.

"Never mind," Rose said after a brief consideration. "It'll probably clear up on its own now the fine weather's a'coming."

And with these wishful thoughts Amy and Rose waited for the appointment. But now there was an unwelcome thought rising in their minds which neither dared to confide to the other. If it's only the remnant of a cold – and everybody gets a sore throat after all – why's a specialist needed? And once these doctors gets hold of you and starts poking about… Far better to leave things as they are! It's only a sore throat after all.

Within the week Amy received confirmation an appointment for her at a hospital in Birmingham. And upon receipt of it she had sat and written her letter to Lilly, telling her that they'd had a rotten winter in Worcester too, and that she wasn't too bad although she'd had to go and see the doctor…

"He's not a Dr. He's a Mister," Amy said archly to Rose, gazing at the letter from the hospital for the tenth time that day and trying to read significance into his lack of formal title. And then she added bleakly, "Queen Elizabeth's? Ain't that the hospital where our Cyril…?" And both she and Rose hurriedly suppressed the dreadful memories of cousin Cyril's last weeks with the cancer gnawing at the inside of his head all those years ago.

"Let's have another look at that letter Ame."

Rose took it and scanned it and handed it back to Amy.

"It don't say anything about what it is anyway! I wouldn't worry too much about it," Rose said reassuringly. "They has all sorts of places in these big hospitals nowadays."

'No', Amy thought, 'it don't say anything about anything.' She wished she'd never gone to the doctor in the first place now. "Anyway," she said with a forced brightness that belied her spirit, "come on Rose. This'll never get the shopping done."

Despite all that Rose did she couldn't stem Amy's apprehension as the appointed day approached. Now the apprehension was mounting in her as she waited for Amy to come from the consulting room, listening as the minutes ticked endlessly in the big clock on the waiting room wall. Finally the door opened and Amy emerged.

"Well, that's that! Shall just have to wait now shan't we." It wasn't what she wanted to say and it wasn't the way she felt but she had to say something to Rose. There wasn't much else to tell. A lot of questions from a very competent and reassuring man who did everything with simple economy and a professional manner. It hardly seemed worth the effort to make such a long journey to see him.

Returning back home they watched the fields of Worcestershire through the windows of the bus. They had a look of green freshness as they passed and the trees were in leaf again. Everything was bright and new in the spring sunshine. But Amy and Rose travelled with silences hanging between them. Now all they could do was wait. It was so simple and so impossible. If it had been someone else, a mutual friend or acquaintance then their journey would have been absorbed in reminiscences and comparisons with other mutual friends. But this was between the two of them and it concerned Rose just as much as Amy and they hadn't the heart. And so they tried to bury their private apprehensions beneath a determined satisfaction that the ride through the countryside was a nice break from routine.

David's conscience was troubling him with recollections of a visit to Sheffield that Aunty Ame and Uncle Albert had made two years after Judith and he were married. The memory of their visit shocked him. Thirteen years! Was it really that long ago?

Aunty Ame and Uncle Al could only come to Sheffield for the week and Lilly had been so pleased to see them. Arrangements had been made for Amy and Albert to go to tea with George and Myra and that had been followed by tea with Bill and Betty two days later. David and Judith were in a small flat and couldn't fit everyone in. However, and it seemed to David in recollection that he had acceded to the arrangements with some reluctance, the family were going to come round en masse in the evening after tea and bring Amy and Albert with them to pay their homage to the newly weds at home. But meanwhile, with scan't regard to these arrangements, David had received a better offer. Richard, who was now married to Jennifer, and two other couples who were close friends, arranged a run out to a country pub in Derbyshire for the same evening.

"You can come can't you?" Richard coaxed.

"It's me aunty. She's coming over special to see us."

"Well can't you get 'em to come another night? They're staying for a bit aren't they?"

"Well…" and David knew himself to be weakening, "I don't know. All the arrangements are made now."

"Aw come on. Mick's going and Barry and Shirl."

David allowed himself to be persuaded. If Aunty Ame came early enough he reasoned, he could show 'em around, Judith'd give 'em all a quick cup of tea and then they could say they had friends to see and... That's it! Get Richard and Barry and the others to come and call for them to go out. Then he'd be able to say 'Sorry' to Aunty Ame and she would see how it was. Besides, Uncle Al would be ready to get down to the pub for his evening session by then so it would all work out alright.

Only when the week of their holiday came and Aunty Ame and Uncle Al began their round of visits to relatives and the appointed evening arrived, David began to resent the imminence of their visit. He changed into his new suit and Judith had her summer frock and a cardigan on ready to go out but when he went to answer the knock at the door, instead of grandma and grandad, and his dad and Betty and Aunty Ame and Uncle Al standing there, it was Jennifer and Richard and the rest of the gang.

"Come on then, are you ready? Have they gone?" Richard cried.

"No!" David answered irritably and he jerked his head towards the interior with a surly expression. "You'd better come in. They haven't arrived yet!"

"Well how long are you going to be?"

"I don't bloody know do I! I don't know what time they're coming. They're supposed to be here!"

The gang stood kicking their heels around the doorway in varying degree's of impatience.

"You'd better go without us," David said peevishly.

"No they'll wait," Judith protested. "You'll wait won't you? They won't be long."

"But how long are they going to be once they get here?" Mike demanded.

"He's right," David said to Judith. "There'll be cups of tea and all that. They'll be here hours. No you'd better go without us."

"You sure?" Mike said.

"No wait a minute, hang on a minute." Richard looked at David. "Do you have to? You can see 'em later in the week can't you? Tell 'em you got the nights mixed up."

"I can't do that!"

"Why not?"

"Well what're we doing?" Mike demanded.

David turned to Judith. "You ready?"

"We can't," Judith protested.

"Come on," David said, and he added self righteously, "Anyway they said they'd be here by now. It's their own fault. Come on, before they come!"

With a sudden rush David put his jacket on, urging Judith to grab her things and they locked up and left. But as they poured out of the flat into the street, anxious to be out of sight, fate intervened and the gang were met by Bill and Betty, grandma and grandad, Aunty Ame and Uncle Al arriving at the gate.

It wasn't what was said, the lame excuses David made, mumbling about 'getting the night wrong' with the gang standing by in embarrassment for him. It wasn't Bill's scarcely concealed scorn and anger. It was the look that didn't condemn that Aunty Ame gave him as he turned her from his door…

The memory filled him with shame.

David sat on the beach at Falmouth with the memory upon him watching his own children at play. He turned to look at Judith where she lay sunbathing on the beachtowel beside him.

"Would you mind if we stopped in at Aunty Ame's on the way back?"

"You're not thinking about going back already are you?" Judith answered lazily without opening her eyes behind her sunglasses. "We've another six days yet."

"No. It was just a thought," David replied. "It's just that it's been so long since I've seen 'em. I was just thinking about what grandma said that's all."

"I don't mind," Judith said lazily and she turned onto her side. "Are my shoulder's looking red? I don't want to get burned."

David reached into the beach bag and began anointing her with cream and Judith purred with satisfaction.

"That sun's really hot now. Who'd have thought it a fortnight ago." Judith adjusted her sunglasses and reclined again. "This is the life," she sighed.

David sat and watched Philip and Julia playing at the water's edge where Philip had excavated a moat around a castle just beyond the reach of the tide. Now he was digging a channel to the sea to fill the moat with energetic help from his sister. Their cries of excitement as the water surged into the channel came to him.

"We'll do that then," David said. "We'll stop off and have a cup of tea or something. If you're sure you don't mind."

"Of course I don't mind." Judith replied. "Are the kids alright?"

"Yes." With sudden energy David rose to his feet. "I think I'll go and build 'em a real castle. Shan't be long."

"If it's any good," Judith called, "I'll come and take a photograph of it."

And so, when the holiday was over, David turned the car off the motorway and headed down the hill past Fort Royal towards the cathedral and the familiar streets of long ago with another sad realisation that neither Aunty Ame nor Aunty Rose had met his children. Oh, photographs had been sent when they were born of course but in recent years even the correspondence between him and his aunts had been sparse. An exchange of Christmas cards and nothing more. Now David primed the children with anticipation, reliving the memories of earlier arrivals at Aunty Ame's as a boy for his holidays.

"You watch," he said, "when she opens the door, you just see what she does. You'll like her. And Aunty Rose. They're ever so nice. Both of them, they're lovely."

He pointed out the cathedral as they swept by in the swirl of traffic. "King John's buried there. I once climbed up to the top of that tower."

The children looked up at the towering building and David heard their intake of breath, suitably impressed.

Philip said, "Can we go up daddy? Will you take us?"

"Not today, we won't have time. But another day perhaps. When we come again."

Then down to the handsome Rennie bridge spanning the Severn, and David turned right before crossing it and followed the embankment where the pleasure steamers had once been moored and drove beneath the high lattice bridge carrying the railway line from Hereford and Malvern into the city.

"They have horseracing here," he said, pointing out Pitchcroft as they passed it on their left and the grandstand across the racecourse in the distance. "When I was a little boy like you I used to come here to the fair."

In vain Julia and Philip, whose ears had pricked at the mention of a fair, searched the racetrack for evidence of it but Pitchcroft was empty. David turned the car away from the racecourse, climbing towards the street where the spire of St. Mary's could be seen rising above the distant roofs. Past the 'George and Dragon' and past the 'Saracens Head' and memories of warm summer evenings spent in the cosy darkness of their yard with a bottle of Vimto, making friends with other kids, and then going with Aunty Ame and Uncle Al to the grammar school. Now they were there, searching for somewhere to park.

"When I was here as a little boy there were no cars at all in these streets. You could play out all day long and never see a car."

He led the way up the entry to the back door, marvelling at the familiar forgotten ring of his footsteps between the houses, just as it had always sounded. There were the roses at the top of the garden by the gate and a profusion of golden rod, just as it had always been. Nothing changes, he noted with satisfaction and a phrase returned briefly to his mind from somewhere and was gone. 'All is well and will be forever more.'

As they turned into the yard David put his fingers to his lips. "Shhh! Don't make a sound. Let's give her a big surprise."

They crowded into the porch around the back door and David knocked and then turned to Judith and the children with a conspiratorial smile of anticipation with his finger against his lips again. They heard a footfall in the kitchen beyond the door and David braced himself to relive the pleasure of her welcome.

The door opened and Rose stood there, taken aback with surprise, searching for recognition of the family standing before her. Her gaze rose from the children to David. "Well bless my soul!" Rose exclaimed.

But oh, how David had wanted to be greeted by Aunty Ame in the way she used to, in the way he had described it to Philip and Julia, with her smile of delight and her arms opening to him. He shrugged off his disappointment. "We've come to see you," he said, and as he spoke he heard a voice from beyond Rose, the voice of Aunty Ame calling,

"Who is it Rose? Who's there?"

"Come in," Rose said and she stepped back from the door, turned and called, "It's our David Ame. He's brought his family. They've come to see you." She beckoned to Judith and the children. "Come on, go on through."

David failed to see the air of anxiety in Rose as he glanced about him, taking it all in with satisfaction; the copper boiler, the old gas cooker, the pantry opposite the roller towel on the wall. The yard outside smelled faintly of roses and everything was giving him a feeling of wellbeing.

"Go on," Judith said to him, "you go first."

With a smile of anticipation David went through into the living room. Amy was sitting at the table in front of a small fire despite the heat of the summer afternoon and looking at the door with a look of puzzlement, wondering if she had heard Rose correctly, wondering which 'David' she could mean.

"Ahh!" Amy gave an involuntary sigh of pleasure. It was David! She hadn't dared to believe it could be but it was! "What brings you here?" Amy said, but there was reserve in her greeting. Beyond Amy, David could see Albert rising to his feet from the armchair by the stairs door as Judith, entering with a smile ushered the children in with Rose following behind.

"We thought we'd just pop in to see you. We've been down to Cornwall," David said. "We're on our way home."

"Oh what a nice surprise." And suddenly David sensed the forced pleasure in her greeting. There was something wrong despite Amy's words. She was older of course but her features had not altered remarkably. She was still strikingly good looking with dark, silver streaked hair. But there were lines of anxiety around her eyes and notwithstanding that David and Judith's visit with the children was a surprise, there was apprehension too.

David moved forward to the table and bent to kiss her but Amy recoiled away from him and cried, "No!" and averted her face. David stopped as though he had been shot. She had a tissue in her hand and she raised it to cover her mouth. "I don't want you to catch my breath." Amy said in a dejected tone of apology. She wiped the tissue round her lips; and he saw she was secreting something into it then she folded the tissue carefully and placed it in the flames of the fire. Then she reached out to the tissue box on the table and took another and folded it ready for use as she spoke and her voice was unsteady.

"I had to go back and see my doctor this week," she said. "He got the results of my examination... I... I got..." She turned her face from them so they wouldn't see the tears. Rose pushed past Philip and Julia and went to join Albert at her side while David and Judith watched helplessly, holding the children close to them.

"Come on Ame," Rose said "Come on love." Crouching at Amy's side Rose cradled Amy to her and raised her face to David and Judith. They saw Rose's mouth silently forming the word 'cancer' and the shock went through David as though the very life had drained from him. He tried to think of something to say but his mind was empty, as empty as the years of neglect.

"I'll be alright in a minute," Amy murmured. She dabbed her eyes with the tissue and turned back to them. All pretence was gone. Now David saw the fear that was consuming Amy and there was a look of hopelessness in Amy's eyes.

"Don't let the kids come near me." She said the words with bitterness. "I loves 'em. You know's that. It's not that I..." Albert stroked her hair as she spoke but her voice faltered and Amy shook her head in denial and her words failed away as she raised the tissue to her mouth again, and again discarded it in the fire.

"I know that aunty," David said. "I'm sorry." He turned to Judith, helpless. Oh God! He'd had no idea. Why didn't anybody...?

He heard Amy saying, "Make 'em a cup of tea Rose." but Judith intervened.

"It's alright Aunty Ame. We hadn't come to stop more than a few minutes anyway. We don't want to put you to any trouble. We've still got a long way to go."

Amy raised her eyes to Judith in compassion. "It's no trouble love.

491

It's no trouble is it Rose."

"No, 'course it ain't. I'll go and put the kettle on," Rose said leaving Amy's side.

"No really!" David protested. "We hadn't intended staying more than a few minutes anyway. Its just that we were passing and…" Again David's words failed him.

Judith could see it was all a big mistake. They couldn't stay. Not with Philip and Julia. Despite their brave hospitality both Rose and Amy were struggling to come to terms with the diagnosis and it was clear that Amy was terrified both for herself and for the children.

"I think we really ought to think about moving on," Judith said as gently as she could.

"I understands love." There were tears in Amy's eyes. "It's lovely to see you anyway. I just wish things were a bit better then we could welcome you properly. Couldn't we Rose?"

"I'll give you a cup of tea if you wants one." Rose nodded. "It won't take a minute. Really."

David looked at Judith and he saw agreement in Judith's eyes. "Well, alright then." It would be churlish to refuse. "Then we'd better be going. It'll be late for the kids when we get home." He paused. "I'm so sorry to see you like this," he said helplessly.

And again David approached to kiss her and again she averted her face with a cry as the children watched with incomprehension.

"Come and take a seat. Make yourselves at home," Albert said, indicating the armchair under the window and David steered Judith to it with Philip and Julia sitting on each arm close to her, watching Amy.

Rose bustled in the kitchen and David listened to Judith as she tried to make small talk and answered their questions about the holiday but it seemed so unreal. What had happened to the happy reunion and the lightly spoken words of comfort he had come to deliver? Now there were other things that David wanted to say but he couldn't. The words were unclear and his thoughts were crowding his brain. Rose came in with the teapot and cups and spread them on the table.

"You having one Ame?"

"I'll have a cold drink," Amy replied and Albert went off to bring it for her.

"Your Uncle Bob's up at home," Rose said, handing out the cups. "Come up and see him before you goes won't you."

"Yes. I'll pop up now if you like." David turned to Judith. "Shan't be a minute."

"Do you want to go up and see Uncle Bob?" Judith asked and Philip and Julia scrambled down from the chair, glad to be given freedom from the sombre room.

"Shan't be more than a couple of minutes." David tried his tea but it was too hot to drink. "I'll have that when I come back."

Amy started to protest but Judith said, "Don't worry Aunty Ame. He always leaves his tea to get cold."

Bob greeted David with a smile that combined pleasure at seeing him with relief from the stagnation that Amy's ailment had introduced into their lives. After the preliminary greetings during which Bob revealed again his unfailing knack of being able to strike an immediate rapport with children, he sent Philip into the garden with Julia to play while David asked him about Aunty Ame.

"Her's got cancer. You knows that?"

"I only just found out," David said sadly. "We just thought she'd been to see the doctor about tonsilitis."

Bob shook his head. "Her's got it in her throat. Sometimes her can hardly swallow." David wanted to ask but he felt the question on his lips would be an intrusion, and so he sat as Bob continued. "We thought it was just a cold and sore throat. It's been such a lousy winter. But she couldn't seem to shake it off. Spent a fortune at the chemist on sweets and lozenges. Then she goes to the doctors and he comes up with this."

"Will she get better? I mean, have they said anything about treatment or…?

Bob watched David carefully and said, "Three months. At the most. That's what they told Rose. Might be quicker."

David opened his mouth to speak but there were no words to express the sudden shock that overcame him. He looked away. Three months! From out of nowhere, and then the end comes suddenly into view.

"I'm so sorry," he murmured. "I don't know what to say."

"None of us knows what to say Dave. Only, your Aunty Ame don't know. Not yet."

"What? You mean…?"

"Oh she knows it's cancer. They couldn't keep that from her. Oh God! you should have seen 'em. Her and Rose! I thought they was never going to stop crying. But she don't know how long they thinks she's got. We thought it'd be kinder…" Bob's voice faded away and he smiled gently at David as if to say you won't let us down, will you.

"I won't say a word. Thanks for telling me."

Philip and Julia came running in with a handful of daisies each from the lawn.

Bob said, "Why don't you two stay with me a minute and I'll show you how to make daisy chains while your daddy goes back down to see Aunty Ame." He looked up at David. "Go on, they'll be alright up here with me. Better than down there."

"Thank's uncle. We shan't be staying much longer anyway. We've got to get back." He returned to number nine leaving Bob happy for a brief moment with the children.

Judith looked up at him as he entered and Rose delivered a good humoured reprimand. "Your tea David. You'll have it stone cold! It won't be fit to drink."

And he saw Amy looking at him, trying to hold back the reproach that he knew she must feel at being excluded from the conspiracy of intimacies that were denied to her. And he felt guilty at the secret he carried, and tried to cover it, saying, "Uncle Bob looks well," and immediately wished he could bite the words back.

But Amy smiled at him and Judith said, "Where's the kids?"

"Making daisy chains."

"They'll be alright with Bob," Amy said and David saw Albert hovering behind her chair stroking Amy's hair once more.

Philip and Julia bounded in, followed by Bob, proudly showing the chains that they had made and it became time for them to leave.

Then Judith said her goodbyes to them all and waited as David, denied Amy's kiss nevertheless took her hand and pressed it to his lips.

"I'll come and see you," he said earnestly. "Soon. I promise." And then he felt hotness rise behind his eyes and turned from her.

"Come on, I'll see you to the door," Rose said. She turned to her sister. "I shan't be a minute Ame."

"I mean it," David said, turning to look back at Amy. "I'll come down again soon."

iii

There was so much to be said that couldn't be said and so much time to try and make up. David visited Amy at every opportunity and they talked. He tried to comfort her during the short time that his visits lasted and she took such pleasure as she was able from them. They talked of childhood and summer holidays but David couldn't say the things he really felt; a mounting need to discharge the emotional debt he owed her. She had preserved the happiness of childhood, its carefree innocence all those years ago.

In the autumn David wrote to her, a letter filled with reminiscence and thanks so that she knew that his visits were made from love, not duty. And things that could not be spoken were carefully phrased and written so as not to give offence, especially to Uncle Al who pursued his vain self appointed task of planning his and Amy's continuing future together. On David's visit after she had received the letter, David looked for some way of making reference to it, searching for the right words to

494

say.

Amy helped him. "I got your letter," she said.

"I hope you know what I meant," David said gently. "I wasn't just saying 'thank you' for looking after me. I hope it was alright."

"It was a lovely letter. I'll treasure it always."

He had wanted to find a way and be able to say 'I don't want you to die but I have to say these things' but he still couldn't find the right words and the words he'd used seemed inadequate. Above all he didn't want to hurt her. Sitting beside her David took Amy's hand in his and she smiled at him, an earnest smile of understanding and said, "It's alright."

They sat together hand in hand while Amy's little world bustled about them. In vain David tried to persuade Uncle Al to let him take Amy for a ride into town to see the river, the cathedral and the countryside with the Malverns on the horizon. But Uncle Al was adamant.

"She must stay where she is, inside where it's warm."

Amy said, "It doesn't matter. But thanks for asking me anyway."

Was there something else? David looked at her, searching for extra meaning but Amy just smiled at him, her bright eyes twinkling moistly.

"I'm glad you liked it anyway," he said lamely. He hadn't wanted it to sound as though he was writing to say farewell but he wanted her to know and understand.

Their conversation passed to other things. Perhaps in the spring, if she was well enough…? But they both knew they were pretending and it didn't matter; there was no falseness about it for it helped Amy to live today and gave a sense of immediacy and purpose to her existence…

As the weeks slipped away Amy didn't lose her fear and she didn't become brave, just accepting so that every precious day was lived instead of shunned. Small things took on meaning and Amy saw and heard with added clarity and awareness. The ticking of the clock, so steady and reassuring, the sound having its own place within the spectrum of other sounds which came to her. The sudden fall of embers in the fire; someone whistling as they walked along the path at the back of the houses leading to moments of speculation; 'who would that be? It don't sound like… Too early for him yet…' And the silences which built up at certain periods of the day, almost tangible in their intensity, engulfing Amy in an ocean of time. The long greyness of autumn afternoon's… The familiar bursts of activity…

"Here Ame, drink this." Rose, caring, hoping. "You'll soon be better."

Amy knew it was a well intentioned lie. It was strange but she sometimes felt as if it was they who needed reassurance, that the statements they made were made for them, to give them comfort, not her. And it was as much for their sakes that Amy went along with it and allowed their false hopes to be accepted without challenge.

But Amy wished she could participate with them and share in their secret conversations as she lay amongst them, remote, talking of Spring and better days to come whilst in reality they knew it could not be. And she knew it was all to do with 'keeping spirits up', theirs as well as hers, but things were failing in her and more and more Amy began to depend on their assistance and she saw with dismay the accelerating changes that were being wrought. How thin she had become and the different shape evolving in her face, the weakness, lethargy and the pain... pain...

"You looks a bit better today Ame. How's you feel?"

And the voice within her cried, as she mouthed trite words of reply, 'But I want to talk about when I die, and how it'll be and what'll happen to Albert. I'm going to die Rose.'

"Now you mustn't talk like that Ame. Come on, drink this, you'll soon be better. That's it."

And Amy did her duty, looking up at the smiling concern of Rose, sipping the tiny droplets past the source, the painful source of her affliction. 'But you talk about me dying between yourselves Rose. Why won't you talk about it with me? Help me! Help me to understand... and perhaps I can help you to understand as well... While we have the time...'

Until it is all too late and Amy is taken finally into the care of the hospital and the opportunities for honest intimacy are gone. Now all that is left are the measured formalities of visiting and watching, caring for Albert, waiting...

The end accelerates towards them and all the months of care are brought to this, gazing at the slight figure, listening to the long, slow, laboured exhalation of breath.

'We came to see Amy. Our Ame.'

And what they see are memories of the past, the times they had known together, all of them laughing, laughing together. But now I see's her looking like...

No sound now. Only stillness!

They put an arm about Albert's shoulders and lead him away from the shrouded figure on the bed with words of comfort. But they find no comfort in themselves. And only time will do its work until they can lay down their grief and begin to live again.

iv

496

Albert made bold statements.

"Life goes on you know. She wouldn't want me to mope about the house."

Rose made sure her brother in law was being looked after properly.

"You'll come and have your dinner with me and Bob now won't you. And I'll call and collect your dirty washing as usual."

"No," Albert replied stubbornly. "I think I'll stay at home for my meals."

"Oh but surely you'll come and have your dinner with us Al," Rose persisted.

"No ta."

He had managed at home while Amy had been ill and incapable! He had looked after them both, caring for himself as well as her and taking the meal which Rose had brought down for him sitting close to Amy, ready to respond to her needs. Now the house was empty without her but he couldn't abandon it, not even for occasional meals. Rose resigned herself to continuing to bring Albert's dinner down to him.

"But you mustn't sit round moping round the house Al. That'll not do you any good you know."

"No," Albert replied with sudden energy. "I thought I'd go up to Sheffield for a few days. When the weather gets a bit better. I ain't been up there for years. Our Billy asked me up. We was having a bit of a chat about it at the funeral. I thought I might. Be a change. Lilly mentioned it too."

Boldly Albert put about the plans he was making and Rose and Bob were pleased at his resolution. He deserved to give himself a little treat and it did them good to see it too. He set about renewing acquaintances in the pubs from which he had been absent for so long, sometimes setting out with Rose and Bob in the evening, often stepping along the street alone and recounting to friends the details of Amy's final weeks.

But it was all sham for Albert was a lost soul without her. The house was without the comfort of her presence and each day yearned endlessly before him. The drink helped but it could not bring oblivion. Albert strove against neglect and Rose's visits helped too but the solitude grew within him.

It was only one month after Amy's funeral when Rose called as she entered the kitchen, to ask if there was anything he needed from the shops and there was no reply to her call. She called again as she walked through to the living room.

"Al? Is you ready? Anything you wants?"

But the living room curtains were still closed and Albert was fast asleep in his armchair.

'Oh Lord' Rose thought to herself and she groaned with dismay.

'He's not going to bed properly. Whatever's we going to do with him?'

She put her shopping basket on the table and drew the curtains.

"Come on Al." She took his arm and shook him. "You can't sleep like this."

Albert sagged and his head rolled to one side; his face was bright blue. Rose gave a cry and recoiled with shock, staring at the body.

"Oh my God!" she said. "That's both of 'em gone."

The summer streets are deserted and the hot afternoon sun imparts a quietness and solitude, as though, by the simple act of shining it absorbs noise, cloaking it in its own golden radiance. There is a sleepiness about the afternoon, something unique to childhood, to be recalled from adult memory but never again to be savoured of itself and impossible to recapture; the sense of timelessness and benevolence, the prospect of a whole afternoon of sunshine in which to play.

In memory our summers are always thus, warm and endless with day upon day of holidays. The houses are silent before the onset of the teatime bustle, the men are at the factories and in the well ordered routine of the day the women have done their shopping. For David, the dusty afternoon is his alone.

He has come to Worcester for the holidays!

It seems in many ways as if Sheffield is the place he visits whilst Worcester is a brief return to his home. The intervening months vanish and last year is just like this year and Aunty Ame is ageless and constant. Aunty Rose and grandma are down there too at their afternoon game of cards; all is well and will be for evermore...

The hop fields of Bromyard stretch endlessly into the late summer haze. David should be back at school but he is not; his holiday is extended for two more weeks to stay with Aunty Ame. The morning fields are fresh with dew and a pale mist lingers across the river as they arrive and are directed into the gloom of the vines.

The picking begins, it is a race and the coarse bine cuts their fingers but still they pluck the hops, filling the crib then carrying it along the row once the section is bare. David picks leaves, hops, stalks until they let him go to play, free to roam in the virginal gloom of the foliage. Then the chatter of the women becomes remote and the jungle closes around him.

Now there is another sound, something moving with stealth in the dense foliage. David, the hunter is moving with caution as the leopard stalks him. But the hunter knows the way of the jungle beasts and picks his way warily, circling about among the vines until he gets a clear shot and the leopard drops lifeless in the dappled shade. Now there is a moment's panic until the right track is found and the hunter returns to the camp where the kettle is boiling on the primus and Aunty Ame is getting out the egg sandwiches for dinner.

The smell of the earth rises in the afternoon sun. Beyond the rows of cribs the picked vines lay desolate and strewn on the ground. Here and there on the bare wires overhead a stray branch hangs abandoned. The rows of poles stretch skeletal into the distance like a battlefield, a wood shelled to destruction with bare trunks standing as memorials to trees.

The soldier moves amongst them; with caution now for there is no cover and blood will be hot and sticky in the sun. Flies buzz and bees hum, enhancing the stillness of the afternoon. Somewhere, an ambush is laid. There! There they go! The enemy! The commando drops to the ground firing his sten gun as he falls. One of the Germans is hit but another is firing steadily, keeping him pinned down. But not for long; he is a commando!

Throwing a stone into a distant heap of foliage, he distracts the enemy's fire then the commando makes a charge, firing from the hip. The enemy is routed! There are more but they are fleeing. No mercy, he shoots them one by one as they run, all except one who gets away. Now begins the wary job of tracking this dangerous adversary down. All afternoon the adventure continues and tomorrow will be the same…

They return in triumph in the evening and sing through the city, grubby, tired, glowing with pleasure. For David the hop picking season is short, a two week extension to the holidays then back to Sheffield; new school, new uniform, new shoes. The bittersweet parting at the station. Why can't it always be like this?

From his vantage point above the old allotments, David is leaning against the wall, surveying the city and the streets below. Of all the images crowding in upon him none makes any lasting impression, just a kaleidoscope of memories; of life, childhood as it used to be and as it never can be again. Aunty Ame has gone and she has taken a part of him with her. Oh! but David will treasure her memory and the precious gifts that she bestowed; security, happiness, a home. She had never been a mother and David had never seen her that way for she had always occupied a more precious place. And although the time he had devoted to her in recent years had been scant he realised now that he would miss her more than he thought possible.

For all through his childhood Aunty Ame had been there, always there. The smiling face of welcome at the door, her arms opening wide, mock surprise, playful.

"Why it's our David! What a nice surprise – come on in then."

He knew without question that this was his home, from where his life began and whatever went before was confined to limbo, beyond memory. Only why did she have to suffer so? For never was it less deserved.

David drank in the scene below him greedily, gratefully and behind him is the simple grave where Albert lies, covering his beloved Amy. A small mound of the precious red earth to contain them and preserve the memories of them both. An urn of fresh flowers and David's own, carefully strewn upon the ground and nothing more; no headstone, no names, no recognition for the curious, just 'Rest in Peace', a peace so richly deserved, a final anonymity. But David will keep faith and remain constant to her memory.

"You won't forget about us now they've gone will you?"

Dear Aunty Rose, you have been so much a part of David's life too and he turns from the wall where he is leaning to make his way down to the house in the quiet streets below. The sun flares in glorious sunset over the Malvern Hills and the bells of the great cathedral begin to peal over the city. But the bells of St. Mary's will never ring again. The steeple, which used to ring out the quarters and the hour stands silent, a landmark against the sky. Beneath the urn upon the silent mound David's final message lays carefully folded, and though the written words may fade and the paper fall to dust, the quiet thoughts are sent upon their way.

'I came to see you both today.
Did you know?
I stood in the sunshine of the still,
warm evening
at the place where you lie in dignity,
and tried to recapture the fabric of
my memories.
As easy might I capture the wind.

Oh! but you have peace
there on your hillside beneath the yew.
Only the hum of the bees and the faraway
call of the dove where
the summer air blows
from the distant Malverns.
Just I, in the stillness, in the sun
    with my memories,
                and you...'

Brian Jackson is a Yorkshireman, born in Sheffield. During a successful career, he has travelled extensively in Europe and the USA, although he and his wife now live in Herefordshire.
He is an avid reader, mainly of history and biography. In addition, Brian shares a love of theatre with his wife, in which are both active, and he has won awards both as a performer and Director.

As a writer he has contributed a regular business column in the local newspaper as well as producing numerous technical works.

'The Tears of Autumn' is his first novel.